CW00688829

CONTENTS

FOREWORD

On Monday (Bank Holiday) the steamships *Florence* and *Carham* made several excursions from Bournemouth to Swanage, and brought a great number of passengers, but owing to the very stormy weather, they had a sorry time of it, and presented a most woe-begone appearance.

(*Wessex Gazette*, August 1880)

To attempt to encompass the entire history of the British pleasure steamer in one volume would be a task which could end in an unjustifiable cramming of facts culminating in pages which would resemble crib sheets for examinations! What I have set out to do is to identify and record the main areas of operations of these delightful little vessels, now alas almost extinct, and in doing so I have taken the term pleasure steamer in its widest context, to include a number of motor vessels which in many cases supplanted their steam-driven counterparts.

What was the magic of these smoky, crowded steamers that formed an integral part of the seaside scene for over a century? Why was the marine excursion often the highlight of a summer Bank Holiday or the pinnacle of the annual vacation? In today's age of easy jet travel, it may be difficult to discern the reason for the magic of the 'butterfly boats' as they were often known, flitting gently from pier to pier, but to our forbears of a century ago they provided an excitement hitherto unknown to few except the rich, an opportunity to view and observe the coastline on a new dimension of wave and foam.

If ever such a creature as a typical excursionist existed, his trip on board might have begun long before his careful crossing of the gangway on to the broad open decks of his chosen vessel. The Victorians, in particular, loved to plan their excursions well in advance and a careful perusal of the weekly sailing bill by 'papa' would have resulted in the family nodding or shaking their heads in approval or otherwise. The costing would have been examined, when a day on the briny could have meant the expenditure of as much as 10s (50p)* per head (half price for children) for a full-day excursion or the available funds might have dictated an evening 'moonlight cruise', probably with musical entertainment on board, for 1s (5p). The choice of vessel and captain would also have to be considered, for the pleasure steamers followed the tradition of their larger transatlantic sisters in having their own devotees, who were always ready to extol the virtues of a particular master or their own favourite steamer and company. Decisions would have to be made concerning catering; should mama provide the picnic hamper to quell the insatiable appetite of the children? Or perhaps the occasion merited a meal on board, for often catering was of an excellent standard with a choice of a cold collation or a table d'hôte menu.

Thus prepared, the party would venture on board, the more judicious noting the quarter of the wind and the direction of their voyage. They would then carefully choose their seats from which sorties could be made for refreshments or a stroll around the decks. If the chosen steamer was a paddle-driven vessel, the children would not be long in finding the engine room where they would gaze with rapture at the gleaming cranks and valve gear, which, as soon as the journey began, would emit the hiss of steam and a rhythm of contentment. Mama and papa might by this time be well ensconced in deck-chairs, reading or idly chatting to their immediate neighbours.

*These amounts must be equated with the average weekly wage of £2–£3 which was the norm around the turn of the century.

Seldom out of sight, the coastline would provide a slow-moving panorama on which to comment.

A murmur of excitement would occur as the destination was reached, with eyes and necks straining to watch the securing lines thrown as the steamer berthed. If time ashore was allowed, a steady stream of passengers walked sedately down the pier — to run would have identified the family as proletarians. After their time ashore and the purchase of souvenirs, such as postcards or a small item of Goss china with a glazed crest emblazoned in colour, our family would make its way slowly back to the pier head once more, to repeat their outward pattern on the return journey. They would watch with an amused expression the efforts of latecomers to gain access to the steamer before departure, as the captain sounded the ship's siren to remind them that time and tide wait for no one.

On board *Cambria*, making passage along the North Devon coast in 1937. Note the reserved deck abaft the funnel for which an extra 1s (5p) single journey was charged and which was a feature of several Campbell steamers

Around the coast of Britain this pattern was enacted from Easter until October, uninterrupted apart from two world wars, until the ageing vessels sailed away for the last time, to resound to the breaker's hammer, with the exception of the paddle steamer *Waverley*, which now proudly boasts of being the last sea-going paddle-propelled excursion vessel in the world. Built in 1947, she is now owned by the Paddle Steamer Preservation Society which endeavours to provide as many opportunities as possible for the vessel to give excursions from seaside towns.

It is to these travellers, the captains and their crews that this volume is gratefully dedicated.

BERNARD COX

DEVELOPMENT AND DECLINE

To examine the growth in popularity of coastal excursions during the nineteenth century and its eventual decline after World War II, one needs to look not only at the emergence of the holiday habit, at first unpaid and of short duration, but also at the movement of population during the Industrial Revolution. The urban population of Great Britain increased from 25 to 75 per cent of the total populace between 1801 and 1901, leading to overcrowding in towns and cities and the need, if and wherever possible, to escape from the conglomeration of bricks and buildings which surrounded the urban worker. Fortunately the rapid advancement of the railway network and the competition between rival companies led to fares which were reasonably priced, and the introduction of specially reduced excursion tickets on a day or weekly basis.

Thus, for the first time, there existed a means of travel within the grasp of many families who began the tradition of the 'great escape' from the environment in which they found themselves, and a day or a week at the seaside became a pleasurable reality. The procession of families with their chattering friends and children, sometimes travelling on their own account and sometimes partaking in a works outing, became a major source of revenue for the railways and in turn led to the rapid expansion of seaside resorts. In the thirty years between 1871 and 1901, thirteen resorts were added to an original list of forty-eight in contemporary census reports.

Parallel with this demand for sea-air entertainment, there developed an ever-increasing number of marine excursions from the piers that jutted proudly from new or extended promenades, constructed to entertain the trippers from London and the growing centres of industrial production. Prosperous businessmen were able to join a regular weekend exodus; middle-class management and the better-paid workers found themselves able to visit the seaside on less numerous occasions, but were still able to join the throngs of marine trippers on several occasions during the summer season, whilst the ordinary workers, from the middle of the nineteenth century, began to find at least some increase in real wealth through the bargaining of trade unions and social pressure for an increased standard of living. With income tax at only 1s (5p) in the £1 at the turn of the century, there was a little money to spare, not only for the journey but also to pay the price of a marine experience.

The main excursion areas developed where easy access by rail, and later by road, became possible. These can be broadly defined as the network of routes on the Clyde, the North Wales coast, the Bristol Channel, the South Coast (with a particular proliferation of routes east of Torquay as far as Sussex) and the Thames, drawing on the great passenger potential of the capital. Development of routes along the north-east coast was sporadic, probably due to the more exposed coastline and the chilly waters of the North Sea. In all these areas the pleasure steamer quickly became an established and almost indispensable part of a visit to the seaside.

The term 'pleasure steamer' was not always appropriate, for although the wide, wind-swept decking of the pleasure steamer gave an outing and untold pleasure to millions of excursionists, there were also a large number who returned wet, uncomfortable and suffering greatly from 'mal de mer', when caught in a sudden squall or other vagaries of the English weather. Nevertheless many steamer operators flourished and prospered for over a century and the seascape was incomplete without the sight of tall smoke stacks emitting a trail of soot and steam as the vessels journeyed majestically to the next pier, at the commencement of a long day-excursion to a distant resort or perhaps an island within sailing distance. The steamers even ventured abroad

occasionally, crossing the waters to France or the Isle of Man.

And what of the companies that operated them? In the main they had strong local connections, the more successful being those that could augment the income received from trippers by some form of seasonal ferry service. Although attempts were made by individuals to run one or perhaps even two vessels, in the main private ownership resulted in severe financial loss, especially when they faced opposition from larger concerns which were able to initiate price cutting and had the advantage of their own repair yards. The larger companies were able to demand the loyalty of their seamen by offering work throughout the year, whilst the smaller concerns were largely dependent on picking up scratch crews at the start of each season.

The steamers themselves were mainly paddle propelled and steam driven by their reciprocating engines which were nearly always open to view, providing a source of wonderment to old and young alike. The paddlers with their shallow draught and ease of manoeuvrability were ideal ships to come alongside and complement the ornate piers from which they sailed. Turbine vessels, although more economical to run, were unable to cope so well with the currents that are

The *Heather Bell* was the first vessel to operate regular excursions between Swanage, Poole and Bournemouth from 1871–6, establishing a service which was maintained in peacetime until 1966

prevalent around coastal piers and scarcely challenged the supremacy of the paddlers, whilst the development of the motor ship came too late to provide a great deal of tonnage. However, they were able in several cases to prolong the running of some routes by replacing the paddle steamers which, because of their age and heavy operating costs, were sent to the breakers' yards.

The causes behind the decline of the British pleasure steamer were varied: besides the more obvious economic factors such as the cost of fuel, crews' wages and maintenance, one of the main challenges to the popularity of these vessels came from alternative forms of entertainment and opportunities for spending money. Many of the mid-Victorian seaside resorts were slow in providing entertainment for the new crowds that descended upon them; hence the popularity of promenading, the act of walking up and down the seafront, exchanging gossip, studying fashion and giving an opportunity for the strollers to indulge in their penchant for health by imbibing fresh air. By the turn of the century, entertainment had established itself in the form of concert parties, bandstands and alfresco concerts, all of which were normally located on the piers or in nearby gardens. There were no undue pressures to take the holiday-maker away from the immediate confine of the seafront. This pattern continued unabated up to the outbreak of World War I and extended, to a large degree, into the 'twenties and 'thirties. After World War I, the charabanc, a long open coach with transverse seats, began to make inroads into steamer traffic but as these were uncomfortable, with minimal weather protection, further development was required before their threat became serious. The motor car was appearing in increasing numbers, but as yet was the prerogative of the well-to-do or higher middle-class strata of society. However, as both these forms of transport improved and increased in popularity, there was cause for the steamer operators to feel concern, a fact which probably affected the amount of new tonnage ordered between the world wars. Already some of the longer routes were being abandoned, especially those which had been instituted and maintained for purposes of prestige. In addition, the traditional forms of entertainment were being supplemented by cinemas, dancing, greyhounds and hobbies such as photography, sport, walking and camping. All these activities took up the time and available cash of the would-be excursionist.

In general, those connected with the steamers looked forward optimistically to an increase in custom following the passing of the Holidays with Pay Act of 1938, which naturally increased disposable income.

Holidays without pay had been initiated for some workers by the efforts of trade unions and certain far-seeing employers in the latter half of the previous century. Previously the majority had coped with the absence of paid holidays by weekly contributions to holiday funds; consequently the number of new visitors was less than was expected, and the outbreak of war in 1939 took place before the act had taken its full effect.

In both wars, the majority of pleasure steamers was impressed into some form of Admiralty activity. After the second conflict those which survived were hurriedly placed back in service and the excursion trade enjoyed an Indian summer in the immediate post-war years, when returning servicemen spent their gratuities freely on holidays and petrol rationing severely curtailed transport by road. In the late 'forties another trend detrimental to the steamers was to manifest itself – the demand for more independent holidays, in particular camping and caravanning, once petrol restrictions were lifted. A greatly enlarged holiday industry emerged and with the advent of cheaper air travel in the 1960s, package tours became popular, especially those to more temperate resorts in Europe and further afield. By 1962, one third of the money spent on holidays went on foreign travel. By this time also the possession of a motor car was regarded as being more of a necessity than a privilege.

It was little wonder that pleasure steamer operators were feeling the pinch. Faced with ageing ships and little likelihood of any capital outlay being reimbursed by additional traffic, the great withdrawal began and one by one vessels were laid up or scrapped. By the end of the 'sixties the process was practically complete, as far as vessels certified for trips on the open sea were concerned.

The excursion trade did not sink completely into the sea of oblivion; often the traditional pleasure steamers were replaced on the shorter coastal or inter-resort ferry services by smaller motor ships, usually locally owned and of a size suitable for the much-decreased trade. Today these vessels maintain the shorter, sheltered-water trips of their predecessors and long may they continue to be patronised.

By 1980 there remained only one sea-going paddle steamer, from the several hundred that had paddled their way majestically along the shores of Britain. The *Waverley*, one of less than a handful of pleasure steamers built after World War II, was reboilered in 1981 and it is to be hoped that through the efforts of her owners, the Paddle Steamer Preservation Society, she may continue to remind her passengers of the maritime traditions of the British pleasure steamer for many years.

And what of the seaside piers, those pillars of Victorian respectability that jutted proudly into the sea at nearly all the main seaside resorts? Although it cannot be claimed that the existence of pleasure steamers led directly to the construction of the principal pleasure piers, clearly the finances of both the steamer operators and the pier companies were entwined, and it was no coincidence that in the final years of the nineteenth century, some fifty

Birnbeck Pier at Weston-super-Mare was an unusual structure being partly constructed on an island. The Campbell steamer *Glen Usk* was employed on the Weston to Cardiff run in the immediate post-war years and is seen at the landing stage which was approached by a part of the pier set at right angles to the approach decking

piers were built just as the network of steamer services was reaching its zenith. Just as the pier represented an extension of the seaside promenade or undercliff drive, the steamer represented an attempt to extend the use of the pier, which at the turn of the century was regarded either as being the place where residents, holiday-makers and day visitors assembled to exchange the gossip of the day and to view the changing modes of fashion or, at the less 'select' resorts, to participate in the growing craze of penny-slot machines, the old time equivalent of video games.

The Victorians were proud of their piers; they represented a pinnacle of engineering. Unfortunately a factor which is currently leading to their decay and demise is the lack of income derived from intending sea-going passengers. This income was accumulated in two ways, either by charging the steamer operator a fixed sum for the use of the landing stage for the season, based on the number of ships that were operated or by charging an individual toll on each passenger, a small amount which was in many cases hidden within the price of the sailing ticket. Some resorts blatantly charged the normal entrance price of 1d or 2d at the time the passenger passed through their ornate turnstiles.

Additional revenue was generated by passengers using the facilities provided on the pier decking such as telescopes and refresh-ments. The stately pleasure piers of the South Coast, in particular, derived their principal income from their pavilions, concerts and catering, whilst the more modest promenading piers such as Swanage and Cromer, because of the immediate lack of other forms of entertainment nearby, were able to retain a fair proportion of custom. An exception was the more exposed structures of East Anglia and the north-east coast where the steamers gave a sorely needed boost to takings. At the turn of the century Southwold Pier (1900) and the Claremont Pier (1902–3) were constructed expressly to accommodate the steamers and their passengers, but such was the simplicity of their design that it is hard to place them in the same league as those of Brighton, Eastbourne and Llandudno.

Just as the introduction of new tonnage declined drastically after both world wars, so did the construction of piers. It is fair to say that nearly all the principal seaside towns possessed a structure of some kind by 1914, but Simon Adamson, a pier historian, lists the only completely new structure after Fleetwood of 1910 as Deal, built as late as 1954–7. Alterations and additions are excluded from this list, as the main structures remained basically unaltered. Of recent date the piers at Bournemouth and Paignton have been extensively rebuilt in an attempt to provide a traditional seaside attraction, but alas too late for their decking to vibrate to the approaching paddle wheels or screws of the once numerous pleasure steamers.

Before entering into the main narrative of the ships and companies, we should perhaps give a thought to the officers and crews that were engaged in the seasonal trade of pleasure steamers. The officers were mainly employed on yearly contracts, being responsible between seasons for the maintenance and preparation of their vessel to obtain the following year's passenger certificate. Very few companies were able to offer permanent employment to their seamen, although such was the attraction of the vessels that many returned season after season, having obtained other employment nearby or gone 'deep sea' in the winter months. Whilst employed in the excursion trade, their working week, usually of six days, was often arduous on both long- and short-distance excursions.

A formal crew photograph of the crew of *Devonia*, believed to have been taken in 1927

The study of contemporary sailing bills provides interesting information on the hours of work undertaken by the crews. Their working day was long by modern standards, especially for the officers and stokers, the latter working in two shifts. For example, when scheduled for a cross-Channel trip from Bournemouth, the *Balmoral* would leave the Royal Pier at Southampton at 7.00am which entailed the crew reporting at least one hour before sailing time in order to 'work up' the ship. She would proceed via the Solent direct to Bournemouth Pier where the majority of her passengers would embark, and be issued with identity cards in lieu of passports. Promptly at 9.20am her ropes would be cast off and her course set for Cherbourg.

A sailing bill for August 1921 stated rather pompously: 'By arrangement with the French Government, passengers to Cherbourg by the P.S. *Balmoral* will not require passports but identity cards will be given in lieu thereof, and the particulars required must be filled in by the passenger before arriving at Cherbourg.' The sailing bill also issued the warning that, 'Under no circumstances will luggage be allowed', and it further stated: 'The Company will not be liable for unavoidable delays, accidents, personal injury, or sea risks of any kind whatsoever.'

THE HALF-WAY 'DOONE'

THE RETRE

And so the passengers and crew would settle down for the 3½ hour voyage to France. The more affluent passengers would obtain one of the deck-chairs provided at a cost of 2d or 3d return, probably handing the deck-chair boy a sixpenny piece and magnanimously telling him to keep the change. They would then scatter their hand baggage around and under the deck-chair as a token of their occupation of that particular space on the deck. Other passengers would sit on the wooden slatted seats which could be turned into liferafts in an emergency.

Meanwhile the captain and helmsman were on the open bridge setting course, whilst below the sweaty stokers were busy shovelling coal in order to obtain and keep a good head of steam so that the ship would arrive on time on the 'other side'. Cherbourg was usually reached about 1.00pm. Apart from the catering staff, other members of the crew were more fortunate in having little to do once the ship had left Bournemouth. *Balmoral* carried an extra crew member after World War I, for she had been fitted with Marconi wireless dur-

The bar of the *Lorna Doone* was aptly named 'The Half-Way "Doone" ' and was situated below the promenade deck at the entrance to the well-appointed restaurant. The saloon on the lower deck was named 'The Retreat' and provided comfortable wicker chairs together with tables on which passengers who did not fancy the upper decks could play cards or partake of refreshments

ing her post-war refit and a radio officer now worked in his own small cabin. The aerials of this new 'marvel' were clearly seen running from a cross-tree on the ship's foremast to a stump mainmast situated near the stern. The main tasks of the radio officer were to obtain the latest weather information, to signal times of arrival and departure and to keep a listening watch on distress frequencies.

The catering staff were kept busy throughout the voyage. The Southampton company was justifiably proud of its catering service, and in *Balmoral*'s main saloon the hungry tourist could obtain breakfast, morning coffee or early lunch, whilst on the return journey one could indulge in either tea, high tea, supper or dinner. For those whose interest lay in a more liquid form of refreshment, the bars supplied every popular drink with the advantage of duty-free prices once the ship had steamed past the three-mile limit. Suitably refreshed, the excursionists would make their way down the gangplank on to French soil.

The vessel left Cherbourg at 4.00pm for the return journey to Bournemouth Pier, and woe betide those passengers who were late returning to the ship and missed the warning note of her whistle a few minutes before departure. It was not unknown for these latecomers to be left behind, to make their own way back to England. The paddler would arrive back at the then Hampshire resort shortly before 8.00pm and a few minutes later steam away on the last leg of her long day to Southampton, finally ending about 200 miles of paddling close to 10.30pm.

Tired officers and crew were lucky if they set foot on land before 11.00pm, thus ending a seventeen-hour working day. Nevertheless there was never any shortage of crew for the *Balmoral*, the high unemployment figures of this period no doubt contributing to this fact, nor is there any record of unrest at the long hours of duty. *Balmoral* always had a reputation of being a happy ship and was extremely popular amongst holiday-makers and residents.

The reasons for the popularity of cross-Channel trips can be summarised under two main headings, social and economic. In the 'twenties, long before the advent of package tours and easy air travel, the fact that one could boast of 'going abroad' would evoke and provide interest amongst one's friends once the excursion was over. There was also the patriotic feeling of visiting the country with which so many soldiers had become acquainted during the war. For some it would provide the opportunity of once again putting into practice their knowledge of the French language, this time in front of their families. Economic reasons included the good exchange rate. The franc was worth about 8d and a glass of best cognac was never more than the equivalent of 1d or 2d ashore. Should the *Balmoral*'s passengers wish to partake of an excellent French 'repas' then this also could be obtained on equally advantageous terms. There was also the old English tradition of trying to avoid customs duty, ill-advised, but for the foolhardy few an opportunity of adding extra adventure to the journey.

Customs facilities at Bournemouth were rather primitive and consisted of officers, sent by tram from the nearby port of Poole, scrutinising passengers as they disembarked. In 1928 a searching shed of canvas was set up on the pier decking, this being maintained by the Council.

The *Bournemouth Echo* recorded the fate of an unfortunate young lady who, attracted by the prospect of obtaining duty-free scent, bought a large bottle and hid it under her dress. At the critical moment, after having denied that she had anything to declare, there came a smash and a splash as the bottle fell from the folds. The story had a happy ending, however, as the paper stated that 'Her fiancé paid the extra duties summarily imposed which amounted to £3.1s.6d.'.

THE NORTH WALES COAST
AND THE NORTH WEST

There is little to gladden the heart and eye more than the River Mersey with a light breeze ruffling its surface; our decks and yellow funnels bathed in sunshine, and the thought of the sea voyage that lies ahead. Whether we journey from Manchester, Bolton, Birmingham, Oswaldtwistle or Oldham to sail to the North Wales Coast, a sense of freedom and well-being is ours.
(*Handbook of the Liverpool & North Wales Steamship Company, 1953 ed*)

The history of excursions from Liverpool and along the North Wales coast is dominated by the Liverpool & North Wales Steamship Co, a concern that was founded by amalgamation as late as 1891, following seventy years of competition between numerous small vessels and concerns. The Fairfield Shipbuilding & Engineering Co had shown a keen interest in the North Wales coastal trade, and when the newly formed concern commenced operations with the *Bonnie Princess*, built in 1882, and the *St Tudno*, which entered service that season, the future looked secure due to the capital invested by Fairfields.

Bonnie Princess, with a capacity of 620 passengers and a speed of 14 knots, remained in service until 1895 when she was sold to a company on the Sussex coast for service from Sussex resorts. The *St Tudno*, as to be expected, was a product of Fairfields, capable of 19 knots and with a capacity of 1,061 passengers. On occasions she crossed to the Isle of Man from Llandudno, as well as undertaking regular work from Liverpool along the Welsh Coast.

To replace the *Bonnie Princess*, the company took delivery in 1896 of another new Fairfield steamer with an increased passenger capacity. The *St Elvies*, like the two vessels already mentioned, was twin-funnelled and the two vessels rapidly became a popular local and tourist attraction, operating on routes from Liverpool and Llandudno around the Isle of Anglesey, from Llandudno to the Isle of Man and from Liverpool to Llandudno.

In 1899 the company acquired the assets of

the Snowdon Passenger Steamship Company which, since 1892, had run the paddle steamer *Snowdon* along the same coastline. She was smaller than the two 'Saints', with a passenger certificate for only 462 and a service speed of about 14 knots. Nevertheless she became a useful member of the fleet, being their final paddle-propelled unit when finally broken up in 1931.

In 1904, the fleet was augmented by the transfer from the Thames of *La Marguerite* which was over twice the tonnage of any vessel hitherto seen in North Wales (1,554 gross

The paddle steamer *St Elvies*, belonging to the Liverpool & North Wales Steamship Co, leaves Liverpool on her final excursion to North Wales in 1930

The second turbine-powered *St Seiriol* leaving Liverpool. Built in 1931 she was withdrawn in 1962, having served on most of the North Wales routes

tons). This steamer was another Fairfield product (1894) in which the shipyard had maintained a financial stake since her launch. With an immense capacity for 2,077 passengers, she gave a great boost to the company. It is doubtful, however, that she was able to pay her way and her running remained largely a matter of prestige for Fairfields and the North Wales company.

In 1907, there appeared the smallest ship so far to serve the area, when the *Southampton* of 1872 was acquired and renamed *St Elian*. This vessel had been constructed for service between Southampton and Cowes and owned by the Southampton, Isle of Wight & South of England Royal Mail Steam Packet Co. She undertook the shorter excursions, but following the outbreak of war was withdrawn and broken up in 1915. Some three years previously the *St Tudno* was sold to the Hamburg-Amerika Line for use as a tender at Southampton. Being a German-owned ship, she was seized by the government on the outbreak of World War I, and after some Admiralty service, broken up in Holland during 1922.

If the *Southampton* of 200 tons was small, then the *St Trillo* of only 163 tons which entered the fleet in 1909 deserved the title of baby of the flotilla. Another ex-member of the Southampton, Isle of Wight & South of England Royal Mail Steam Packet Co fleet, she had been launched in 1876 as the *Carisbrooke*. The *St Trillo* had previously been in competition with the Liverpool & North Wales vessels when operated by the Mersey Trading Company and Walter Hawthorn between 1906 and 1908 under the name of *Rhos Trevor*. Like the *St Elian*, *St Trillo* was single-funnelled and had a speed of 12 knots, adequate for the ferry service from the Hampshire port to the Isle of Wight. Despite her smaller tonnage, she had a greater passenger capacity with a certificate for 463 against the 200 of her former fleet mate. After war service, *St Trillo* returned to the Welsh Coast, being eventually withdrawn and sold to Spain in 1921.

The company abandoned paddle propulsion in 1914, and were hopeful of taking delivery of their first twin-screw turbine steamer which was named *St Seiriol*. The outbreak of war precluded her entry into service, and she was unfortunately lost whilst engaged in minesweeping operations off Harwich in 1918. Following hostilities it was neither practicable nor possible to replace *St Seiriol* and the company once again turned to second-hand tonnage. Having disposed of *St Trillo* and with the fleet depleted, their choice fell upon a German vessel named *Hörnum*, which had operated on the River Elbe as a tender, strangely enough for the same Hamburg-Amerika Line which had bought *St Tudno* a decade previously. Entering service in 1922, the *Hörnum* was described as a very smart-looking craft with a single funnel and two masts. Renamed *St Elian*, she was largely based at Llandudno, but after only five years' service she was sold into Italian ownership for the service from Naples to Capri.

When *La Marguerite* was withdrawn in 1925, the company decided that her replacement would be turbine driven and accordingly took delivery of yet another Fairfield product for the 1926 season. The name *St Tudno* was revived and the new product was the most ambitious vessel yet seen along the coastline. Her gross tonnage of 2,300 made her one of the largest British excursion steamers; with a speed of 19 knots and a capacity of 2,493 passengers, she was capable of providing a comfortable and speedy passage for her patrons. To cope with the company's secondary routes, *St Tudno* was joined in 1931 by the *St Seiriol* of 1,586 gross tons, basically a smaller version of her fleet companion. Turbine powered, she was only slightly slower at 18½ knots and sailed on nearly all of the principal North Wales routes for her owners. Prior to her arrival, the paddle steamer *St Elvies* was withdrawn and broken up at Birkenhead.

By 1936 there was a further need for a smaller vessel to undertake local cruises and excursions from Llandudno and the first and last motor vessel to be owned by the Liverpool & North Wales Co appeared with a Fairfield hull but powered by Crossley engines. It is said that the original intention was to name her *St Tysilio*, but when she appeared this had been shortened to *St Silio*.

In 1939 all coastal passenger services were terminated and the three remaining 'Saints' changed their yellow funnels for a more sombre grey. All three vessels survived the war and in the immediate post-war period were able to regain a large amount of patronage, aided by the fact that the piers of North Wales had not been breached like their counterparts on the South Coast (in an attempt to prevent them being helpful to an invading force).

The *St Silio* was renamed *St Trillo*, and services recommenced on a similar pattern to those of the 'thirties. As was to happen elsewhere, the late 'fifties saw a serious decline in the number of passengers and at the end of 1961 *St Seiriol* was withdrawn and offered for sale. No buyers were forthcoming and the ship was sold for breaking up in Belgium during October of the following year. The company found that it was unable to continue in business after the end of the 1962 season and both the remaining vessels were put on the disposal list. *St Tudno* followed *St Seiriol* to the scrapyard but the more economical *St*

The turbine vessel *St Tudno* was delivered in time for the 1926 season and remained with the Liverpool & North Wales Steamship Co until their final withdrawal from excursion services in 1962

An unusual clipper bow graced *Lady Orme*, built as *Fusilier* in 1888, seen here along the North Wales coast in the 1930s. To many she seemed to have the lines of a private steam yacht rather than an excursion vessel

Trillo was purchased by P. & A. Campbell Ltd for service in the Bristol Channel and occasionally in the more familiar waters of her old routes. In November 1962 the Liverpool & North Wales Steamship Co sadly went into voluntary liquidation and the once-familiar buff funnels were to be seen no more.

Other North Wales Operators

One of several short-lived attempts to operate excursion vessels in the North Wales area was undertaken by W. Horton who, in 1902, chartered a River Tay steamer and ran her under the name of *Albion*. His sailings comprised a summer service between Rhyl, Rhos and Llandudno, with occasional trips to the Isle of Man. Having gained some experience with this vessel, Horton returned her to Scotland and looked for another steamer to run on similar routes during the following season. He was able to purchase the *Sussex Belle* (1899) of 981 gross tons from her South Coast owners, and a

concern named the Colwyn Bay & Liverpool Steamship Co was formed to operate the steamer which was renamed *Rhos Colwyn*. At the end of 1905 *Rhos Colwyn* was disposed of to the Barry Railway Co, presumably to raise part of the capital required to purchase two ex-Southampton steamers which became available during the winter of 1905–6. These were the *Carisbrooke* and *Prince Leopold* which were renamed *Rhos Trevor* and *Rhos Neigr* respectively. Horton seems to have given up steamer ownership about this time and the two vessels were almost immediately transferred to the Mersey Trading Co Ltd which, in 1906, also purchased two ex-Mersey ferries named *Daisy* and *Snowdrop*. In 1907 the fleet was augmented by obtaining the ex-Clyde steamer *Viceroy*, built as early as 1875. Renamed *Rhos Colwyn* she proved more useful than the Mersey ferry vessels which were quickly withdrawn. In June 1908 the three 'Rhos' steamers came under the ownership of Walter Hawthorn of Rhyl. Only a month later, however, *Rhos Neigr* struck a rock in Penrhyn Bay and had to be driven ashore. Her damage proved fatal and the vessel was ultimately broken up. *Rhos Trevor* was sold to the Liverpool & North Wales Steamship Co in

1909, as already related, whilst the elderly *Rhos Colwyn* paddled on alone until the end of the 1911 season when she too went to the breakers.

With the demise of these steamers, the opposition to the Liverpool & North Wales Steamship Co became negligible. In the 'thirties, however, an attempt was made by the Alexandra Towing Co to place a former Liverpool tender on services from Llandudno. She had been built as the *Magnetic* by Harland & Wolff in 1891 and had transferred hundreds of thousands of passengers to and from the White Star liners anchored in the Mersey. The *Magnetic* remained with her original owners until December 1932, when she was purchased by the tug company and renamed *Ryde*. At the time it was thought that she was destined for service to or from the Isle of Wight, since her new title was spelt in the same way as the southerly ferry terminal of the island. Nothing came of this, however, and the twin-screw vessel appeared and operated services from Llandudno, possibly with the agreement of the Liverpool & North Wales Co. The *Ryde* appeared to have outlived her usefulness and was sold in August 1935 to Clyde breakers.

In 1935, a concern known as the Cambrian Shipping Co operated an ex-Scottish steamer named *Fusilier*, built in 1888, under the more appropriate name of *Lady Orme*, but in the following year she was transferred to the South Coast and commenced a limited number of excursions from Ramsgate under the ownership of Frederick Perry of Llanrhos. The English Channel venture was unsuccessful and in 1937 the elderly vessel became the property of the Ormes Cruising Co, operating on her previous routes along the North Wales coast. Somewhat inexplicably she was yet again renamed in 1938, and sailed her final season as *Crestawave*. Laid up in 1939, this nomadic vessel was unable to find a buyer and was broken up for scrap.

The post-war scene left these waters entirely to the Liverpool & North Wales Steamship Co.

Morecambe and Blackpool

The history of pleasure steamer operations along the Lancashire coast is not easy to chronicle, as the record of private individuals, pier companies and other concerns that owned vessels is complicated by amalgamations, take overs and financial crises. One of the early vessels to sail from Morecambe was the *Helvellyn* of 1842 which ran on charter, until her purchase by the Furness Railway in 1848. A paddle steamer named *Morecambe Queen* appeared in 1853, but apparently met with little success as she was sold during the following season. In 1867 the *Queen of the Bay* took up station at Blackpool and was replaced after the 1872 season by another vessel of the same name, when the former steamer was sold for further service in the Scilly Isles. Her departure may have been on purely speculative grounds or the need for a larger vessel, since the 189 gross tons of the second *Queen of the Bay* was 51 tons greater than her predecessor.

A partnership between R. Wilson, R. Birkett and J. Brown resulted in the formation in 1872 of the Morecambe Steamboat Co, which ordered and ran the screw steamer *Morecambe Queen* followed by the paddle steamers *Roses* (1876) and *Sunbeam* (1885); in 1888 they acquired a twin-screw steamer named *Britannia* and finally the PS *Express*, delivered in 1892. From their heyday in the 1890s, this fleet gradually declined when faced with competition from vessels owned by other companies, although their screw vessels *Morecambe Queen* and *Sunbeam* were not disposed of until after the 1908 season.

In 1912, Samuel Cordingley purchased the Clyde steamer, *Isle of Bute*, which had but a brief career under his ownership; she collided with the Central Pier at Morecambe and sustained such damage that she was scrapped in the following year. Her loss led Cordingley, who was financially concerned with the Morecambe Central Pier Company, to purchase the twin-screw steamer *Robina* of some 306 gross tons which remained under his control until the early 1920s. She was employed on several charters, being seen at Blackpool in 1919 and on the Bristol Channel during the subsequent two seasons. In 1922 her ownership was transferred to Samuel's sons, W. A. and P. Cordingley. Some three years later the Cordingley brothers seem to have given up steamer ownership but *Robina* was again sailing from Blackpool, this time operated by the Blackpool Steam Shipping Co and in 1924 by H. D. Bickerstaffe. The post-war resurgence was only temporary and the need to charter was not subsequently

The flush-decked Blackpool steamer *Greyhound* on trials in 1895. She ran trips to Llandudno and Douglas before ending her days in Turkish waters

repeated; at the beginning of 1925 *Robina* was sold for service as a tender on Belfast Lough.

Like the Cordingley family, the Bickerstaffes were also steamship operators on their own behalf, J. Bickerstaffe owning a vessel which bore the family name in 1879. He formed the Blackpool Passenger Steamboat Co in December 1894 to finance the building of the *Queen of the North*, which entered service in the following season. Whilst the *Bickerstaffe* lasted until broken up in 1928, the newer vessel became a war loss whilst on Admiralty service in 1917.

Anxious to increase its tolls, the Blackpool North Pier Co had formed a steamship company, taking delivery in 1895 of the *Greyhound*, a paddle steamer of 542 gross tons and some 230ft in length. She was in direct competition with the *Queen of the North*, their displacement and size being similar. The *Greyhound* was a flush-decked steamer with her promenade deck extending the complete length of the vessel. She undertook trips to Douglas and Llandudno and was also employed on runs from Preston to Llandudno. After World War I she resumed her sailings, but in April 1923 she preceded the *Robina* in being sold for service on Belfast Lough, on which she only lasted two seasons before sail-

ing in March 1925 to Turkey where she was renamed *Buyuk Ada*. In 1901 the North Pier Steamship Co took delivery of a twin-screw ship which they named *Deerhound*, but she never attained the popularity of her elder sister and was sold after only four years to the West Cornwall Steamship Co, later ending her days in the ownership of the Canadian Government.

Following the withdrawal of *Bickerstaffe* in 1928, there were no locally operated vessels until the formation of Blackpool Pleasure Steamers in 1933. This concern purchased the Mersey Ferry *Bidston* and renamed her *Minden*. In 1935 they acquired a twin-screw ex-minesweeper of 1918, which had latterly seen service as a South African survey ship, named *Protea*. The following season she was renamed *Queen of the Bay*. In 1937 a further addition was made when the ex-Clyde turbine steamer *Atalanta* was acquired. The company had overreached its potential, however, and at the end of that season, the *Queen of the Bay* and *Minden* were sold and scrapped. The *Atalanta* was then run by an associated concern known as the Blackpool Steam Navigation Co, and operated alone until the outbreak of World War II, during which she saw service as a net-layer. Although surviving the conflict unscathed, she was never reconditioned on her return and was towed to Belgium in 1947, thus ending the history of major pleasure steamers along the North Wales and Lancashire coastline.

THE BRISTOL CHANNEL

While the Company endeavour to inform passengers generally of the steamers' arrival at the different places en route, they do not in any way bind themselves to do so by issuing tickets for the same, or to disembark passengers off Lynmouth when circumstances prevent the boats from coming out to the steamers. And it should be clearly understood that passengers to and from Lynmouth, and all other places where landing and embarkation is effected by means of boats, are conveyed to and from the steamers entirely at their own risk.

(Bristol Channel District Guide, 1921)

When in 1886 a group of speculative Bristol businessmen chartered the Clyde steamer *Bonnie Doon* to run excursions in the Bristol Channel, their action was laying a seed that would result in the birth of a white-funnelled fleet of steamers that would serve the area for close on a century. In the following year, *Waverley*, an improved vessel offering a greater speed and comfort, was chartered and operated under the management of Captain Alec Campbell who, together with his brother Peter, also a Master Mariner, had for many years been associated with pleasure steamers on the Clyde.

Such was the success of this charter that Captain Alec Campbell ran the *Waverley* on his own account in 1888. He foresaw the full potential of the Bristol Channel area, including the possibility of lucrative steamer connections between the South Wales ports and the south-west of England. Captain Alec Campbell persuaded his brother to forego the possibility of expansion in their native waters, and subsequently to base their operations in the Bristol Channel, an action which led to the formation of their own company, P. & A. Campbell Ltd.

An immediate necessity for the new company was to order a steamer to add prestige and credibility to their flag. Delivered in time for the main part of the 1891 season, the *Ravenswood* made her maiden voyage from Bristol on 3 July. The Campbell concern was well received and a presentation was made to Captain Alec at the Royal Hotel, Bristol on 23 April 1892, at which he received a diamond scarf ring in the form of the company's flag, a diamond stud, a pair of marine glasses, a Davenport writing desk and an illuminated address which bore testimony to the care and skill with which Alec and his brother were developing passenger traffic in the area.

The success of *Waverley* and *Ravenswood* led to the building and acquisition of three more paddle steamers, *Westward Ho* (1894) *Britannia* (1895) and *Cambria* (1896), all of which were built to a broadly similar design that included for the first time an extended promenade deck from stem to stern. The *Britannia*, possibly in recognition of her patriotic name, remained the flagship of the fleet until 1946. All three vessels, together with *Ravenswood* were to survive two world wars, the *Waverley* having been withdrawn and scrapped in 1921. But only *Ravenswood* and *Britannia* were fit enough to re-enter service after the second conflict. *Westward Ho* was not thought worthy of reconditioning after World War II and *Cambria* caught fire before she could be reconditioned. From time to time other vessels were acquired and operated, but in 1911 the company embarked on the construction of three further vessels, the *Lady Ismay* (1911), *Glen Avon* (1912) and *Glen Usk* (1914). Of somewhat smaller dimensions than the Victorian members of the fleet and more economical to operate, they were ideal vessels to open and close the excursion season and to supplement the Cardiff to Weston via Penarth service, which had become an important source of revenue to the company

19

(*opposite above*) A fine view of *Westward Ho* as she approaches the pier at Ilfracombe in the early 1920s

(*opposite below*) The magnificent paddle-box of *Glen Avon*, lost in World War II, complete with gold paint and scroll work, hiding the thrashing red painted floats of her paddle wheel

(*above*) The *Lorna Doone* leaves Ilfracombe in the 1890s. As built she had an open foredeck but this was later plated in during her service on the South Coast

and which was a profitable and well-patronised ferry service between April and October. The service was thought of as a ferry rather than an excursion trip, although the ships carried both commuters and holiday-makers. No attempt was ever made to operate on a year-round basis.

The main competition to the Campbell brothers had come from Edwards & Robertson, a company set up in 1882 by Fredrick Edwards, the son of a Cardiff tug owner, and George Robertson, one-time secretary of the Taff Vale Railway. They made a strong bid for the Bristol Channel excursion trade and in 1889 took delivery of the *Lady Gwendoline* to combat the expansion of the Campbell operations. This vessel, although a 'flyer', was extravagant on fuel and after only

two seasons was sold to Charles Tricquot of Cherbourg, her replacement being a vessel named *Lorna Doone* which entered service in 1891. At the end of 1895, Edwards & Robertson sold their vessels to John Gunn of Cardiff, but by March 1899, he had financial problems and his fleet was dispersed, two of the vessels, *Bonnie Doon* (known locally as the Bonnie Breakdoon) and *Scotia* entering the Campbell fleet. The *Bonnie Doon* was the same vessel that had undertaken the original charter of 1886. Before their demise, Edwards & Robertson had made a last attempt to compete with Campbells' new *Westward Ho* by managing the *Lady Margaret*; this vessel had been built in 1895 for a company largely composed of the directors of Penarth Pier who had sought to acquire a proportion of the South Wales traffic. After only one season she too passed to Campbell ownership.

Further opposition to the Scottish brothers came from the Barry Railway Co, a profitable concern which wanted to diversify. Two of their vessels were sister ships, delivered in 1905 and named *Gwalia* and *Devonia*. Large and with twin funnels, they were fast and expensive to operate, although the railway company had no

21

need to fear the price of coal, due to their trade contracts from the pits. Peter and Alec Campbell viewed this new threat to their profitability with the utmost concern, and in a bid to stop the railway company's expansion, took their case to the courts, stating that although the vessels were running under the title of the Barry and Bristol Channel Steamship Co this was a 'colourable and fraudulent device'. At this time railway companies were limited by Act of Parliament to operate steam trains only and not to indulge in other enterprises such as steamship services. Railway steamers had to be operated by a separate company, often wholly owned by the railway concerned. The Campbells were partially successful and an agreement was entered into which limited the ports of call of the railway steamers. A further vessel, the *Rhos Colwyn*, was acquired second-hand by the Barry Railway in 1905 from North Wales and named *Westonia* to run on the Cardiff to Weston ferry, followed two years later by a new paddler named *Barry*. By this time the company was operating under the title of the Red Funnel Line. There seems little doubt that the geographical restrictions placed on their routes affected profitability, with the result that on 7 May 1910, *Gwalia* was sold to the Furness Railway for service from Barrow under the name *Lady Moyra*. Five days later the other three vessels were sold for £60,000 to Joseph Davies and Claude Hailey who continued to operate the vessels under the title of Bristol Channel Boats Ltd.

As there were no longer any railway connections or restrictions, it was now possible to operate the vessels over a wider area, but after only two seasons, the company decided to accept a Campbell offer for their three vessels and ceased trading. By 1914 the Campbell fleet numbered thirteen paddle steamers, including a number which had operated on the South Coast. Every vessel was requisitioned for war service:

Waverley	Brighton Queen
Ravenswood	Lady Ismay
Westward Ho	Barry
Cambria	Devonia
Britannia	Glen Avon
Glen Rosa	Glen Usk
Albion	

With the entire fleet operating under Admiralty instructions and many involved in the dangerous task of minesweeping, losses were to be expected and neither the *Brighton Queen* nor the *Lady Ismay* survived the conflict, both being sunk by enemy action in 1915.

When peace returned, it was not considered to be worth reconditioning the *Waverley* or *Glen Rosa* and they were scrapped. With the Campbell fleet depleted by four vessels, further trouble was experienced when the tug-owning firm, W. H. Tucker and Co of Cardiff, decided in 1919 to offer opposition on the Campbell routes. They purchased the *Lady Moyra*, which as we have noted previously had already seen service as the *Gwalia* on the Bristol Channel before passing to the Furness Railway in 1910, and the *Lady Evelyn*, built in 1900 for the same company. Their first season was reasonably successful, and in 1920 Tuckers chartered the screw steamer *Robina* from Cordingley of Morecambe. This charter was repeated in the following year, but by this time all Campbells' vessels were back from reconditioning and the Tucker concern was in financial difficulties. To meet this opposition in the Bristol Channel, no Campbell steamers were sent to the South Coast during this period. But after Tuckers' liquidation in 1922 they acquired the *Lady Evelyn* and *Lady Moyra*, and were able to reopen services along the Sussex coast the following season.

Prior to this, however, they had taken delivery of a new vessel named *Glen Gower* in 1922. She received the engines of the *Albion* which was then scrapped. The new ship was intended as a general-purpose vessel rather than a repeat of the faster *Britannia*, *Westward Ho* and *Cambria*. *Lady Evelyn* was renamed *Brighton Belle* and *Lady Moyra* became *Brighton Queen*. No further tonnage was added to the fleet in the inter-war period, although the company's first turbine vessel, *Empress Queen*, was ordered in 1939, but because of hostilities was unable to fly the Campbell flag until 1947.

During World War II, the *Brighton Queen*, *Brighton Belle* and *Devonia* were lost at Dunkirk, and both *Waverley* and *Glen Avon* became casualties during later Admiralty operations. At this time few shipyards were able to accept orders for pleasure steamers because of the need to replace merchant shipping losses. But because of their losses, the com-

Owing to the absence of piers at Lynmouth, Clovelly and Lundy Island, passengers were rowed ashore by local boatmen under charter to the steamship operator. Here passengers wait patiently to disembark from the *Lorna Doone* in a photograph taken just before the turn of the century at Clovelly

Although such occurrences were rare, it was not unknown for an excursion steamer to become stranded. Such a misfortune befell the *Albion* in 1907 when she was left high and dry at Blacknose Rock, Portishead. No serious damage was caused and the ship was refloated

(opposite above) The Duchess of Devonshire, seen here on the Bristol Channel and painted in Campbell colours was sent from Exmouth to maintain the link between Cardiff and Weston, whilst the other members of the Campbell fleet were on war service

(centre) Part of the crew of Cambria in 1914. One wonders if they all survived the holocaust of war

(below) With her bridge behind her funnel the helmsman had sheltered if uninteresting view of the voyage on board Lady Rowena

(above) The Bristol Queen passes through the Town Bridge at Weymouth in 1963, the ship having received attention by Cosens whose work-force were well used to paddle-steamer maintenance performed on their own fleet

pany was allowed to have two paddle steamers constructed, the first of which, named *Bristol Queen*, undertook her trials in September 1946, whilst the second was delivered in the following year with the title of *Cardiff Queen*.

The *Empress Queen* had been launched in 1940 and immediately pressed into service under Admiralty control, seeing service as a troopship between Stranraer and Larne. Returned in 1946, she was refitted during the following year and reopened Campbell services along the South Coast in 1948. With a gross tonnage of 1,781, she was by far the largest Campbell vessel ever operated; at the time of her conception it was envisaged that she would provide a challenge to the cross-Channel vessels of the General Steam Navigation Co, but government restrictions on travel abroad

meant that day trips without passports were not feasible, and *Empress Queen* became somewhat of a white elephant, with the result that in 1955 she was sold, re-engined as a motor ship and went to Greece for further service.

The veteran ex-Campbell flagship, *Britannia*, was reboilered in time for the 1948 season, emerging as an oil-fired ship with twin funnels. The Campbell fleet then numbered seven vessels, the largest post-war fleet of any British excursion company. In addition, the board of directors had plans for two more paddlers, but they remained that since it was already clear that on both the South Coast and Bristol Channel, passenger receipts were beginning to be affected by the large number of motor coast trips being offered to the public. As is usual with ageing forms of machinery, the older members of the fleet were becoming more expensive to maintain, and the time was fast approaching for their withdrawal. The first post-war deletion came in 1955 when the veteran *Ravenswood* went to the breakers, followed the next year by *Britannia*. Trade was hampered by poor weather in the peak of several summer seasons and by 1959, a receiver was appointed. A financial arrangement was made for P. & A. Campbell to become part of the expanding George Nott Industries Ltd, with the result that all but one of the remaining vessels were able to sail on into the 'sixties; *Glen Gower*, still fitted with the original engines of the *Albion*, was scrapped a few months after the take over. The sole

25

In 1947 *Britannia* was reboilered and emerged as a twin-funnelled vessel. Her old boiler is seen here being removed at Fairfields' yard on the Clyde

remaining pre-war paddler, *Glen Usk*, was laid up at the end of 1960, and after three years at the dockside was towed to the breakers.

The time had come to look around for more economical vessels; the cost of new tonnage had become prohibitive so the reconstituted board was fortunate in being able to obtain the small motor ship *St Trillo* in 1962, following the collapse of the Liverpool & North Wales Steamship Co. For the following seven years, she was operated on her former Llandudno to Menai service and occasionally at the beginning and end of the season in Bristol Channel waters. The next addition was the former Southampton vessel *Vecta*, which was chartered at the end of 1965 and, following successful trials, purchased in time for the following season for which she was renamed *Westward Ho*.

There was yet another arrival in 1968, when the *Queen of the Isles*, owned by the Isles of Scilly Steamship Co, was chartered for that and the following two seasons. The last conventional Southampton excursion vessel, *Balmoral*, was chartered in 1969 and thereafter became a useful member of the Campbell fleet. The arrival of these motor ships resulted in the withdrawal of the remaining two post-war paddle steamers, which had progressively seen a shortening of their season, as their size and operating costs meant that they were only able to pay their way for some six to seven weeks of each season. The *Cardiff Queen* steamed for the last time in 1966 and was broken up two years later, closely followed by *Bristol Queen*.

George Nott Industries in turn became part of Townsend Ferries and was incorporated in the mighty European Ferries Group, and it is to the credit of these concerns that they allowed the Campbell excursion business to continue without any real possibility of substantial or increasing profit. (Perhaps the days of sentiment were not completely finished.) Indeed, several interesting experimental services were operated during this period, including a brief romance with Hovercraft, which operated between Weston and Penarth and on the South Coast across the Solent. Both the *Balmoral* and *Queen of the Isles*, under Campbell direction, operated excursions from British ports as far apart as Douglas and Eastbourne in an attempt to obtain patronage. With the withdrawal of the General Steam Navigation Co's operations in 1966, plans were made to purchase the *Royal Sovereign* and to maintain their cross-Channel excursions, but the idea encountered difficulties in meeting Board of Trade requirements and had to be abandoned.

(*above*) Even in *Glen Usk*'s final season of passenger service (1960) the shining telegraphs and wheel bore testimony to the care with which her crew maintained the vessel

(*below*) The *Cardiff Queen* was broken up at Newport. An undignified end for a vessel which had given pleasure to thousands

The world's last sea-going paddle steamer *Waverley*, seen here off Portland in May 1978, is now the last chance for many to savour a traditional 'marine excursion'

Sadly further withdrawals were about to take place; *St Trillo* entered her final season in 1969 and was subsequently laid up. She never again entered passenger service and was broken up six years later. *Westward Ho* made her last sailings in 1971 and was then sold to be converted to a floating restaurant on the Manchester Ship Canal. There was to be one final arrival, however, when the *Scillonian*, a combined passenger and cargo vessel was acquired in 1977 and renamed *Devonia*. Built in 1955, she had previously been employed on service to the Isles of Scilly, as her name suggests. The 'seventies resulted in a further fall in passenger receipts whilst costs, particularly those of fuel, were rapidly escalating. The inevitable result was that at the end of 1979, the Campbell company finally decided to cease sailings. A final attempt to continue some form of excursion service in the Bristol Channel was mounted by the Landmark Trust, concerned at the loss of sailings to Lundy Island. In 1980, the Trust formed White Funnel Steamers Ltd, and the *Balmoral* was chartered to this concern under Campbell management. At the beginning of 1981, an announcement was made that no further sailings would take place and the *Balmoral* and *Devonia* were put up for sale. In 1982, *Balmoral* sailed under her own power to be converted for use as a floating restaurant at Dundee, whilst *Devonia* was purchased for further use from Torquay, to be operated by Torbay Seaways with her name changed to *Devoniun*. With the demise of P. and A. Campbell, the Bristol Channel and South Coast lost an operator whose ships provided entertainment and a form of communication and travel for millions of passengers throughout its existence.

Mention must be made of a praiseworthy attempt to revive Bristol Channel sailings in 1981, when the ex-Sealink ferry *Shanklin*, from the Portsmouth to Ryde service, was purchased by a group of enthusiasts. This motor vessel was operated by the Firth of Clyde Steam Packet Co Ltd on their behalf, with the intention that any profits should be allocated to help towards the operational preservation of the paddle steamer *Waverley*, an ex-Clyde vessel which had become the world's last sea-going paddle steamer. *Shanklin* was renamed *Prince Ivanhoe* and, working in conjunction with *Waverley*, she was placed on some of the old Campbell routes in the Bristol Channel. Whilst on a cruise off the Gower Coast in August 1981 she struck an underwater obstruction at Port Eynon Bay, had to be beached and became a total loss.

The *Waverley* (1947) is mainly employed in Scottish waters during the summer, but undertakes occasional tours in British waters at the beginning and end of each season in an attempt to provide coastal excursions from the piers and ports which otherwise would be completely devoid of the sound and sight of a traditional excursion steamer.

THE SOUTH COAST

The Cosens Fleet is well equipped and this ensures to its passengers a very
high standard of comfort and convenience. Catering is on up-to-date lines, not
only in the case of the meals taken in the dining saloon, but also as regards the
refreshment bar, which is open all day. One of the features of the fleet is a
special landing apparatus which can be thrown out to beaches, thus enabling
passengers to land at many charming places without the discomfort and in-
convenience of being transferred to small boats.

(English Channel Guide, 1933)

The South Coast, because of its temperate
climate and multitude of resorts, harbours and
ports, has undoubtedly been the base of more
pleasure steamers than any other part of the
English Coast. The main fleets were based at
and operated from Weymouth, Bournemouth
and Southampton, and two of the principal
operators, Cosens of Weymouth and Red Funnel of Southampton are still happily in
existence, albeit in different and diversified
activities. The network of services operated by
these concerns, supplemented by the vessels of
the Bristol-based P. & A. Campbell fleet and
various local operators, extended from
Plymouth to Dover.

The Weymouth-based Cosens & Co was
established in 1852, following a public meeting
in the previous year at the Portland Arms Inn
for the purpose of 'floating a company to
provide steamboat communication between
Weymouth and Portland'. The founders were
Captain Joseph Cosens and J. Drew, a newspaper proprietor. Captain Cosens had been
associated with excursions from Weymouth to
Lyme Regis and as far as Southampton from at
least 1845. When the company was formed,
three vessels were in operation: the *Princess*,
Wave Queen (on charter from J. Scott Russell,
the builder of Brunel's famous *Great Eastern*)
and *Highland Maid*, purchased second-hand in
1848 to provide a ferry service to Portland.
The *Wave Queen* was filling a gap until the
delivery of a new paddle steamer named
Prince, which was at that time being built on
the Thames at Scott Russell's yard. In fact
when the *Prince* was ready for launching, her

slipway was so constructed that the steamer
slid through the middle section of the *Great
Eastern*. Surely a unique way of finding her intended element!

About this time an opposing company was
inaugurated under the control of John Tizard,
a solicitor who brought the *Bannockburn* and
the *Premier* to the Dorset port to run in direct
competition with Cosens. The latter was not to
be outdone and quickly added two more ships
to its fleet, named *Contractor* and *Ocean
Bride*. After a few years of keen competition,
the two companies amalgamated, with Tizard
joining the Cosens concern in 1876. The
Premier was absorbed into the fleet, whilst the
Bannockburn suffered the ignominy of being
turned into a coal barge for supplying steamers
in Portland Roads.

Some three years later the company took
delivery of *Empress*, the £8,000 capital having
been raised in about 48 hours. During the
'eighties the company expanded, helped by the
increasing number of holiday-makers at Weymouth and the fast-growing resort of
Bournemouth. The *Queen* was built in 1883,
followed by the *Victoria* in the following year
and the twin-funnelled *Monarch* in 1888. By
this time the Cosens fleet was serving places as
far apart as Torquay and Brighton, and cross-
Channel excursions were operated from Weymouth and Bournemouth to the Channel
Islands and Cherbourg.

Along the coast at Southampton, steamship
communication to the Isle of Wight had
become well established, and in 1861 the
articles and constitution of the Southampton,

The number of excursion vessels lost by stranding has been remarkably small, but a major loss on the South Coast was the *Bournemouth* in 1886, seen here after the ravages of the weather and salvage crew

Isle of Wight & South of England Royal Mail Steam Packet Co (said to be the longest title of any shipping company in Lloyds' Register) had been ratified. Formed by the amalgamation of two smaller companies, the concern had been created largely by the efforts of Andrew Lamb, previously a superintendent engineer with Peninsular & Orient. The revenue of the new company was derived from a number of well-established ferry routes from Southampton and Portsmouth to the Isle of Wight, serving the piers at Cowes, Ryde and Yarmouth, supplemented in the summer by excursions around the island by seven small steamers.

The first new vessel ordered by the company was the *Vectis* in 1866, followed six years later by the *Southampton* from the yard of Barclay, Curle on the Clyde, a concern which was to build several other vessels to serve from Southampton, including the *Carisbrooke* and *Prince Leopold*, delivered in 1876. All four vessels were constructed with an open foredeck where luggage could be stored, a single funnel and narrow first-class saloon aft. They were intended as all-year-round vessels, capable of excursions and charters when required.

The popularity of the Isle of Wight increased year by year, helped by the frequent visits of

Queen Victoria to Osborne House near Cowes, with the consequence that four further vessels were added in the 'eighties: *Princess Beatrice* (1880), *Princess Helena* (1883), *Her Majesty* (1885) and the first twin-funnelled member of the fleet, *Solent Queen*, in 1889. This last vessel was constructed primarily for excursion work and replaced the *Princess of Wales* which had been launched the previous year, but had been cut in two by a collision on her trials over the measured mile at Skelmorlie in the Firth of Clyde. One of the lifeboats from the ill-fated vessel was recovered and subsequently carried on board the *Solent Queen* for the remainder of her career. The final Victorian addition came in 1891, when the *Prince of Wales* was constructed locally to a similar design to the Barclay, Curle ships by the Southampton Naval Works (although there has never been a royal dockyard at Southampton, this rather grand sounding title reflects the Victorian pride in the Royal Navy). Designed by Sir John Biles, she was designed with a hog-backed keel; this was intended to stop the tendency of paddle steamers to sag amidships under the weight of their machinery, but the *Prince of Wales* was so soundly constructed that she refused to bend and thus carried this peculiarity until scrapped. A hog-backed vessel was one that was designed with a slightly convex line in the contour of the keel, so that in service the weight of the engines would gradually straighten this distortion.

Midway between Weymouth and Southampton, the seaside town of Bournemouth had developed as one of the fastest growing resorts in Great Britain, with a population exploding from 5,896 in 1871 to 50,762 in 1901, a tenfold increase. Following the successful running of a small steamer named *Heather Bell* during the 'seventies from Swanage to Bournemouth, a local steamship company had been formed by David Sydenham in 1877. In subsequent seasons a number of vessels were chartered, and by 1881 the Bournemouth, Swanage & Poole Steam Packet Co were ready to purchase their first

Visits to view warships of the British navy were a valuable source of income to steamer companies, and on this occasion in May 1937, passengers are elevated rather precariously on board HMS *Shropshire* at Spithead from the paddle steamer *Bournemouth Queen*

steamer to operate from Bournemouth's new pier. Their choice fell upon the *Lord Elgin*, built five years previously for service on the Firth of Forth. The Bournemouth company was immediately faced with competition from Cosens of Weymouth, who had also set their sights on the potential traffic. Rising to the challenge, the local concern ordered a new vessel, delivered in 1884 and named after the resort. Unfortunately the career of the *Bournemouth* was short lived; when returning from a day trip to Torquay in 1886, in dense fog she ran on to the rocks at Portland. There was no loss of life but the vessel became a total loss. (It should be noted that the safety record of excursion steamers within British waters has always been of a very high standard; the loss of the *Bournemouth* was the only serious accident on a long day excursion, in the entire history of the South Coast sailings.)

The Bournemouth, Swanage & Poole Steam Packet Co replaced their ill-fated flagship with the *Brodick Castle*, built in 1878 for service in Scotland. Upon hearing that their rivals, Cosens, were taking delivery of the *Monarch* in time for the 1888 season, they immediately raised further capital to reboiler the *Brodick Castle* to give her extra power and speed with which to meet the challenge. Four years later they commissioned the *Windsor Castle*, built at Southampton and at that time the largest paddle steamer seen on the South Coast with a gross tonnage of 847. Unfortunately this vessel was a heavy coal burner and never really paid her way, with the result that after only three seasons she was sold to the Glasgow, Ayrshire and Campbeltown Steamboat Co with which she entered service in 1895.

The effect of Queen Victoria's Diamond Jubilee and the naval review, which took place in June 1897, upon the future development of routes along the South Coast was considerable. Such was the amount of feeling and support for the monarchy and the interest in maritime matters, especially where the Royal Navy was concerned, that vessels were chartered from coastal companies from the Thames to the Bristol Channel. The review not only saw the greatest array of warships ever assembled, but almost certainly the largest assortment of pleasure steamers in the same waters.

One of the vessels to sail south to witness the review was the paddle steamer *Cambria*, constructed for service with P. & A. Campbell on the Bristol Channel some two years previously. Her arrival was to have a profound effect on future South Coast services. Flush decked from stem to stern and capable of a speed of 20 knots, she represented the most modern type of excursion steamer to operate in these waters. Her owners were not slow to appreciate the potential traffic that could be obtained from the fast-developing coastal resorts, and follow-

ing the review they decided that the time was right to try to obtain a share of these passenger receipts. Having successfully disposed of any major opposition in the Bristol Channel and possessing an effective fleet of vessels, they sent the *Cambria* back again a few weeks after the review to operate from Southampton, along the Hampshire coast. In the following year the Campbell flyer returned again, together with their *Glen Rosa* which had been purchased during the previous year. With these two vessels they quickly extended their routes as far as Hastings and Weymouth. In 1899 *Cambria* operated alone as *Glen Rosa* was retained on the Bristol Channel to combat possible opposition from the Barry Railway's operations, and during the following three seasons *Cambria*'s long day trips were augmented on the shorter runs by the *Albion*, another recent acquisition of the White Funnel fleet.

Cambria's arrival brought forth a flurry of activity from the established South Coast companies. The Southampton company was the first to react, seeing its profitable excursions to the Isle of Wight in danger; they purchased the *Lorna Doone* in March 1898 from John Gunn of Bristol. She was immediately reboiled and improved, and with this vessel the company was able to increase the frequency of trips from Bournemouth and Weymouth. Although the *Lorna Doone* was a useful general-purpose excursion steamer, her service speed of about 16 knots was about 4 knots slower than *Cambria* and consequently an order was placed with S. McKnight & Co of Ayr for a flush-decked vessel of very similar appearance to *Cambria*. Commencing service in July 1900 and named *Balmoral*, she entered into immediate competition with *Cambria*. Meanwhile, Cosens, who had also been affected by the Bristol-registered vessel, wisely awaited the arrival of *Balmoral* before ordering their own reply. They considered there was no useful purpose in obtaining another 20-knot flyer, and instead contented themselves with a 16-knot vessel which was to be fitted out to provide comfort and luxury rather than speed. This new vessel was to be fitted with triple diagonal machinery, rather than the twin-cylinder engines of *Cambria* and *Balmoral*. Named *Majestic*, she entered service in May 1901 and almost immediately gained her own share of the market. All three vessels held cross-Channel certificates and crossed to

The *Lorna Doone* off Egypt Point, Cowes, in the early 1930s. Built for service in the Bristol Channel, after purchase by the Southampton, Isle of Wight & South of England Royal Mail Steam Packet Co in 1898, most of her service was on excursions in the Isle of Wight area. It was not unknown for holiday-makers to return year after year for the express purpose of sailing on the 'Lorna' as she was affectionately known

(*below*) Another view of the saloon of *Lorna Doone* in the early 1930s complete with mosquito netting which was seldom required in British climate, but added a touch of gentility to the decor

The elegant lounge of the PS *Lorna Doone*. Note the oil lamp on the right of the picture. The standard of cleanliness of excursion steamers in the inter-war period was generally very high

Cherbourg, *Cambria* and *Balmoral* sometimes competing directly with each other for the fastest crossing. Exciting days indeed!

Rather unexpectedly Campbells withdrew after the 1902 season from Southampton and Bournemouth. Although the competition for trade had become tougher with the arrival of *Balmoral* and *Majestic*, the main reason for their departure lay in the fact that more fruitful waters were becoming apparent along the Sussex coast: during the winter of 1901–2, Campbells were able to take over the assets and two steamers of the Brighton, Worthing & South Coast Steamboat Co. This company, which had been set up in 1891, had operated a number of vessels by the time of its demise, obtaining its revenue mainly from the two resorts mentioned in its title. The two vessels taken over by Campbells were the *Brighton Queen* and *Princess May*. The former, built in 1897, was a long-distance vessel with a cross-

Channel certificate, whilst the *Princess May*, some four years her senior, was a slower pier-to-pier vessel. After a few weeks on the Bristol Channel and some excursions in connection with King Edward's Coronation Review at Spithead, she was sold to Italian ownership in January 1903. The *Brighton Queen* was refitted and restyled, and served along the South Coast until the outbreak of war in 1914, being seen in places as far apart as Ramsgate and Swanage. She was unfortunately mined in 1915 and sank off the Belgian coast.

We must now revert to Bournemouth and Southampton. Another new vessel was added to the Southampton fleet in 1902. Named *Queen*, she was again designed as a twin-purpose vessel for the company, useful as both a ferry and excursion steamer. She replaced the *Southampton* which, after a brief spell of service from Newhaven, eventually ended her days in service along the North Wales coast. Following the disposal of *Carisbrooke* and *Prince Leopold* in 1905 to the Colwyn Bay & Liverpool Steamship Company, the Southampton fleet set about obtaining more modern vessels. The first to arrive was the

Princess Royal in 1906, in many ways similar to the *Queen* but with a single funnel. Unfortunately she never matched her design speed and was returned to her builders, the local shipbuilders J. I. Thornycroft; she was never accepted by the Southampton company. Instead they purchased from Leith the *Stirling Castle* which, after suitable internal modifications, was placed on the Bournemouth station in April 1908. Their attack to gain further trade at Bournemouth was increased three months later when the *Bournemouth Queen*, the first ship built expressly for excursion work from the resort, was delivered from Ailsa's of Troon. In appearance a scaled-down version of *Balmoral*, the arrival of these two vessels showed that the company meant business.

Cosens of Weymouth appear to have been caught napping, their only reply being the acquisition of the rejected *Princess Royal*, renamed *Emperor of India*. She had been lengthened by her builders but still possessed an open foredeck, which was plated in to the bows during the following winter, making the then fashionable full-length promenade deck.

The unfortunate Bournemouth, Swanage & Poole Steam Packet Co also came to the end of its days during the Edwardian period. Beset with financial difficulties, an agreement with Cosens was entered into during 1901 for joint sailings to be advertised. The *Brodick Castle* was transferred to Cosens' ownership, leaving the Bournemouth company to paddle on alone with the *Lord Elgin*, which was operated mainly on the shorter route to Swanage. In 1909, however, they sold this steamer and their goodwill to the Southampton company, probably as a result of the latter's determination to gain patronage from Bournemouth. The *Lord Elgin* was transferred to Southampton, converted to a cargo steamer and for the next forty-four years paddled faithfully between Southampton and Cowes, laden with everything from cattle to pins.

In 1909, Cosens disposed of *Brodick Castle* and the ship was prepared at Weymouth for the journey to Buenos Aires for use as a cattle boat. The old ship was loath to leave British waters, however, and sank whilst under tow to South America. Three more vessels were added to the Weymouth fleet before the outbreak of war, each of them being mostly employed at Weymouth. The *Helper* arrived in 1911 purchased from the Great Western Railway,

whilst two years later two other ex-railway paddlers arrived, the *Lune*, renamed *Melcombe Regis*, from Fleetwood, and *Alexandra*, an ex-Isle of Wight ferry. The company had obtained a lucrative Admiralty contract to transfer sailors to and from the warships in Portland harbour and a number of their vessels were kept in steam throughout the year for this purpose. The final Southampton addition before the war was named *Princess Mary*; she entered service in 1911 but had only a very short life, becoming a war casualty, as did the *Stirling Castle*. Both ships were lost in the Mediterranean.

In 1912 Captain S. G. Shippick, who had been employed by Cosens, decided to set up on his own account. He purchased a small wooden-built paddle steamer named *Advance* of 72 gross tons, renamed her *Studland Belle*, and commenced a service from Bournemouth to Studland and Swanage. Since there was no pier at Studland beach, his passengers were landed on a small pontoon from whence they were ferried ashore by local boatmen. The *Studland Belle* became the first Sabbath breaker in 1913 when she landed passengers at

With her funnel grossly out of proportion by modern standards, *Audrey* was operated out of Bournemouth in 1914, later seeing service with New Medway Steam Packet Co. En route from Bournemouth to Swanage she would call off Studland beach where passengers were first landed on a small floating pontoon before being rowed ashore by local boatmen

Poole Quay, an event which did not pass unnoticed in the local papers and did not become a regular part of Captain Shippick's programme. During the winter of 1913–14, whilst wintering in the local waters of Poole harbour, she unfortunately caught fire, due to the night watchman leaving a stove unattended, and she became a total loss. She was replaced by a larger steamer named *Audrey*, built in 1897 for the Cork, Blackrock & Passage Railway. *Audrey* ran for the 1914 season only, her service being interrupted by the outbreak of war. Captain Shippick subsequently became involved with the New Medway Steam Packet Co.

Thus at the outbreak of war in 1914 there were no less than twenty-four paddle steamers operating in Hampshire and Dorset waters, owned by two companies:

Cosens & Co	Southampton Co
Majestic	*Balmoral*
Monarch	*Bournemouth Queen*
Empress	*Stirling Castle*
Emperor of India	*Princess Helena*
Victoria	*Lorna Doone*
Alexandra	*Queen*
Melcombe Regis	*Princess Mary*
Helper	*Duchess of York*
Queen	*Prince of Wales*
Albert Victor	*Solent Queen*
Premier	*Her Majesty*
	Princess Beatrice
	Lord Elgin

When services resumed in 1920, besides the two Southampton steamers already mentioned, Cosens' flagship, the *Majestic*, had been lost. No new or second-hand tonnage was added to either company until 1927, when the *Princess Elizabeth*, built closely to the design of the *Princess Mary* of 1911, entered service at Southampton. She was destined to be the last but one new paddler designed for South Coast usage, as subsequent units in the Southampton area were motor-driven screw vessels, whilst Cosens, although remaining faithful to paddle propulsion, only acquired further second-hand tonnage.

The first of the motor ships, delivered in 1931 and named *Medina*, was employed mainly on the Southampton to Cowes ferry run. She was rarely used on excursions, as the paddlers were more adept at manoeuvring

alongside piers. In 1939, there appeared a vessel with the then revolutionary (in both senses of the word) Voith-Schneider propellers. Named *Vecta*, she undertook excursion work to the Isle of Wight and maintained the ferry service when not so employed. The last Southampton paddle steamer had been constructed in 1936 and named *Gracie Fields* after the well-known artiste who launched her. Basically an improved version of *Princess Elizabeth*, she was again intended as a dual-purpose excursion and ferry vessel.

In 1937 Cosens scrapped the ageing *Premier* and replaced her in the following season with the *Duke of Devonshire*, which had been operating from Torquay. Renamed *Consul*, she was shortly joined by an ex-ferry steamer, the *Duchess of Norfolk*, which had previously been owned by the Southern Railway, and worked between Portsmouth and Ryde. She emerged as the *Embassy*. It was with these vessels that both companies operated in the season prior to World War II. As in the previous conflict, the buff-funnelled Weymouth fleet was impressed for war service, several of the steamers operating as contraband control vessels in local waters. Cosens were fortunate in suffering no losses, and when their ships were returned, looked forward to reopening services on most of their pre-war routes as soon as possible. The *Empress* and *Victoria* were able to sail from Weymouth in June 1946 as their departure point was the stone pier or jetty, which, unlike the piers at Bournemouth and most of the other South Coast resorts, had not been breached as an anti-invasion measure. A temporary connection to the landing stage of the pier was hurriedly constructed at Bournemouth, enabling the Southampton steamer *Princess Elizabeth* to call during the following month. It was this ship, together with Cosens' *Monarch* which reopened the Swanage service in the following year.

The *Embassy* appeared in September 1947, with a further refit planned for the following winter; this included additional superstructure and an enclosed wheelhouse. The remaining Cosens vessels were ready in 1948, when the *Emperor of India* and *Consul* had passed

After her disposal by Cosens of Weymouth, the *Consul* of 1896 receives a pre-season survey at Southampton. She was later to revert to her original name of *Duke of Devonshire*

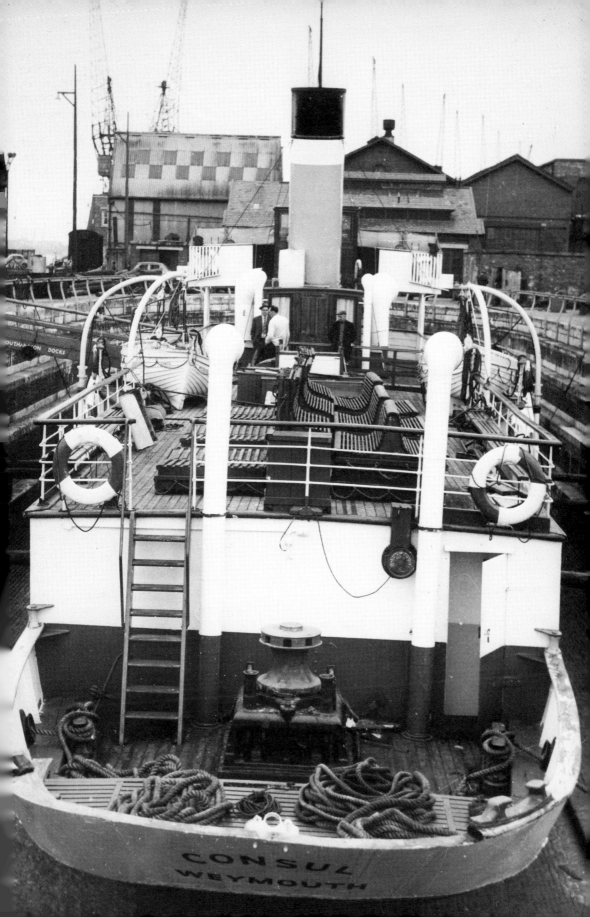

through the company's yard for refurbishing. The former, like the *Embassy*, emerged with additional top hamper, comprising a wheelhouse, covered companion-way and a greatly enlarged funnel; both ships received enclosed wheelhouses which must have greatly assisted the comfort of their masters in the more exposed waters outside Weymouth and across Poole Bay to the island piers.

Whilst the Weymouth company was content to utilise their modernised fleet without any additional tonnage, at Southampton a number of second-hand vessels were purchased to augment their remaining vessels. The *Gracie Fields* had been lost at Dunkirk, and the ferry, *Her Majesty*, sunk in an air raid at her home port. The company's two main excursion steamers, *Lorna Doone* and *Balmoral*, although returned by the Admiralty, were found to be in such a poor state that both vessels had to be scrapped. In May 1946 the company bought the ex-Birkenhead ferry *Upton*, a twin-screw vessel which, after trials on the Swanage service, was found to be unsuitable for the task and was then allocated for trips from Southampton to Ryde and Southsea within more sheltered waters. In 1948 they acquired *Robina*, which, since her service along the North Wales coast, had undergone several changes of ownership. Like the *Upton*, she was employed on the shorter cruises within the Solent or on the Island ferry service. *Robina*'s arrival enabled the *Solent Queen* to be sold for scrap at the end of the season.

The year 1949 was to see a great revival in excursion work for the Southampton concern. The company received a new twin-screw motor vessel of 688 gross tons, which revived the name of their cross-Channel paddler *Balmoral*. The new motor ship was able to commence the round the Isle of Wight and day return trips to Bournemouth. In addition to this new flagship, two paddle steamers, the *Queen of Thanet* and *Queen of Kent* were purchased from the New Medway Steam Packet Co and renamed *Solent Queen* and *Lorna Doone* respectively. With three large-capacity excursion steamers, plus their dual-purpose pre-war steamers, the company may have been over-optimistic in their estimates of potential traffic, but the South Coast was experiencing a greater boom in tourist and holiday trade than other parts of the coastline.

In 1946 there was an amalgamation of in-terests when Cosens were taken over by the Southampton company, which since the 'thirties had traded under the shortened title of Red Funnel Steamers and later as Red Funnel Services. The acquisition of five ships since the war had brought the Southampton fleet up to strength, and the *Duchess of Cornwall* and *Princess Helena* were scrapped. The *Lorna Doone* was placed on the Bournemouth station, whilst the *Solent Queen* augmented *Balmoral*'s excursions, this motor vessel having never received a cross-Channel certificate. The service of these two ex-Medway vessels was to be shortlived. Whilst preparing for the 1951 season, *Solent Queen* caught fire with the result that her sister ship was withdrawn from Bournemouth to take her place, but she too was to finish her passenger service at the end of that season. At the same time it was decided that the *Bournemouth Queen*, which had also served the resort since her return from war service, should also be restationed, thus beginning the withdrawal of Red Funnel Steamers from Bournemouth. A new arrival in 1951 was the ex-Southern Railway paddler *Shanklin*, dating from 1924. The vessel was renamed *Monarch* and operated under the Cosens' house-flag, as a direct replacement of the former holder of the name.

Although the commencement of the 'fifties had augured well with the arrival of so many new vessels to the area, withdrawals were not far away, led by *Lorna Doone* in 1951 and the stop-gap steamers *Upton* and *Robina* in 1953. Cosens disposed of *Victoria* in the same year and a further withdrawal was announced at the end of the 1955 season, when Cosens' *Empress* sailed under her own steam to Southampton to be broken up. She had become the last paddle steamer with oscillating engines, and these were fortunately preserved at the Southampton Maritime Museum, where they can still be seen. Another 'last' was the scrapping of *Lord Elgin* in the same year, her claim to fame being that she was the last paddle-propelled cargo vessel on the British Register.

The list of withdrawals became longer with the demise of *Emperor of India* at the beginning of 1957 and her one-time rival, *Bournemouth Queen*, at the end of that season. This left only the two motor vessels, *Vecta* and *Balmoral*, together with the paddle steamer *Princess Elizabeth* at Southampton, and the

The Southampton, Isle of Wight, and South of England Royal Mail Steam Packet Co. Ltd., and
————————— Cosens and Company, Ltd. —————————

have pleasure in presenting

BOURNEMOUTH'S FIRST GRAND

SHOWBOAT CRUISE

(Weather and circumstances permitting)

WEDNESDAY, AUGUST 25th, 1948

8.30 P.M. TO MIDNIGHT

DANCING ON DECK	CONTINUOUS CABARET below DECK
with RASTUS and his DIXIE SWINGSTERS	8 VERSATILE ARTISTES 8 presented by LEO WELLS

A HEATWAVE OF ROMANCE AND RHYTHM

Fully Licensed Saloons   ::   **Refreshments at Moderate Charges**

The Cruise will be in smooth water, leaving Bournemouth Pier at 8.30 p.m.
Landing at Poole Quay at midnight, where Hants & Dorset motor coaches
will be awaiting the arrival of the Showboat to return passengers along
the main bus route to Bournemouth, Boscombe, etc.

TICKETS (Limited) 10/6 Including Return Coach Fare

Obtainable in advance at the Steamer Office
8 BATH ROAD : : : BOURNEMOUTH

EARLY APPLICATION ADVISABLE. Free List entirely suspended

Richmond Hill Printing Works, Ltd., Yelverton Road, Bournemouth   H. H. BAKER, Bournemouth Manager

The ex-railway paddler *Freshwater* was purchased for service along the Sussex coast in 1961 and renamed *Sussex Queen*. She is seen here leaving Newhaven. She was transferred to Bournemouth for the following season and renamed *Swanage Queen*. She was broken up in Belgium during 1963

latter's days were clearly numbered. She paddled on for two more seasons and was sold at the end of the decade to commence a rather chequered career under private ownership in 1960. Red Funnel Steamers had wisely realised that their future lay in providing an efficient and more profitable car ferry service and for this purpose all their subsequent vessels have been purpose-built as car ferries. *Vecta* was sent on charter to the Bristol Channel at the end of her 1965 Solent season, leaving *Balmoral* as the sole Red Funnel excursion steamer. She too was destined to join her former fleet mate under the P. & A. Campbell flag in 1969, thus ending the tradition of 'Round the Island' and Solent cruises from Southampton.

After the *Empress* was withdrawn in 1955, this left the Cosens fleet with three vessels, *Consul, Monarch* and *Embassy*. In the ensuing seasons, the *Consul* was employed mainly at Weymouth and the other two vessels from Bournemouth. *Monarch* was sold for breaking early in 1961 and her departure opened the way for two private concerns to attempt to fill

the gap left by her departure. First to arrive was the aptly named *Swanage Queen*, owned by Herbert Jennings who had previous experience with the running of a small passenger vessel in Devon waters. In 1959 he had purchased the ex-railway paddler *Freshwater* which had operated between Lymington and Yarmouth (IOW). His original intention had been to operate the vessel from Sussex resorts, which he did in 1961, naming her *Sussex Queen*, but seeing an opportunity to run on the long-established Swanage service, he transferred the 263-ton vessel to the Bournemouth area in 1962. Berthing each night at Poole, she ran to Swanage and the Isle of Wight. Cosens did not take kindly to this intrusion and some price-cutting took place. The *Swanage Queen* was withdrawn at the end of the season and subsequently scrapped.

The second intruder was the last of the Southampton paddle steamers, *Princess Elizabeth*, which, after service at Torquay, tried her chance at Bournemouth during 1962. At the end of that season Cosens put the Weymouth-based *Consul* up for sale and the *Princess Elizabeth* was then transferred to Weymouth, where it was thought there would be no sizeable excursion vessel in 1963. After a poor season along the Sussex coast under private ownership, *Consul* was returned to Weymouth for 1964, and thus two privately owned vessels entered into competition in an area where established operators had already withdrawn. The result was obvious and *Consul* was sold during the winter to become an accommodation ship at Dartmouth, reverting to her original name of *Duke of Devonshire*. Unfortunately *Princess Elizabeth*, although now in sole possession of the Weymouth station, could not pay her way and remained laid up in Weymouth's inner harbour from 1966 to 1968. On a happier note, after languishing at Weymouth and Hayling Island for some time, the steamer was eventually converted to a floating restaurant and is currently still serving in that role near Tower Bridge, London.

After three seasons as the sole remaining excursion paddle steamer on the South Coast, Cosens' *Embassy* made her last sailing in September 1966 and was sold to be broken up in Belgium in the following spring. Bournemouth was thus without its own paddle steamer for the first time since 1871, but the popular run to the Isle of Wight was continued using Fairmile-type motor vessels and other tonnage operated by Crosons Ltd of Poole. This firm, which is still providing a much needed service, had developed some years previously from a long-established local boat and pleasure trip family concern with extensive knowledge of local waters and an associated shipyard at Hamworthy. They were able to purchase from Bridlington, the twin-screw motor vessel *Thornwick* of 127 gross tons, constructed in 1948. She entered service in June 1967, operating from Bournemouth to Totland and Yarmouth, Isle of Wight. During the following winter she was extensively refitted and renamed *Swanage Queen*, but her speed of about 10 knots was rather on the slow side and Crosons looked around for a faster and more suitable vessel for the island runs, the *Swanage Queen* being put up for sale and eventually being purchased by Meridian Line Cruises of London in 1969.

Crosons was able to acquire the *Coronia*, a 227 gross tons motor vessel, built in 1935, from Scarborough. In June 1968, renamed *Bournemouth Queen* and with a class III certificate for 452 passengers, she was able to operate a regular service to the Isle of Wight. The service lasted until the end of the 1974 season when she was sold to Sir Robert McAlpine & Sons Ltd to be used as a workers' ferry service between Rothesay and Ardyne

and renamed *Queen of Scots*.

With her departure went the last remaining regular passenger vessel with an open waters certificate. It is to their credit that Crosons constructed three modern passenger motor ships between 1974 and 1977 and continue to run short excursions from Bournemouth pier, but as their combined gross tonnage is less than 200, they cannot rank as traditional excursion steamers in the sense used in this book.

Plymouth and Torquay

Neither the port of Plymouth nor the bustling resort of Torquay has ever become the centre of widespread or intensive excursion steamer activity, relying instead on locally based motor launches or river craft to provide marine opportunities. Nevertheless it was a Plymouth-based company, as we shall see later, that was responsible for ordering a vessel which was to have repercussions in far away Sussex, and it should be recorded that Torquay has provided a base for a number of steamers owned by established excursion operators.

One of the first vessels operated from Torquay was the *Prince*, built in 1852 and previously operated by Cosens of Weymouth, which had decided to dispose of this small, iron paddle steamer at the end of 1887. She was purchased by two local businessmen, Ellett and Matthews, who spent a considerable amount of money on a refit which included reboilering. She was based at Exmouth and ran trips to several of the Devon beaches. Her bow was put ashore whilst two stern anchors held the vessel steady, her passengers disembarked from her bows on to a gangplank, which then connected with a small wooden jetty on wheels that was pushed out from the shore. This rather precarious method of landing was commonly used by several South Devon- and Weymouth-based steamers throughout their service.

Having received a reasonable financial return from the operation of *Prince* in 1891, Ellett and Matthews formed the Devon Steamship Co and ordered a new vessel, named *Duchess of Devonshire*, for delivery in the following year. At the same time they disposed of *Prince*, which then ran for several years from Lee on Solent before being scrapped around 1897. The *Duchess of Devonshire* was of 221 gross tons, much larger than the 61 gross tons of her predecessor, and appears to

The last of the line. The world's last sea-going passenger paddle steamer *Waverley* provides at least a taste of former regular services by undertaking annual 'around the coast cruises'. She is seen here at Bournemouth in 1978. The ship evokes great interest and nostalgia at her various ports of call

have made a profit, for in 1896 a second steamer was delivered, basically similar, with an open deck forward, but 5ft longer and a tonnage increased to 257. Named *Duke of Devonshire*, she was destined to have a long career on the South Coast and elsewhere, and to become the last operational Victorian paddle steamer in British waters.

In 1898 the company was reconstituted and emerged as the Devon Dock, Pier & Steamship Co, reflecting other interests that had been acquired. Both ships were operated, virtually without competition up to the time that services were suspended in 1914. After the outbreak of World War I, the *Duke* was impressed as a minesweeper and the *Duchess* sent to the Bristol Channel under the management of P. & A. Campbell to operate on the Weston to Cardiff service. The *Duchess of Devonshire* was needed to maintain the link between Cardiff and Weston as all the larger Campbell steamers had by 1917 been impressed into Admiralty service. She maintained the service alone in 1917 and 1918 and the first part of the 1919 season.

The two ships were able to re-enter passenger service from Exmouth and Torquay in 1920, serving Plymouth and Weymouth with shorter trips to Teignmouth, Brixham, Dartmouth and Lyme Regis. The Devon company met with their first real taste of opposition between 1925 and 1927, when Cosens placed their vessel *Alexandra* at Torquay, in direct competition. After 1927 Cosens withdrew, realising that *Alexandra* could be more profitably operated at Weymouth. It would seem that South Devon traffic was declining, and as a result, the *Duchess of Devonshire* was withdrawn and laid up in 1930. Two years later, the Devon company had to contend with Campbell's *Westward Ho*, operating in their territory from both Plymouth and Torquay. A much faster steamer than the *Duke* or *Duchess*, she sailed eastward from Torquay to Bournemouth and westward to Looe; whilst at Plymouth she visited Penzance, Fowey, Mevagissey and Falmouth. This Campbell incursion lasted only two seasons; like Cosens, they probably realised that no great financial gains were to be forthcoming. Unfortunately, the presence of *Westward Ho* had made the operation of the *Duke of Devonshire* unprofitable, with the result that she was put up for sale and sold for further service in Irish waters. At the same time the *Duchess of Devonshire* was also offered for sale and purchased by a new concern named the South Devon & West Bay Steamship Co. She ran out of Exmouth during 1933 and returned, in the absence of any Campbell steamer, to Torquay in 1934. Unfortunately the *Duchess* was wrecked at Sidmouth in August of that year. She had nosed on to the shore, but her stern anchor failed to hold and she was swept broadside on to the beach, fortunately without loss of life. Thus the area had no excursion steamer in 1935, but in the following year Alexander Taylor of Torquay purchased and brought back the *Duke of Devonshire* from her exile at Cork. She was operated for two more seasons and then sold at the beginning of 1938 to Cosens, who had been looking for a vessel to replace their *Premier*, which had come to the end of a long and useful life. Subsequently there were no vessels operating from Torquay or Exmouth until after World War II.

It is now opportune to consider steamer operations at Plymouth, from where a number of small steamers were operated on the River Tamar and to Cawsand for many years. In 1895 W. Dusting, a local businessman, formed the Plymouth Belle Steamship Co and took delivery of a large full-length, flush-decked steamer of no less than 654 gross tons. She was faster and larger than any vessel hitherto seen on any part of the South Coast, with the exception of the Bournemouth steamer *Windsor Castle* of 1892, and all seemed set for the *Plymouth Belle* to obtain the cream of the excursion traffic for years to come. As is often the case, however, a new company with little or no experience of short sea operations has much to learn, and mistakes once made are costly and hard to rectify. The *Plymouth Belle* was placed almost entirely on long-distance trips. These included three-day excursions to Guernsey and Jersey and two-day visits to the Isles of Scilly. In practically every area of sailing, it has been the shorter excursions or those allowing time ashore at another resort that have provided the 'bread and butter' for steamer operators.

Consequently her services fell between normal coastal ventures and short-distance cruis-

The *Duchess of Devonshire* arrives at Exmouth with one of her officers keeping an eye on her sponson from the wing of her bridge. She was later lost after being stranded on the beach at Sidmouth in August 1934

ing, an area into which few had ventured. As a result, after only one season, she was made available on charter to Collard of Newhaven, where we shall meet up with her again. For many years a number of short excursions from Plymouth were carried out by the tenders of the Great Western Railway, when they were not required to transport passengers to and from the many transatlantic liners which stopped in the English Channel outside Plymouth Sound.

Returning to Torquay, which had no service in 1938–9: in the early post-war years several attempts were made to exploit the area, none of them meeting with any real success. The first arrival in 1947 was named *Pride of Devon*, previously the *Essex Queen* of the New Medway Steam Packet Co and now owned by the South Western Steam Navigation Co. She ran to Dartmouth and operated a number of cruises along the coast, but unlike her predecessors was unable to nose on to the Devon beaches, as her bow had not been strengthened to run ashore. She sailed in 1947 and 1948 only, before being laid up at Southampton. Plans were afoot to replace her with a converted naval ship to be named *Pride of the West*, but promised support for the scheme was not forthcoming; the ship never appeared, the company sold their *Pride of Devon* to the breakers in 1951 and ceased to operate.

The *Plymouth Belle*, seen here at Eastbourne at the turn of the century, was the largest and most palatial excursion steamer seen on the Sussex coast. Built in 1895, she saw little service at the port of her name, being mainly employed at Brighton, Eastbourne and Hastings

In 1950 a twin-screw turbine vessel named *Lady Enchantress* appeared, three years after an unsuccessful attempt to run her on the Thames. She was in service for the month of August only, running from Torquay to Guernsey. Of 1,474 gross tons, she was too large for any coastal work and, following a boiler failure near the Channel Islands, was towed back, laid up and in February 1952 went to the breakers. P. & A. Campbell returned to Torquay in 1951 with their *Empress Queen*, which had proved to be too costly to operate along the Sussex coastline. She ran to Guernsey three times a week and also sailed occasionally to Bournemouth or Falmouth. Because of her size, 1,781 gross tons, *Empress Queen* was unable to visit many of the small picturesque ports and harbours of Devon and thus lost some potential traffic. The public were deprived of the shorter half-day excursions and with only a limited demand for the long and consequently more expensive excursions offered, *Empress Queen* did not return for subsequent service.

There followed a void in Devon sailings, enlivened only by a number of cross-Channel excursions operated by railway or ex-railway vessels which were not true excursion steamers in the accepted sense of the word. The final attempt to run a vessel of suitable size came in 1960 when E. Rhodes purchased the last of the Southampton paddle steamers, *Princess Elizabeth*, and formed a company known as Torbay Steamers Ltd, offering some of the traditional trips once operated by the *Duke* and *Duchess of Devonshire*. She ventured to Plymouth, Lyme Regis and Dartmouth, but unfortunately a dispute arose between her owner and Torquay Corporation when the 388 gross vessel sailed on a day when a flag signal had been hoisted prohibiting the sailing of small craft! As a result *Princess Elizabeth* was withdrawn from Torquay and sailed in 1962 from Bournemouth, leaving the area once again without a vessel holding a class 3 certificate for open waters.

In 1982 another attempt was made to base an excursion vessel at Torquay. Following the final demise of P. & A. Campbell in 1981, one of their two remaining screw vessels, the *Devonia*, was purchased by a number of local businessmen. Her name was changed to *Devoniun* and in 1982, she was able to provide a mixture of cross-Channel and coastal excursions from Torquay.

River Dart

The inception of excursions on the picturesque River Dart from Dartmouth and Kingswear to Totnes appears to derive from the formation of the Dartmouth Steam Packet Co in 1859, although, as elsewhere, private owners had paved the way for the formation of the company. Their first vessel was a wooden, clinker-built paddle tug built in 1852 and named *Pilot*. She had previously seen service on the Tyne, and in 1858 had been operated by C. S. Hayne of Dartmouth. The newly formed company operated the 101-ton vessel not only on the Dart but also as far as the Channel Islands. Without modern navigation aid or wireless, such a voyage must have been quite an undertaking, but such was the ambition of Victorian owners and mariners that it was not uncommon to use vessels on journeys that would be immediately forbidden by today's safety standards. The Dartmouth Steam Packet Co also acquired an even smaller vessel named *Dartmouth* which for the previous three seasons had operated privately in Devon waters.

When the railway station at Kingswear was opened in 1864, there was a need to transfer passengers across the river to Dartmouth and a new iron paddle steamer named *Newcomin* was immediately placed in service. Of only 47 gross tons she soon became too small for the increasing trade and was replaced by the *Dolphin* in 1869, the *Newcomin* becoming the relief steamer used only in the height of the season. Eight years later a screw steamer, the *Hauley*, certificated for 160 passengers, was also used on the Kingswear to Dartmouth service, as well as for excursion work on the Dart.

In 1880 the *Berry Castle* appeared, to a design which was to form the basis of seven subsequent paddle steamers. In order of building and withdrawal, they were:

		Built at
Berry Castle	1880–1917	Kingswear
Dartmouth Castle	1885–1907	Hayle
Totnes Castle	1894–1912	Dartmouth
Kingswear Castle	1904–1923	Falmouth
Dartmouth Castle	1907–1939	Falmouth
Compton Castle	1914–1962	Falmouth
Totnes Castle	1923–1963	Dartmouth
Kingswear Castle	1924–1965	Dartmouth

All were built with an open foredeck, single funnel and mast, and steered from a raised platform in front of their funnel.

A tranquil scene on the River Dart at Totnes with the *Dartmouth Castle* of 1885 ready to commence her return journey to Dartmouth. It was not unknown for businessmen to use these little steamers as a means of communication, their speed and comfort being vastly superior to a coach and horses

The *Kingswear Castle*, laid up at Old Mill Creek, Dartmouth, in 1966, prior to her purchase for preservation by the Paddle Steamer Preservation Society in 1969. She can currently be seen undergoing extensive restoration on the River Medway

The steam packet company was reorganised in 1906, thereafter being known as the River Dart Steamboat Co. Besides owning the paddlers, two diesel-powered vessels were operated from 1922 and five other screw vessels placed in service between 1926 and 1949, varying in gross tonnage from 17 to 81. To replace the three withdrawn paddle steamers in the 1960s, two larger diesel units were added in 1963 and 1964, the *Conway Castle* and *Cardiff Castle*. The latter was built by J. Bolson & Son of Poole, Dorset, and was the first vessel since the *Compton Castle* of 1914 to be built outside the confines of the River Dart for the company.

A peculiarity of the eight paddle steamers built between 1880 and 1924 was their reluctance to be scrapped. The first *Kingswear Castle* (1904) was hulked on the banks of the river a little way downstream from Totnes where remains can still be detected. The *Dartmouth Castle* (1907) was similarly treated at the company's base at Old Mill Creek, and likewise her hull lies rotting at the present time. The *Compton Castle* was converted as a floating restaurant at Kingsbridge and later towed to Looe in Cornwall, where she also

awaits her final fate. The *Totnes Castle* (1923) was converted in 1963, together with the ex-Cosens paddler *Consul*, to provide floating accommodation for yachting holidays on the Dart, but whilst in the process of changing her base from Dartmouth to Plymouth in 1967, sank whilst under tow off Burgh Island in Bigbury Bay. The last Dart paddle steamer *Kingswear Castle* (1924) is still happily in existence, having been purchased for restoration in 1967 by the Paddle Steamer Preservation Society, and is currently being restored to an operational condition on the River Medway near Rochester.

Sussex Coast

After World War I the excursion scene along the Sussex coast was dominated by the presence of the white-funnelled steamers of P. & A. Campbell, who after a short tour of operations from Southampton, concentrated their efforts on establishing a network of services from Brighton and Eastbourne, which spread its tentacles as far as Swanage and Dover. Before the Campbell arrival, however, nineteenth-century excursions in Sussex waters can broadly be defined as those operated by two established companies with offices at Brighton and Hastings, together with the frequent charters of an astute Sussex businessman, Richard R. Collard. It is convenient to deal with these three operators in chronological order, although to some degree their services overlapped during varying periods of co-operation and competition.

A useful date to commence the story of the Brighton steamers is 1878, when a wooden paddle steamer, named after the resort, commenced local trips. Of only 100 gross tons she should not be confused with another *Brighton* which operated cross-Channel services from Newhaven for the London, Brighton & South Coast Railway. Both ships dated from 1878. The *Brighton* (at Brighton) was originally operated by W. S. Gardner. Some nine years later, he sold the vessel for £1,500 to Captain J. Lee who in 1891 formed the Brighton, Worthing & South Coast Steamship Co (which will now be referred to as the Brighton company).

During the previous season, Captain Lee had chartered and operated from Brighton and Worthing a larger vessel named *May*, of 123 gross tons and built in 1875, which later served from Hastings. Shortly after the formation of the Brighton company, the Clyde steamer *Adela* of 1877 was purchased and renamed *Sea Breeze*. With an eye for expanding business in 1893, the company took delivery of their first new vessel which was named *Princess May*. Of 260 gross tons, she replaced the *Sea Breeze*, which was then operated for one season on the Bristol Channel by Campbells, before ultimately finding her way to Marseilles for further service as *La Corse*.

By 1896, competition from Hastings and Newhaven was having its effects on the receipts of the Brighton company, especially after the arrival of the large and fast *Plymouth Belle* on charter to Collard during that year. As an interim measure, Captain Lee chartered the Bristol-based *Lorna Doone* for some two months, and at the same time took steps to order a vessel of no less than 603 gross tons for delivery in 1897. Named *Brighton Queen*, she immediately became a popular and reliable steamer, undertaking many long day and cross-Channel excursions from the Sussex piers. The Brighton fleet received another vessel on a short charter during August and September 1900, named *Jupiter*. She may well have been required during a breakdown or overhaul of one of the other steamers, and no subsequent trace of her on the South Coast has been established.

Captain Lee appears to have had some disagreement with the Brighton company about this time, because in 1901, he set up once again on his own account and purchased the *Diana Vernon* of 1885 from the North Bristol Steam Packet Co and the nearly new *Tantallon Castle*, built in the previous year for the Galloway Steam Packet Co. The former was renamed *Worthing Belle* and the latter

The *Brighton Queen* approaches the Palace Pier at Brighton at 10.10am on a summer morning in 1911. The main structure of the pier remains little changed today, although regular calls by pleasure steamers are but a memory

The *Worthing Belle*, although slow and of modest size, operated many successful short excursions from Littlehampton and Worthing under the ownership of Captain Lee between 1901 and 1913. She was then sold to Turkish interests for a further spell of duty

Sussex Belle. There were probably financial difficulties from the start, and by the following season both ships were operated under separate financial arrangements. The *Worthing Belle* became the property of Lee Ltd (surely the shortest name of any steamer operator), whilst the *Sussex Belle* ran for the Sussex Steam Packet Co. At the end of 1902, following the introduction of regular Campbell excursions along the Sussex coast, the *Sussex Belle* was sold, renamed *Rhos Colwyn* and operated along the North Wales coast (q.v.). The *Worthing Belle*, operating from Worthing and Brighton, was able to continue in service for Captain Lee until after the 1913 season, when she was sold to Turkey for service on the Bosphorus under the name of *Touzla*, thus ending Captain Lee's association with the excursion scene.

The Brighton company had no need for additional tonnage after the delivery of *Brighton Queen* in 1897 and continued in business for a further five years, despite Lee's opposition, until 1902, when the company was

bought outright by P. & A. Campbell. They considered the elderly wooden *Brighton* too obsolete to run under their flag and she shortly came to a rather untimely end for a veteran, being burnt out whilst berthed at Shoreham. *Princess May* was not operated by Campbells on the South Coast; instead she was transferred to the Bristol Channel and after a brief spell on the Cardiff to Weston service was sold to Italian interests at Costellamare with the name of *Princepessa Yolanda*. *Brighton Queen* was modified during the winter of 1902 and reappeared with the typical Campbell profile of a fully plated flush-decked steamer.

We should now consider operations at Hastings, which were of course affected by Campbells' arrival. Prior to this, a number of vessels had sailed under various local owners and the resort was a popular call for most, if not all, of the other Sussex-based concerns. The first Hastings vessel appears to be the *Carrick Castle*, an ex-Clyde vessel built in 1872. She had been operated at Leith since 1881, and was purchased four years later by A. Payne, who had formed the Hastings and St Leonards Steamship Co. (This practice of forming companies which incorporated the names of the principal resorts from which its steamers were intended to sail was prevalent at this time, as will be noted elsewhere.) In the following season, her sailings were augmented by a small steam launch named *Albatross*, which could hardly be classed as an excursion steamer and appears to have been operated in 1886 only, presumably on short trips between the piers at Hastings and St Leonards and may well have been used as a feeder to the 176 gross tons *Carrick Castle*.

In the following season the paddle steamer *Nelson* appeared on charter to J. Buckett, a local wine merchant, both vessels sailing against opposition provided by R. Collard of Newhaven, of which more anon. Buckett and a Mr Wood appear to have joined forces to combat Collard's intervention with the result that the original Hastings company was reconstituted into the Hastings, St Leonards and Eastbourne Steam Boat Co in 1888. The new concern took delivery of a new twin-screw steamer named *Lady Brassey*. In the same year *Carrick Castle* was sold to Edwards & Robertson of Cardiff and became the *Lady Margaret*. Before the start of the 1889 season, *Nelson* was bought by Collard. This rather unexpected change of ownership may have been necessary to finance the new *Lady Brassey*. For the height of that season the Hastings company chartered a paddle tug named *Conqueror* which, in common with many of her type, possessed a passenger certificate. She had been previously owned by Sandford & Co at Gravesend, where she operated mainly in her role as a tug. Further financial problems beset the Hastings concern when trade did not match expectations, and the *Lady Brassey* was sold. In her place a second-hand vessel of 107 gross tons named *Seagull* was acquired. Built in 1877, she had previously been owned by J. Steel of Glasgow and was another example of a passenger-certificated tug.

In July 1892, she was joined by the *Glen Rosa* of 254 gross tons on charter from the Thames. The following season was operated by the *Seagull* and a further charter of the *Conqueror*, the latter even venturing as far as Boulogne, Dover and Brighton. A similar arrangement occurred in 1894. The success of the long day and cross-Channel excursions was instrumental in the Hastings company acquiring two larger, fully equipped passenger steamers in 1895 and 1896. The first was the ex-railway cross-Channel vessel, *Alexandra*, which had been previously occupied on the Newhaven to Dieppe service since 1863. After an accident in which she ran on to the rocks near Dieppe, she had been salvaged, reconditioned and sold for further service in the Bristol Channel and along the North Wales coast. Although elderly, she was reboilered in 1893 and, with a passenger certificate for 600 and a gross tonnage of 332, was considered suitable by the Hastings company to accommodate the potential trade from Sussex piers. *Seagull* was withdrawn and broken up shortly after *Alexandra* entered service. The second cross-Channel vessel was named *Ruby* and was an even older vessel, constructed in 1854 to run between Weymouth and the Channel Islands. She had originally been titled *Aquila* and like her consort had seen a brief spell of service in the Bristol Channel. *Ruby* was either too old or too slow, and after a short season of only seven weeks was withdrawn and is recorded as having been broken up at Calais in 1899. The company looked around for a suitable replacement and acquired the *Bonnie Princess* from the Liverpool & North Wales Steamship Co. Although a comparatively new vessel, she was mainly employed on short runs between Hastings and Eastbourne; her 440 gross tons would have made her an ideal cross-Channel vessel. No attempt was made to retain the vessel in service in 1897, despite the extra trade that was generated by Queen Victoria's Diamond Jubilee and the Naval Review. It appears that the purchase of *Bonnie Princess* was only a stop-gap measure whilst plans and contracts were drawn up for a new steamer which entered service in 1897. She was named *Britannia*, a flush-decked steamer with a gross tonnage of 318 and speed of some 14 knots. (This vessel should not be confused with Campbell's ship of the same name, which was then running the Bristol Channel.)

The nearby resort of Eastbourne had a steamer of its own in 1898 when C. Dray chartered the former North British steamer, *John Stirling*, which latterly had been owned by the Ship Canal Passenger Co of Manchester. Her main excursions were between Eastbourne, Hastings, Newhaven and Brighton but she made one epic three-day voyage to Weymouth, leaving Hastings and calling at Eastbourne, Southsea and Bournemouth. Since *John Stirling* did not return in subsequent seasons, we can assume that Dray was out of pocket at the end of his charter.

Alexandra and *Britannia* kept on sailing for the Hastings, St Leonards and Eastbourne Co, but by the end of 1903, the opposition from the recently arrived Campbell steamers was having its effects and early in 1904, *Britannia* was sold to the Glasgow & South Western Railway which renamed her *Vulcan*. *Alexandra* ran for one more season before being sold at the end of 1904 for £900 to the breakers.

The demise of the original Hastings company led to a brief flurry of competition in 1905, when a new company bearing the same title ran the *Cynthia* of 1892, on charter from H. C. Jones of London, and another concern, the South of England Steamboat Co, operated the ex-General Steam Navigation Co's steamer, *Halcyon*. Both concerns finished the season licking their financial wounds and passed into oblivion.

Having related the histories of the two main Sussex companies, we must now examine the services provided by Richard Collard of Newhaven, whose charters and purchases were all too often a thorn in the side of his competitors. Collard always operated as an individual and never formed a company. He was a man of substance and tenacity, with a flair for steamer operations which lasted from 1887 until 1911. In the same year as Captain Lee purchased the *Brighton*, Collard chartered a small wooden steamer named *May* from John Wood of Hull. She proved a slow but reliable vessel, taking nine hours to steam from Hastings to Ryde to witness a Naval Review. Whilst at Ryde, Collard was offered a lucrative charter to take passengers to view the assembled fleet, with the result that his original Sussex complement were informed that they had the choice of staying at their own expense a further twenty-four hours on the Isle of Wight or to return home by rail! *May* was retained for the 1888 season but as already related Collard acquired Lee's *Nelson* in 1889 and ran her until 1897. *May* was returned to Hull and was subsequently purchased and used as a tug for the Great Western Railway until 1930. To supplement the services run by *Nelson*, a number of charters took place: *Lynton* in 1893, *Halcyon* in 1894 and *Plymouth Belle* in 1896 and 1897.

This last steamer was, like the *Cambria* at Southampton (q.v.), to have a profound effect on future steamers and services in Sussex waters. *Plymouth Belle* was bigger, faster and more luxurious than any excursion vessel hitherto seen in the area. She inaugurated cross-Channel trips to Boulogne from all the principal Sussex resorts and was directly responsible for the ordering of *Brighton Queen* to meet her challenge, as well as the charter of *Lorna Doone* in August and September 1896 prior to the delivery of the Brighton company's new vessel. As is often the case, however, there was insufficient custom for two large vessels competing for the same trade, and Collard did not feel inclined to continue with the charter of *Plymouth Belle*, with the result that she was then purchased outright by a concern known as South Coast & Continental Steamers with offices at Southampton in 1898. But before the following season *Plymouth Belle* was sold to be a tender to the Hamburg-Amerika Line, renamed *Wilkommen* and operated between Hamburg and Heligoland until 1925.

Collard now appears to have retired from pleasure steamer operations until 1903, when he purchased the paddle steamer *Southampton* from her owners at that port. She was run from Newhaven, Eastbourne and Hastings and occasionally across the Channel. He seems to have astutely filled the gaps in the Campbell services. When this small vessel was sold to the Liverpool & North Wales Steamship Co in 1907, she was replaced by a former North British Steamship Co vessel which had latterly been sailing from Naples. One of a very few examples of British vessels being repurchased to sail again under the Red Ensign, the *Lady Rowena*, of 332 gross tons and built in 1891, was operated by Collard until 1911 when she was sold to A. W. Cameron for service on the Clyde. (She reappears briefly in these waters again after World War I.) With the departure of *Lady Rowena*, Collard retired permanently as a steamship operator.

Although the extension of P. & A. Campbell activities from the Bristol Channel has already been stressed, it is important to view their arrival in relation to the services operated at the time of the purchase of the ships and goodwill of the Brighton, Worthing & South Coast Co in the winter of 1901/2. With the exception of *Brighton Queen*, all the vessels operated along the Sussex coast were elderly and approaching obsolescence. Neither the Brighton nor the Hastings company was in a position to acquire newer vessels, and Collard had for years played the waiting game, filling

in gaps that the other operators had left in their operational network. Campbells were entering the arena possessing a fleet of comparatively modern vessels and with the psychological advantage that they had seen off most of the opposition in the Bristol Channel. They also had sufficient financial backing to make a prolonged attempt to capture the Sussex trade and could draw upon considerable operating experience. When established in Sussex waters, they operated only two vessels, even in the height of the season, between 1902 and 1905. A third unit was added from 1906 until services were suspended with the outbreak of war. Throughout those years, *Brighton Queen* undertook the longer trips as far as Dover and Bournemouth and was the mainstay of the cross-Channel excursions, being assisted by *Glen Rosa* and *Bonnie Doon* from 1906 onwards until the latter was

Captain Hector MacFadyen of the *Bonnie Doon* from a photograph taken of him between 1906 and 1910. His ship was nicknamed the 'Bonnie Breakdoon', although she does not seem to have suffered any greater number of mechanical misfortunes than other steamers

The *Brighton Belle* was the principal short-distance steamer from the Sussex resorts between 1923 and 1935. Her immediate post-war service was on the Bristol Channel and she was unfortunately lost during the evacuation from Dunkirk in May 1940

P. S. BRIGHTON BELLE.

replaced by *Waverley* for the 1911 season and *Ravenswood* thereafter.

After the war Campbells, because of their war losses and the fact that *Waverley, Glen Rosa* and *Albion* were unfit for reconditioning, were unable to reopen their South Coast services until 1923. Before their return, attempts to provide excursions were made by F. C. Deering who brought the much travelled *Lady Rowena* back again. She ran only in 1921 and was sold for breaking during the following year. Two further attempts were made in 1922 to establish services: a concern known as Channel Excursion Steamers Ltd purchased the *Woolwich Belle* from the Thames and renamed her *Queen of the South*; whilst the newly formed Cinque Ports Steam Navigation Co chartered the *Emperor of India* from Cosens until the return of the Campbell vessels. This charter was not renewed in 1923 and the *Queen of the South* was sold to the New Medway Steam Packet Co at the end of that season.

Campbells' long-distance steamer became the *Devonia*, supported by *Ravenswood* and *Lady Evelyn*, renamed *Brighton Belle*. In 1926 *Ravenswood* was retained in the Bristol Channel, her place being taken by the former *Barry*, now renamed *Waverley*. Further changes took place in 1933 when *Devonia* was replaced by her sister ship *Lady Moyra*, which now sailed as the second *Brighton Queen*. *Waverley* was operated on the Bristol Channel in 1933 and 1934, but returned to take the place of *Brighton Belle* in 1936; the newer *Glen Gower* was sent south in 1934 to maintain the now firmly established three-ship service, up to the outbreak of World War II.

In 1947 *Glen Gower* returned to reopen services again but was replaced in July by the large new turbine vessel *Empress Queen*, which had been ordered before the war with cross-Channel services in mind. These had been forbidden by government restrictions on foreign travel and for the next three years, *Empress Queen* was only allowed to run on coastline excursions, backed up in 1948 and 1949 by the paddler *Britannia* which, although reboilered, was an ageing steamer. In 1950, Sussex services were downgraded to a single-vessel service, *Glen Gower* opening the season with *Empress Queen* replacing her in mid-season. Unfortunately even this did not pay,

with the result that *Empress Queen* was transferred to Torquay in 1951, and for the first time since the turn of the century there was no welcoming plume of smoke at Sussex piers. Campbells returned in 1952, sending their post-war paddler *Cardiff Queen* to regain trade. She returned in the following year, operating to Shanklin and Folkestone, but was replaced for the next three seasons by *Glen Gower*. No-passport trips to France were allowed in 1955, which gave a welcome boost to trade — it was perhaps a pity that *Empress Queen* had been sold in the spring of that same year. *Glen Gower*'s final season in the south was 1956, and complete withdrawal was not far away following a number of seasons of poor weather. Campbells chartered the *Crested Eagle*, a motor vessel of 245 tons in 1957 but after another season of indifferent weather, the company decided that it was no longer feasible to operate along the South Coast and made their final withdrawal.

With no Sussex-based excursion steamer in 1958, the outlook seemed bleak, and coupled with continual withdrawal of steamers elsewhere the prospect of a resumption of services by an established operator was remote. However, two further opportunities occurred in the early 'sixties with steamers that had been withdrawn elsewhere: the railway paddle steamer *Freshwater*, 263 gross tons, which had run between Lymington and Yarmouth (IOW), was withdrawn at the end of 1959 and shortly afterwards purchased by H. Jennings of Budleigh Salterton. Renamed *Sussex Queen*, she ran a number of coastal excursions in 1960, mainly from Brighton and Eastbourne, but unfortunately lacked the speed and size of the Campbell paddlers and was unable to cross the Channel. Her owner transferred the vessel to Bournemouth for the following season. Three years later the ex-Cosens paddler *Consul* was based at Newhaven and she too ran a small number of excursions before returning to the more sheltered waters of Weymouth in 1966.

Although there are no longer any traditional excursion steamers from which to view the Sussex coastline, cheap cross-Channel excursions are abundantly available by coach connections to Folkestone and Dover and a number of small launches continue to provide the opportunity to go to sea.

THE THAMES

The accommodation for passengers is most complete and conveniently arranged. Those travelling with saloon tickets are entitled to the use of the promenade deck, the social hall on the main deck, and the first class dining saloon just below . . .

At the entrance to the social hall there is a retiring room for ladies, fitted with lavatories and with a stewardess in attendance. The accommodation also includes a parcels and cloakroom, where light articles may be deposited during the trip; refreshment bars on the promenade deck and in the fore and aft dining saloons.

(Handbook of the 'Belle Steamers and Royal Sovereign', 1926)

The *Sunday Times* of 3 June 1827 recorded its approbation of pioneer efforts to commence passenger services to Kent in the following words: 'The Public are highly indebted to the General Steam Navigation Company for the public spirit they have so laudably exhibited in applying the great discovery of Steam Navigation to the purposes of trade, warfare, quick communication, and of amusement. They on Tuesday accomplished a design which a few years back would have been considered incredible and impracticable, that of going to Margate and back in one day. This great and singular undertaking completely succeeded. The performance of the voyage (nearly 160 miles) in a little more than 15 hours really constitutes an era in the history of navigation.' The trip was probably undertaken by the paddle steamer *Eagle*, a small vessel of some 56 tons, equipped to travel by sail and steam and with a thin funnel as high as her foremast. The General Steam Navigation Co had been formed some three years previously in 1824, and it was this company that was to develop and maintain marine excursions from London on a regular basis for over 140 years.

It was not until 1887, however, that the General Steam Navigation Co decided, in view of impending competition and the obsolescence of a number of their vessels, that it was time to order no less than five steamers, all of which were delivered within the successive two years. This ranked as the largest number of steamers ever delivered to a British operator within such

a short period. The *Halcyon, Mavis, Oriole, Laverock* and *Philomel* constituted a fleet that other operators would have been foolish to challenge and ensured that the General Steam Navigation Co was able to take full advantage of the increasing London traffic, especially at summer weekends. Besides serving Southend and the Kent resorts of Margate and Ramsgate, existing and additional services were operated along the Essex and Suffolk coasts as far as Great Yarmouth. The quintet were fitted with twin-cylinder diagonal engines, comfortable full-width saloons and were capable of making as much as 17 knots when driven hard. A further addition to the fleet was added in 1898 and named *Eagle* to perpetuate the title of their earlier vessel. In 1909 she inaugurated a service from Tilbury to Southend, Margate, Ramsgate, Deal and Dover.

No further new tonnage was needed until the *Halcyon* was sold in 1905. Her replacement took the form of a turbine triple-screw steamer which bore the name *Kingfisher*. Turbine steamers had been introduced on the Clyde and proved to be faster and in many ways more economical than paddle steamers, with a more pleasing (to some) profile. *Kingfisher* was designed for a speed of over 20 knots and ran from Tilbury on cross-Channel excursions to Boulogne. Unfortunately she proved to be a difficult vessel to handle at piers and rolled badly; consequently she was sold to an Italian company in 1912 for service out of Trieste.

(*above*) Packed to capacity, *La Marguerite* slows as she approaches an unrecorded pier head. Although crowded on this occasion, probably a Bank Holiday, she was never financially successful but retained the distinction of being the largest paddle vessel ever to operate on the Thames – 1,554 gross tons

(*opposite above*)The *Eagle* of 1898 was a regular visitor to Margate for thirty years, commencing her run from Fresh Wharf below London Bridge. In July 1909 she inaugurated a service from Tilbury, calling at Southend, Margate, Ramsgate, Deal and Dover. Following her withdrawal in 1929, she was sold to a Dutch firm of shipbreakers and her hull was converted to a landing stage moored on the River Maas, above Dordrecht

(*centre*) A publicity postcard depicting the first turbine steamer built for the General Steam Navigation Co. Despite her speed of 20 knots, *Kingfisher* was difficult to handle and sold after only six seasons

(*below*) The *Koh-i-Noor* arrives in a blustery wind to pick up her passengers. Built in 1892 she was named after the famous diamond which was presented to Queen Victoria on the annexation of the Punjab in 1850. the *Koh-i-Noor* sailed from the Old Swan Pier to Southend, Clacton and Harwich as well as the popular Kent resorts

The General Steam Navigation Co returned to paddle propulsion in 1909 with delivery of the triple-expansion-engined *Golden Eagle*. Like the *Kingfisher*, she was fitted with the now fashionable full-length promenade deck. At the end of her first season, the last of the original quintet, *Mavis*, was withdrawn. *Philomel* had been sold in 1907 for service from Fleetwood, a year later *Laverock* went to Bordeaux and the *Oriole* ended her days on the Thames in 1912, when she was sold to Dutch interests for conversion to a hulk.

The *Golden Eagle* quickly established herself as a popular steamer, being employed mainly on trips to Margate and Ramsgate with occasional diversions across the Channel to Boulogne. Despite their fleet of up-to-date vessels it should not be thought that the General Steam Navigation Co met with no opposition or competition. Efforts to gain trade and patronage came from the rather grandly named Victoria Steamboat Association and the London, Woolwich and Clacton-on-Sea Steamboat Co which later became more generally known as the Belle Steamers.

The Victoria Steamboat Association was responsible for the running of three of the largest and most palatial paddle steamers ever to run on the Thames: the *Koh-i-Noor* (1982), *Royal Sovereign* (1893) and *La Marguerite*

(1894). Initially the trio were owned by separate companies within the association, but in 1895 all three ran under the title of New Palace Steamers Ltd. They were all products of the Fairfield Shipbuilding and Engineering Co which had a financial interest in their operation. All three vessels were twin-funnelled, constructed of steel and capable of nearly 20 knots. The *Koh-i-Noor* made her maiden voyage on the 3 July 1892 from the Old Swan Pier to Southend and Clacton, but she was shortly transferred to the Thanet service and on Saturdays made a double trip from Tilbury to Margate, a service which was later extended as far as Dover. The *Royal Sovereign* could be recognised from her companions by slightly wider spaced funnels and was slightly broader in the beam. The third Fairfield vessel, *La Marguerite*, was expressly intended and used for cross-Channel excursions and, drawing on the operational experience of her two sisters, was the largest, fastest and better equipped steamer. Of 1,554 gross tons she was nearly twice the tonnage of the other two vessels and for ten seasons became the most popular excursion vessel on the Thames.

Unfortunately, because of their size and fuel consumption, none of the three vessels were able to make a consistent profit. Fairfields demanded that steps be taken to rectify the situation, and in 1904, *La Marguerite* was sold for service from Liverpool. The *Koh-i-Noor* was in need of reboilering in 1914, and just before the outbreak of war had been sent to the Clyde to have them installed. She remained laid up during hostilities but apparently deteriorated, with the result that she was sold for scrapping in 1918 and cut up at Morecambe during the following year. The *Royal Sovereign* had been reboilered in 1909, but she too was laid up during the war. Afterwards she returned to service on the Thames under the ownership of the Royal Sovereign Steamship Company Ltd, changing ownership again in 1929 when she passed for £5,540 to General Steam Navigation. She ran for one season before being sold in February 1930 to Dutch shipbreakers.

The origins of the London, Woolwich and Clacton-on-Sea Steamboat Co are a little more complex. The company had arisen from the desire of the directors and shareholders of Clacton pier to obtain a sizeable proportion of the ever-increasing number of excursionists from London. The company was formed in 1887 and immediately ordered a steamer for delivery during the following year. Aptly named *Clacton*, she entered service on 17 May 1888, leaving the Old Swan Pier daily at 9.30am for a round trip to the fast-developing Essex resorts and arriving back at 8.30pm. She immediately came into competition with the new vessels of the General Steam Navigation Co and after only one season was sold to Turkey for service on the Bosphorus. The Clacton entrepreneurs, however, seem to have had second thoughts and during the next six years ordered from Denny Brothers of Dumbarton, four new vessels: the *Clacton Belle* (1890), *Woolwich Belle* (1891), *London Belle* (1893) and *Southend Belle* (1896). Although generally similar in outline, with a single funnel and open foredeck, they were all of different dimensions with displacements which varied from 198 to 738 gross tons. Thus the company could, if they wished, vary the capacity of their routes at short notice.

In 1897 the company was reconstituted as Belle Steamers Ltd and ordered two more vessels, the *Walton Belle* (1897) and *Yarmouth Belle* (1898). A further financial rearrangement occurred in 1898 and the six steamers passed to the ownership of the Coast Development Corporation Ltd, to be joined by a seventh and final 'Belle' steamer, the *Southwold Belle* of 1900. At the peak of their operations the Coast Development Corporation owned seven steamers, five piers and the Grand Hotel at Southwold.

Thus by the turn of the century, London enjoyed a variety of choice only rivalled by the fleets that operated along the South Coast and the Clyde. The competition that ensued resulted in the sale of *Southwold Belle* after the 1911 season. It was said that her withdrawal was necessary in order to raise cash for a large outstanding coal bill. The oldest member of the fleet was sold in the following year, when the *Clacton Belle* was purchased by the P.S.M. Syndicate Ltd, formed by A. W. Pilchard, two brothers named Shankhand and de Mathos. It was these same four gentlemen who were the original directors of the Royal Sovereign Steamship Co in 1919.

All Thames services were suspended during World War I, but before leaving the pre-war scene, mention should be made of the attempts to run services by the London County Council.

On 17 June 1905 the LCC inaugurated a service between Hammersmith and Greenwich with a fleet of no less than thirty small steamers. The main idea behind their operation was to provide a waterborne bus service along the Thames, but after only two and a half years, a loss of £164,499 had been sustained. The 'penny steamers' as they became known, were hardly excursion steamers in the more accepted use of the word, but because of the cheapness of their fares gave many thousands an opportunity to view the city from the river and perhaps enjoy their first marine excursion.

After the war, London's sailings recommenced in 1919 with a service provided by the *Royal Sovereign* to Margate. At the end of the year there emerged the New Medway Steam Packet Co, in effect a financial rearrangement of a concern without the prefix 'New' which had operated on the Medway since 1881, and which was in turn the successor to a company which had been formed in 1837 with the objective of operating a ferry link between Sheerness and Chatham. The pre-war Medway Steam Packet Co had purchased the *Lady Margaret* from the Bristol Channel in 1888 and ran her in company with two very elderly paddlers named *City of Rochester* (1847) and *Alma* (1855). *Lady Margaret* was followed by a new steamer named *Princess of Wales*, delivered in 1896, which enabled the

older vessels to be withdrawn and scrapped by the turn of the century. In 1904, after a disastrous fire which destroyed *Lady Margaret*, the company took delivery of their second *City of Rochester* but services ceased when both their ships were taken over by the Admiralty during the war. Both vessels were returned in time for the 1920 season.

One of the directors of the New Medway Steam Packet Co was Captain S. J. Shippick who had run two small steamers from Bournemouth before the war (q.v.). One of these was named *Audrey*, and after the outbreak of war had been operated on a government ferry service at Chatham. By 1923 *Audrey* was again available and Captain Shippick acquired the vessel once more to operate under the New Medway Steam Packet flag. From a modest start, operating from Strood to Southend, services were increased to as far as Great Yarmouth, and eventually cross-Channel to Calais and Boulogne.

In 1924 the company acquired the ex-*Woolwich Belle*, which had been renamed *Queen of the South* and had operated for the previous two seasons at Brighton in the absence of the Campbell steamers on that station. They also ordered a paddle steamer, to be named *Medway Queen*, which was the first

The *London Belle* passes through Tower Bridge whilst horsedrawn traffic waits for the roadway to be lowered

(*above*) The *Medway Queen* prepares for a further season of service to Southend and Margate

(*right*) A sad moment as the *Medway Queen*, last of the vessels owned by the New Medway Steam Packet Co approaches Herne Bay Pier on her last service voyage in 1963

new vessel to enter service in the Thames area since the *Golden Eagle* of 1909. With a full-length promenade deck, she was later to gain fame at Dunkirk and to become the last regular excursion steamer on the Thames. In the following year, the *Walton Belle* was also acquired and renamed *Essex Queen*; this made the *Princess of Wales* redundant and she was sold for a further spell of service on the Firth of Forth.

The General Steam Navigation Co also decided to add new tonnage and an order was placed with J. Samuel White & Co at Cowes for a vessel of 1,100 tons to be named *Crested Eagle*. She was 299ft in length and delivered in time for the 1925 season. The *Crested Eagle* has earned herself a place in history as being the first excursion steamer to be fitted for burning oil. In May 1937 she was moored in the Thames off the Embankment and used as a grandstand for the Coronation procession of

King George VI, but three years later she was one of the many pleasure vessels lost at Dunkirk.

The development of new services and the need for steamers to operate them resulted in the conversion of two ex-Admiralty paddle minesweepers in 1928 and 1929 at the company's own yard at Rochester. They entered service as the *Queen of Kent* (formerly HMS *Atherstone*) and *Queen of Thanet* (formerly HMS *Melton*) and were useful additions to the fleet, whose ports of call now included Dunkirk, Gravesend, Clacton, Yarmouth and Dover. With a speed of 16 knots, they were easily recognisable by their widely spaced twin funnels, but as is often the case with former warships, they were expensive ships to run with a high fuel consumption.

The financial slump of this period had resulted in the demise of the four remaining 'Belle' steamers. The *London Belle* and *Clacton Belle* went to the breakers, and the New Medway Steam Packet Co purchased the *Yarmouth Belle*, which they promptly renamed *Queen of Southend*. The *Southend Belle* meanwhile was sold to E. Kingsman who owned Clacton pier; she was also renamed and emerged as *Laguna Belle*. The General Steam Navigation Co had acquired the *Royal Sovereign* but ran her on their own account only for the 1929 season and she was subsequently broken up in Holland. The remaining casualty of this 'shake up' was the little *Audrey*, which was sold for £500 to be scrapped at Grays, Essex. The New Medway Steam Packet Co advertised their vessels as 'The Queen Line' and, together with the vessels of General Steam Navigation, operated successfully throughout the 1930s.

Kingsman's *Laguna Belle* offered some competition as she operated from Tower Bridge, Greenwich and Woolwich to Clacton, rather than the other way about. An interesting development of this period was the operation by the Port of London Authority of dock cruises. They would arrange for the charter of vessels to undertake short sightseeing excursions which became very popular, but the authority did not confine themselves to any particular operator. As a result several second-line vessels were purchased by the General Steam Navigation and New Medway companies to accommodate the PLA traffic and for their own shorter routes. In 1931 and 1932 the New Medway company used the *Essex Queen*, making a morning trip from Chatham to Tower Pier and returning the same evening.

In 1932 a new paddle steamer named *Royal Eagle* was delivered for the General Steam

Navigation Co. Her 1,539 gross tons made her only 15 tons smaller than *La Marguerite*, and she was luxuriously fitted out with observation lounges and a sun-deck. Rather surprisingly she retained the old-fashioned feature of her bridge being situated behind her funnel, this probably assisted going astern in certain reaches of the Thames and was a feature of all the three 'Eagle' paddlers.

In 1933 the General Steam Navigation Co was asked to undertake the PLA cruises and purchased the *Isle of Arran*, built in 1892 and previously operated from Glasgow to Arran. In the same year the New Medway company acquired a twin-screw vessel, which had gained fame during World War I, as being suitable for the PLA work. She was the ferry *Royal Daffodil* that had plied between Liverpool and Birkenhead and had assisted HMS *Vindictive* during the operation at Zeebrugge in 1918. She replaced the *Rochester Queen* which had operated only during the 1933 season and had been better known as the London, Midland & Scottish Railway ferry *Gertrude*, operating between Tilbury and Gravesend. Yet another acquisition appeared at the end of 1934 when

The *Queen of Kent* (later *Lorna Doone*) crowded with passengers for one of the Kent resorts passes Chatham. Note the destroyer in the background. Originally built as a minesweeper in World War I, she was better known as an excursion vessel of the New Medway Steam Packet Co but later served in the Solent area

The dining saloon, deck lounge and cocktail bar of the *Royal Eagle*, a popular and once well-known vessel on her service between London, Southend and Margate. No less than 322 passengers could be served at one sitting, whilst the bar was described as 'a popular retreat for gentlemen passengers'

the ex-Southern Railway paddler *Duchess of Kent* was renamed *Clacton Queen*. The company had little success with this vessel; possibly she was too slow and she was surplus to requirements when a new screw vessel was delivered in 1935. In November of that year, she was sold to operate excursions from Liverpool and New Brighton to Blackpool, rather belatedly being named *Jubilee Queen*, since King George V's Jubilee had taken place some months previously.

The new motor vessel of 1935 had been built by Denny's and was named *Queen of the Channel*. Capable of 19 knots, she was nicely proportioned with an open bridge and dummy fore-funnel. She was operated on cross-Channel excursions from Tilbury to Ostend, Calais and Boulogne. The colour scheme adopted for *Queen of the Channel* and subsequent motor vessels of the fleet consisted of a white hull and buff funnels to which replicas of the company's house-flag were later added. Rather interestingly one of her two Sulzer diesel engines was built in Switzerland and the

other under licence by Denny' at Dumbarton. Such was the success of this ship that the New Medway Steam Packet Co ordered a larger and more commodious vessel which entered service in time for the 1937 season. Reviving the name of *Royal Sovereign*, she was capable of 21 knots and was scheduled to leave London at 8.40am calling at Southend *en route* for Ostend. The return journey left the Continent at 8.00pm but the sea trip was terminated at Tilbury where her passengers disembarked and returned by special train. On other occasions she would be billed to run from Yarmouth, Clacton or Felixstowe to Calais.

By 1937 the New Medway Steam Packet Co and the General Steam Navigation Co had become part of the same concern when the latter purchased the share capital of the Medway company, although the two concerns retained their separate identities as far as the general public was concerned. Before the 1937 dock cruises, the *Isle of Arran* was withdrawn and scrapped, her place being taken by the *Royal Daffodil*, but her capacity proved inadequate and she was sometimes supplemented by other members of the fleet. At the end of the season she was withdrawn and sold for scrapping in Belgium, her place in 1938 being taken by *Queen of Southend* which was then renamed, emerging with the more appropriate title of *Thames Queen*.

No doubt because of their high operating costs, the *Queen of Thanet* and *Queen of Kent* were laid up during 1939; they had in fact been made somewhat redundant by the capacity of the two motor vessels and a third ship which entered service that summer. In an attempt to retain the publicity and fame attached to the previous holder of the name, she was named *Royal Daffodil*. The new ship was nearly 300ft in length and had a gross tonnage of 2,060. All three motor vessels were impressed for service; only the *Royal Daffodil* survived.

Mention must be made of two other short-lived attempts to provide opposition to the vessels and routes of the two established companies. The first was the arrival in 1935 of the *Marchioness of Breadalbane*, a Clyde steamer built in 1890. She was purchased by the Redcliffe Shipping Co and ran a series of excursions from Great Yarmouth and Lowestoft. At the beginning of the following year she operated out of Newcastle upon Tyne before returning to Yarmouth and Lowestoft for the main weeks of the season. Her attempts to be profitable were unsuccessful, and in April 1937 her demise came at the hands of German shipbreakers. The other attempt to gain trade was undertaken by the *Lady Orme* running out of Ramsgate, but this too was short lived and the vessel retreated to the North Wales routes, from whence she had come, by the following season (q.v.).

The post-war scene saw only six vessels of the combined New Medway Steam Packet Co and the General Steam Navigation Co fleets available for commercial use, the remaining vessels having become war casualties or unfit for reconditioning. (The last of the former Belle steamers *Essex Queen* (ex-*Walton Belle*) had survived but had been sold for service from Torquay as the *Pride of Devon*.) They were the *Golden Eagle*, *Royal Eagle* and *Royal Daffodil* in the General Steam Navigation fleet, and the *Medway Queen*, *Queen of Thanet* and *Queen of Kent* in the New Medway Steam Packet colours. Services were resumed in 1946 with *Queen of Thanet* and *Royal Eagle*, with the rest of the vessels being commissioned in time for the following season.

Another ex-warship arrived on the Thames in 1947. Named *Lady Enchantress*, she was an ex-Naval sloop, rebuilt as the Admiralty yacht which had led the Royal Procession around the

fleet in 1937 for the Coronation Review. Under the ownership of The Three Star Shipping Co, she ran from Gravesend to Southend and Margate. After a short season of only six weeks, she was laid up near Gravesend for the next two years, before being towed to Dartmouth to be refitted for excursion work from Torquay during 1950, after which she was again laid up and subsequently scrapped. On a more joyful note, 1948 saw the delivery of the first of two new motor vessels to replace the General Steam Navigation Co's war losses. With the same names as their predecessors, the *Royal Sovereign* and *Queen of the Channel*, together with the pre-war *Royal Daffodil*, they were able to provide a variety of long day trips. To supplement the trio on the shorter and slower runs, the company obtained an ex-landing craft, which was named *Rochester Queen*, and a small motor vessel of 248 tons called *Crested Eagle*, which had previously operated from Scarborough as the *Royal Lady*. The two ex-minesweepers, *Queen of Thanet* and *Queen of Kent*, were now surplus to General Steam Navigation's requirements and were purchased by Red Funnel Steamers of Southampton to replace their war casualties.

The paddle steamer *Golden Eagle* did not enter service in 1950 and the *Royal Eagle* followed her fleet mate into oblivion at the end of that season, leaving the *Medway Queen* as the sole survivor of paddle propulsion in the area.

The motor ships remained in service, and when government restrictions on cross-Channel excursions were lifted in 1954, the *Royal Daffodil* was placed on services from Gravesend and Southend to Boulogne; *Queen of the Channel* ran two days a week from Clacton to Calais and on the other days, excepting Mondays, from Ramsgate to either Boulogne or Calais. A further port of call was opened in 1957 when the new Deal Pier was opened, and for a time it seemed that the remaining vessels were safe from withdrawal. Deal Pier retains the distinction of being the only completely new British pier constructed after World War II.

The final years of *Medway Queen*'s service were affected by the closure, due to the need of repair, of three of her pick-up points: the Sun Pier, Chatham and Sheerness calls were no longer possible, which resulted in her services being limited to those from Strood to Southend

The General Steam Navigation Co., Ltd.

Tuesday, Aug. 12th

Weather and other circumstances permitting

2.40
PROMPT

From Margate Jetty

Back 4.30

2/- Children 1/-

Under 3 Years Free

Free admission to Pier.

(Capt. BRANTHWAITE)

MUSIC

The " Golden Eagle " is now fitted with the Marconi Broadcasting Apparatus which will enable our friends to hear good music while having the benefit of Invigorating Sea Breezes.

GAMES AND SPORTS ON BOARD FOR ALL.

PLENTY OF FUN FOR KIDDIES.

By P.S. 'GOLDEN EAGLE'

Special Long Sea Trip straight out into the North Sea Fishing Grounds towards

THE KENTISH KNOCK

and round the **SOUTH BUOY**

Be sure it is the " Golden Eagle."

Lunches and Refreshments on Board from 1 p.m.

Special Terms to Parties.   Phone: Margate 398

W. L. TOBY, PRINTER, MARGATE.

The ill-fated *Lochinvar* at Newhaven in 1966, a few months before her loss in transit on the north-east coast

and thence across the estuary to Herne Bay, with an occasional diversion to Clacton. At the beginning of 1963 it was announced that it was to be her final season, and in September of that year she made her way to Southend and Herne Bay for the last time. She had gained fame at Dunkirk as being the paddle steamer which had rescued the largest number of survivors from the British Expeditionary Force in 1940, and such was the outcry at her departure that *Medway Queen* was rescued to see further static service as a club and restaurant on the banks of the River Medina, between Cowes and Newport on the Isle of Wight. By the 'seventies her place had been taken by the larger ex-railway paddler *Ryde* and sadly the once proud *Medway Queen* gradually became derelict. By 1982 she was little more than a hulk, holed and resting on the mud of the river, a sad end to a ship which had given pleasure to so many and rescued many thousands from the sands of Dunkirk.

The General Steam Navigation motor ships met with competition in the summer of 1960, when a converted ex-Admiralty Fairmile motor launch was placed in service by C. Harvey and Lt Cdr W. Foreman between Southend and Sheerness. After a successful season she was sold for further service in the Mediterranean and her place taken by the MV *Lochinvar*, built in 1908 and an ex-member of the Scottish MacBrayne fleet. Renamed *Anzio 1*, she had a class 4 certificate for 351 passengers and remained in service until the rebuilding of Sheerness Harbour affected her service and timetable. After a period of lay-up, she was sold in 1966 and was due to operate from Inverness. Unfortunately she foundered on her delivery voyage whilst off Spurn Head, with the loss of her entire crew.

Another more serious threat to the profits of GSN came in the summer of 1965, when a Swedish company operated a passenger and car ferry to France. The ship was of 2,607 gross tons and ran under the title of *The Londoner*, although her registered name was *Stena Nordica*. For the following season this ship was replaced by the slightly larger (2,240 gross tons) *Prinsessan Christina* which still operated under the same pseudonym. The cream of the GSN traffic had been skimmed, and although *The Londoner* took the form of a much smaller vessel named *Stena Baltica*, 1,200 gross tons, the company decided that their days of excursion sailings were over. They sought to diversify and a number of their more experienced staff were becoming involved with a project to open up a car ferry service between Southampton and Le Havre. This operation was originally entitled Southern Ferries but emerged as Normandy Ferries, now, like the General Steam Navigation Co, a part of the P. & O. shipping group.

The final attempt to run excursions by private ownership came in 1966 and 1967 when the ex-Scottish paddle steamer, *Jeanie Deans* was purchased by D. Rose and run by the Coastal Steam Packet Co. Renamed *Queen of the South*, she ran from Tower Pier to Southend, Herne Bay or Clacton. As had been the case in the history of previous vessels run by individuals or comparatively small concerns, financial success was not forthcoming, with the result that *Queen of the South* was towed away in December 1967 to be broken up at Antwerp.

At the end of December 1966, it was announced that the three remaining excursion vessels *Royal Daffodil, Royal Sovereign* and *Queen of the Channel* were to be withdrawn and GSN would no longer provide excursions from Tower Bridge. Their announcement stated in a few words the reason behind their loss of clientele: 'Whereas Mum and Dad used to take the children down the river by ship, they are now taking them by car to the Continent.'

In February 1967 the *Royal Daffodil* made her final Channel crossing to the breakers. The *Royal Sovereign* during the same year was converted to carry cars and renamed *Autocarrier*. The *Queen of the Channel* remained forlornly laid up in the Medway until a buyer was finally found in the following year, when she was sold to Greek interests and sailed away under the much shorter name of *Oia*.

The sun had not quite set on Thames sailings, however. In 1969, P. & A. Campbell sent a former Isles of Scilly motor vessel *Queen of the Isles*, then under charter, to perform a restricted service from Eastbourne and Hastings, but included in her itinerary, a Saturday service from Tower Pier to Southend and Margate. Some Sunday sailings were also operated from Southend to Calais. There were also a few sailings to Ostend from the Kent resorts. Once again the venture did not prove financially successful and at the end of the season Campbells stated that there would be no sailings in 1970.

In December 1970 the *Swanage Queen*, previously owned by Crosons of Bournemouth, was sold to Meridian Line Cruises of Greenwich. Although she is mainly employed on charter work and only runs a very limited public service on short river cruises, she at least provides some opportunity to view the Thames and part of the routes area operated by the many fine vessels mentioned in this chapter.

Me

Myself

And

Weed

Written By Chris Taylor

FOREWORD/ ROLLING PREP.

I've been stoned every day of my life for the last twenty years. I'm thirty eight.

I've used that many excuses over two decades for why I do it that I can't even remember what the true root of it all really is.

  That's what this book is about. I want to try and find out if I do it to numb feelings, pain and emotion or because I just like the feeling of getting high.

 If you're reading this and you're a pure weed geek then apologies in advance.

  For all I've smoked it for twenty years I literally know fuck all about strains and THC and all that jazz. If it's green and it stinks then I'll smoke it. So if you thought this was going to be a guide on how to grow the best chronic then I'm sorry to disappoint.

I've only ever written scripts before so this is my first bash at a book. I've put it off for years because, well I'm usually too stoned. And I never thought I was smart enough. My spelling at times can be atroshus.

  I was always scared to try and write because my knowledge and grammar doesn't match up to "real writers", but one day I thought fuck it, I'm writing this book and I'm writing it my way. That day was eight years ago.

2

I want you to see the mistakes, the dodgy grammar and most of all the way my brain works. I'll go off on tangents and forget where the starting point was. But it'll be me. I don't want to pretend to be a super intelligent novelist. I'm a dope smoking, over emotional bag of anxiety who disguises everything with humour.

This is a mix of stories from childhood to today, all with weed or some kind of drug as the focal point. In no way am I trying to glamorise the lifestyle I lead or the mistakes I made. A lot of people have been hurt over the years due to my addictions and behaviour so I will try to be as sensitive as I can. I have changed everyone's names where the party scene is involved so for any pals reading this, it's all good, yer safe!

I've had a lot of relationships with women over the years and been engaged 3 times but I have left all of this out of the book out of respect for them. And if I did have to mention any I have also changed their names.

Some of them have new men in their lives or have families now and it wouldn't feel right to drag any of them into this. I've been lucky enough to have some amazing girlfriend's/fiancée's over the years , some truly beautiful souls, but I lost most of them to addiction. A couple were just wee cows but we won't go into that.

You'll see my writing evolve with each chapter hopefully as I will not be editing anything when the final draft is complete. Again there WILL be mistakes, there will be discrepancies with dates as I've been stoned for twenty years but it'll be a journey we can hopefully all take together.....Aw man that was wanky as fuck. Wish I hadn't just said I wouldn't edit this. Bastard.

Alright here we go I guess....

If you're a stoner then this book might make you want to stop.

If you're not a stoner then this book might make you want to start.

CHAPTER ONE- FALSE START

My first real experience with cannabis was when I was in first year at Prestwick Academy.

The English block toilets.

All the boys used to go there to smoke the fags they had bought fae old Danny Walsh newsagents that same morning. Danny wasn't known for asking for I.D. If I said the fags were for my mum he would never question it. Most didn't back in the day.

Danny would sell full packs or even individual fags. Singles or singuls we called them.

Each morning I'd use my dinner money to buy a pack of ten Regal Kingsize. They cost one pound thirty six back then. I would sell them to my mates for twenty pence a singul. Seventy pence profit meant I could get two chip rolls from the New Yorker café down Prestwick Main Street at lunchtime and still have enough cash for another pack to smoke for myself. It was a tidy we earner.

The English block toilets were the ideal place to deal and smoke fags. The main door looked right onto the open playground, so we could see teachers coming from every direction thirty yards away. There would always be someone keeping "edgy" at any one time.

We would all be crowded around a bog puffing away like wee Ned goldfish sooking on a hose. Each year would have their designated smoking area.

3rd and 4th year had the back cubicle as that was hidden

around a corner and gave them more time to dispose of any evidence.

2nd Year had the two cubicles in the middle. First years had to congregate around the big dog legged metal urinal with a wet rust stained cream tiled backdrop. We had the worst area because if there was a bust we couldn't hide our fags in the urinal. At least all the other years could flush.

5th and 6th year pupils were usually more sensible. The proof in that being they made it to 5th and 6th year. If any of them smoked they probably did it in the common room.

But in our toilet it was a real working man's environment, for boys. Prison rules applied.

Everyone in there were either pissing, smoking or gambling.

Pogs and Coinsy were the high roller games for kids in the mid nineties. And guaranteed there would always be a couple of boys playing "knuckles" in a corner somewhere. Knuckles was basically when two people played Pontoon/ Blackjack and every time they lost a hand the other player got to wrap the deck of cards right off their knuckles. There was no money to be made, it's just who bled most lost. The trick was to drag the deck downwards as the cards made contact with the skin. It ripped more flesh that way.

I never played knuckles. I was a shite bag.

There was a definite ranking system in the toilets. From fourth year the shite rolled downhill to us first years. Random bog washes were a common practice. A bog wash if you didn't know, was when a group of guys put your head down the toilet pan and flushed it.

Not like in the American movies where they tip you upside down and place your head in the toilet. No it was never as balletic as that in Scotland. A big group of boys would grab you, drag you to your knees then slam you face first into the pan. They usually managed to hit the water by the third or fourth attempt. Split nose and a face full of shitey pish water as they laughed and spanked yer arse.

But you had to laugh. If you didn't they'd kick fuck out you.

Best days of your life.

Despite all that, we did all look out for each other when it came down to smoking politics.

Any time our guard on edgy spotted one of the Jannies (Janitors to all non Scots) they would give us all an "edgy up" and we would all throw our fags to fuck and start filling out the toilet like nervous ants late for work.

For the Janitor this was just a daily routine, but despite the clear cloud of smoke and the floating fag doubts in the urinal, all taken before their time, he never grassed us in. He didn't need to. He just appeared with that scunnered look on his face and we would all run back to class. He was basically a sheepdog for neds.

We respected him more than most teachers. He gave us space most of the time and you could tell he used to be one of us. It was that look in his eyes, as if to say, "I've been there boys, I'll play the game if you do". We never fucked with the Jannie.

One lunch time I couldn't be arsed heading down to the New Yorker café for my chip rolls so I broke routine and headed to the dinner hall for a scran.

I tanned a big plate of chips cheese beans and coleslaw then headed across the playground to the English block for a smoke and a shit. It always felt safer smoking when you were taking a shit because if a teacher was suspect and asked you to open the door you could just yell paedo and they would run like fuck.

Right enough some of them would just stay there and have a wank. (Joke).

As I walked across the playground, the chips cheese beans and coleslaw were swishing about with the Irn Bru in my belly. I can still taste the burps.

As I got closer to the toilets I saw three familiar faces standing at the entrance. My heart fucking sank.

The Sweeney's.

The Sweeney's were Prestwick Academy's equivalent to the Krays Twins, but we had three of them.

Ally, Graham and Walter. They were nice guys, really. But fuck me were they intimidating. Together they were as formidable as a pack of wolves in a petting zoo, but individually they couldn't be nicer. They usually socialised in separate groups, each a general of their own troop. They even had their own patches around the school, like Mafia for minis. They were seldom seen all together. But when they were, you knew some shit was about to go down.

When I saw them all gathered at the English block

toilets, my arse nearly fired my lunch through the dinner hall window twenty feet behind me. But it was too late, they'd seen me. If I'd turned around I'd have got the standard, "Haw ya wee poof are these toilets no good enough for you?" or even the more straight to the point, "Get back here now ya prick!".

Now to let you know a bit about me, I'm a mouthy wee bastard, I can't hold my tongue. So it wasn't only the fear of a doing it was also the absolute terror that ma gub might get me in trouble. It doesn't matter how scared I am I just can't help trying to crack jokes. I think I've got some kind of jokes Tourettes. It's got me in so much trouble over the years as you will find out later on (If I remember to write those stories).

I had no choice but to brave it out and keep walking. I didn't know if it was just because I was getting closer, but their smiles were definitely getting wider. What the fuck were they up to?

I kept walking with my head down, staring at the ground. I'd rather risk a schoolbag off the top of my dome than have to make eye contact with them. I was getting closer and knew I had to look up sooner or later. Between the fear and my lunch swishing about, my arsehole felt like it was trying to deep throat the arse of my boxers.

I looked up.

-Whit you dain here?

It was Walter, the youngest of the Sweeney's. Walter was solid with a heed like a bull, hands like shovels and fingers like fuckin forearms. He always had a shaved head

9

which made him look even tougher.

I looked Glaikit as I tried to come up with something that wouldn't make me sound like a fanny.

-Need a shite.

The brothers looked like three chefs peering down on a big pot, pondering how best to boil this little lobster.

Ally stepped out into the open. He was the middle brother. He was smaller and chubbier than Graham and Walter but just as tough in his own way. One day he's bullying your bully for bullying you and the next he's putting fags out on your cheek because he thinks the "burny noise sounds funny" .

-Only smokers here. Go shite in the music block.

- I smoke, I tell him with a squeak in my already breaking voice.

- Many fags you got, pipes up Graham

Unforeseen predicament.

I know I've got five fags, but if I tell them that then they will take at least five of them. But if I lie and they check my packet they'll kick fuck out me. And then take my fags anyway.

I blurted out without thinking.
-None, was gonnae see if you'd sell me one.

Graham was the quieter of the brothers. He was really tall with almost sheep like blonde wavy hair. A menacing type quiet though. You never knew what Graham was thinking. I think I was intimidated by him more because of that.

He whispers something to Ally.

10

His smile sent my chips cheese beans and coleslaw into full spin.

-Gauntlet! He declares.

A squad of smoker ants flood from the toilets and appear in the doorway faster than it takes my heart to sink. Not the fuckin Gauntlet.

Walter takes the lead.

-Right line up! Nae nose breaks, nae baw punches, nae biting!

All the ants lined up either side of the entrance creating what can only be described as a hostile guard of honour.

The gauntlet was every First Year's nightmare.

A tunnel of fear and pain.

All the older kids lined either side of the entrance to the toilet and you had to get through the man made tunnel as they all threw kicks and punches at you.

Dead arm city.

Some manky bastard always spat at you. There was always a spitter, every time. And there was always at least one blood thirsty cunt that got too carried away .

But you had to laugh, remember?

I didn't even think about it. I just ran head first straight into them all.

I wasn't having anyone think I was weak. But believe me I was.

The first few steps were a painful blur. I stuck a few elbows and jabs back along the way. You had to fight back. If you didn't you'd be seen as an easy target and would be running the gauntlet every day until you left school. But you couldn't fight back too hard as you didn't want to piss them off either.

Just as I was getting to my last pair of swinging gargoyles, some bastard behind me swung his black Slazenger bag onto the top of my head. It slid down the crown of my head and planted me right on the nose.

The straps acted like a lasso around my face and he started to drag me back into the tunnel. I could feel his gym shoes and loose pencils crush my nose down over my top lip.

I landed on my back, cushioned by the odd boot to the spine.

As I looked up an army of soles rained down on me like arrows blotting out the sun.

I shielded as many as I could using my forearms as I clutched my face.

A big rubbery toe punt just missed and grazed my cheek so hard that I swear I could smell burnt flesh.

-Fuckin pack it in ya cunts!

The arrows faded. The sun appeared in form of a flickering lavvy light.

Thank fuck. Had the Jannie saved the day?

-Let him up.

It was Graham.

His smile peaked through the swarm of bodies like the Cheshire Cat's toothy grin lighting up in the darkness.

He throws me one of his fags and nods his approval.

-You Cara's brother?

I was. And still am actually.

-Aye.

Walter the youngest chips in.

-Aw aye, so ye ur. Here, this wee cunts meant tae be daft as fuck. Wur you no stood on a post box telling jokes in Marchburn? Dae something funny.

I was still half conscious from running the gauntlet and now they wanted a fuckin comedy routine.

I'd rather run the gauntlet again.

Think of a joke, think of a fucking joke for fuck sake.

I'd gone blank.

Ally saw the anxiety on my face as a white flag.

-Leave him alone. Let the boy him smoke his fag.

And with those calmly uttered words they all turned back into ant mode and scurried back to their designated smoking/gambling areas.

I gave them a minute just in case they had a change of heart then snuck around to the first years trough.

I couldn't believe it. Not only had I managed to get a pass from the Sweeney's, they'd even given me one of their own smokes.

Then the fear hit and all the radios turned on in my brain.

Hold on, is that me in their debt now? I already had five fags, I didn't need to take one off them. Aw fuck sake Chris that's you in their pocket now. They own you. Dick.

I lit the fag to help me think.

And that's when it happened.

My introduction to cannabis.

I'd literally just started to sook in the cloud of

smoke trapped in my mouth when out he pops from the third year's cubicle. Hammy.

Hammy could hear the spark of a lighter from a hundred yards away while listening to Metallica on his headphones.

Sure as fuck if you lit a fag, he'd pop out of nowhere like a fuckin hologram.

-Twos Taylor!

Two's means, leave me half your fag. You can haggle sometimes and offer three's which is a quarter, depending on how hard the other kid was. If you knew you could beat them in a fight then you would get away with leaving them last draws, two or three good puffs at the most.

But Hammy was harder than me. Most folk were at school.

I knew it would have to be two's but I chanced my luck.

-I'll leave you threes.

-Naw, you'll leemy fuckin twos or ah'll take it aw.

He clearly had his own fags, he always did. But I wasn't going to argue.

Hammy was a fat wee bastard. He looked so pale and unhealthy all the time. But he wasn't scared of anyone. So that's why I was scared of him. People with no fear give me the fear.

He was always sweating and he wore one of those thin gold chains, that was so tight around his neck it left a wee line that made his head look detachable. And his already thinning hair had so much wet look gel in it, it made his napper look constantly greasy

14

Most days he wore one of those woollen navy blue Kickers jumpers. It got tighter on him every year, but he said it was muscle.

-Aye nae bother Hammy, twos then.

I tried to avoid eye contact as much as possible without looking too scared or rude. I started to smoke faster, double reeking it as we would call it. Two puffs in a row, exhale, two puffs, repeat. I just wanted to pass him his two's and get to the toilet to vacate my chips cheese beans and coleslaw. But I had a feeling Hammy wasn't finished with me. I could see his oily wee cogs turning in his brain through his piercing almost grey eyes.

-Here, dae ye puff?

I looked at the cig in my hand. I was confused as surely even Hammy wasn't that thick.

-Fags?

- Naw no fags ya fanny, obviously you fuckin smoke fags.

Now I was the thick one.

-What do you mean then?

I had obviously heard of cannabis here and there by this time but not enough to actually register that this was what Hammy was getting at.

-Dope. Weed?

It registers, but my brain is quick enough to disguise my ignorance.

-Aye course.

-Want tae buy some?

I froze.

Hammy goes into his pocket and pulls out a closed fist.

15

He turns it over and opens his hand to reveal the contents. A few coppers, a pencil sharpener and a tiny little piece of balled up cling film the size of a pea. You couldn't really see what was inside. It was so tightly wrapped the cling film had a light yellow tint.

He lifted the little ball from between the sweaty copper coins and puts the change in his pocket. My hearts was racing. What the fuck was I getting into here? Say something Chris. Abort, for fuck sake, abort! Fake an asthma attack . Shit yourself. Anything, just get the fuck away from this guy. But I froze again and just let him speak.

-Here, there a gram.

He closed his first around the little ball and thrust it towards me. I look around like a meerkat in protective custody in fear that a swat team was about to burst through the windows.

-Fuckin take it then. He thrusts it at me again, this time giving my chest a wee jab. I tried to look for a way out of the situation but everything I said just kept me there longer.

-Much?

-Fiver.

My shoulders relaxed at hearing this. I now had an out. Thank fuck.

-Ah sorry mate, only got a quid.

I passed him his twos with a false look of disappointment. He took the fag but kept an eye on me, using the passing over as time to work out if I was talking

16

shite or not.

-Alright fine, a quid will do, here.

   He thrusts his fist one last time. The jab was more aggressive this time.

- Fuckin take it afore we get caught ya dick.

   I grabbed it from his hand, again without any thought of the outcome. Between his greasy paws and my sweaty palms, fuck knows how I didn't drop it.

   Hammy held out an open palm.

-Quid.

   I gave him a pound then quickly stuffed the cling film into my pocket. I could definitely feel something solid was wrapped inside.

   Hammy finished off the fag with three big draws without exhaling. It was a real talent the amount of smoke he could hold in those fat little fleshy pouches of his. Rumour had it he could finish a full fag in only four draws.

 He flicked the doubt into the urinal. We watched it as it hissed then floated down the trough like an abandoned canoe, bumping into neon yellow icebergs along the way before crash landing into the rusty iron plug grate at the end.

   Hammy exhaled the smoke from his chest. He looked proud of himself. Holding smoke in back in the day was an Olympic sport to us kids.

-I didnae sell you that right?

   I'm half listening but also half shitting my new already deep throated Top Man boxers.

- So do I just like, smoke it then?

He now knew I had never done anything like this before. He smiled, almost relaxed.

-Aye mate, just make a wee roll up, pinch some off the rock then sprinkle it in. Don't show any other cunt though. This is the best of gear. White Moroccan, best stone around. I don't want every cunt knowing I've got it.

I should have clicked there and then. But my naivety prevailed once again.

-Nice one, cheers.

-Grass and yer done in.

I nodded.

Hammy made for the door, counting my pound coin with his coppers in his chubby wee waterlogged palms as he left. The second his surprisingly flat arse disappeared around the corner I went straight into a panic mode again. All my radios turn up full blast.

What if someone searches me and finds this. Why the fuck would anyone search you? What if one of the Sweeney's hears I've got some of the best Moroccan White in town and they want it for themselves? Calm down fuck sake, the Sweeney's hate Hammy, why would he tell them. I'll flush it. But what if it floats? What if they find it and finger print it?

Before I could give my paranoia any answers, I was deafened by the sound of the bell. They had just installed one in the toilets because we always turned up late to class and pretended we couldn't hear it when it rang. I was now stood right underneath it. The fright reminded me I still hadn't been for my lunchtime shit. But it was too late now though. I had to get to Geography.

The last few classes that day were total hell.

I was sweating like Hammy's fingers. I couldn't stop watching the door, half expecting the drug squad to burst in and arrest me at any point .Every second of every hour, just waiting for a teacher to come and haul me to the headmasters office which will now surely be crowded with police, detectives, possibly even the army. I hadn't even smoked anything yet and I was already parra as fuck. If I'd got done with this them ma maw was gonnae fucking kill me. Actually no, this would fucking kill *her.* What would the people at my Granny's church think??

When the last bell finally rang, I shot out of my seat, burst through the doors and ran out of school as if I was doing the gauntlet again. Looking back I was about as covert as a cock in a convent. But I didn't care. I just had to get as far away from that school as I could.

And I didn't stop running.

I Forrest Gumped the shit right out of it.

Adrenaline took over and next thing I knew I was at the Prestwick Oval.

The Oval is a huge patch of land that has two full size 11 aside grass football pitches at the top of a small hill. At the bottom of the hill sits Prestwick baths, an indoor bowling green and a basketball court.

A few feet away from the pool there was a cricket ground and Pavilion.

Two public paths cut up either side of the cricket ground leading to a play park and tennis courts at the top end of the Oval.

It really is a sporting Mecca on reflection.

I hid myself in the bushes on the hills between the football pitches and the pool. I did my Meerkat neck thing again to check for the feds and then raided my pockets for the Moroccan White.

All the radios switched on in my brain again.

What was I doing? Why didn't I just sling it over the first hedge I passed? Well maybe a wee kid could have pick it up and ate it? Even worse….What if a dog scoffed it?

All of these were just excuses though.

In short. I was fucking intrigued.

I hadn't even been drunk before. Yet here I was, in a wee bush staring at a lump of pure Moroccan white. My heart was racing but this time it was different. Not anxious, more like a hot surge of curiosity.

I started to unwrap the cling film. A noise made me panic so I stuck it in my mouth to hide it. The noise was me. My elbow had squished down on an old rusty can of Tizer. I froze for a minute to make sure the coast was clear.

I spat the ball into my hand and continued to unravel it.

How much fucking cling film did he need. The more I unwrapped it the smaller the package began to feel. (A trick I have now become very used to over the years). But what did I know. He said it was a gram and I didn't know what the fuck a gram even was.

I opened the package and the Moroccan White peaked out like a baby crowning. I didn't know what I was expecting, but it wasn't this. It was actually white. I thought hash was brown? But he did say Moroccan *White*.

I started to get excited. Then just like that I made a decision.

Fuck it, I'm gonnae try this. Soon as mum and dad are asleep I'm getting that skylight window cracked open in my bedroom and I'm gonnae see what all the fuss is about.

I had no abuse issues, I had a great childhood, Mum and Dad were strict but loving. Mum was my rock and still is to this day. I had no excuses to start taking drugs. I just really wanted to know what feeling stoned was like. Curiosity has always been a bad influence on me. I just can't help myself sometimes. That's the honest bones of it right there.

-Sheila! Sheila!

Who the fuck was that? I clumsily wrapped the hash back up and forced it into my jacket pocket.

-Sheila! Sheila! A woman kept shouting.

I figure Sheila was her dog. Who the fuck calls a dug Sheila?

She kept shouting.

-Sheila! Sheila darling come to mummy! Sheila!

I spot Sheila.

She's stopped right at my bush and was sniffing away at all the freshly sprayed pishes of the day. She was a golden lab. You could tell she was old as her coat was lighter and she had that sagging bit in the middle dogs get when they've had too many puppies.

Sheila gets a whiff of me all of a sudden and looks straight into my eyes. Her front legs fall as her rear pokes

21

up. She was wanting to play.

It's bad enough I'm carrying drugs, but if that woman caught me in the bush then I would have been done for being a pervert as well as a drug mule.

-Fuck off Sheila, I whispered to the dog as if the dog would reply, "Aw sorry mate, I'll leave you to it".

-Sheila! Sheila! The woman was getting closer

Luckily Sheila spotted her, sprung back onto all fours and bolted away from her owner towards the football pitches. For an older dog she can still fair move. I liked Shiela.

Her shouts turn to screams.

- Sheila! Sheila!! You get back here! Sheila!!!

Her cries fade but I can still hear her frustration.

She was gone.

I flew out of my bush like a starling and legged it down past the cricket pitch and onto Ayr Road.

I gave myself an inner pep talk as I headed for home.

-Play it cool. Go home, plant the hash and wait for everyone to go to bed.

I was starting to enjoy the thrill of it all now.

When I got home, Mum was making a curry in the kitchen. I was so nervous.

-Alright Mum? Everything ok?

She gave me a squint.

-Yeah, why wouldn't it be?

-Just asking. Right I better go get my homework done.

Fuck knows how my Mum didn't twig something was up there and then, because I never did my homework.

I swivelled on my heels and went upstairs to my room to hide my hash under my bed, then waited for dinner. I was acting as cool as a shite in a freezer, but Mum didn't bat an eyelid. She was too busy boiling rice.

After we had all eaten I lay on my bed counting down the hours until everyone went to sleep.

Dad always went to bed first on a week day. He worked hard all his life and was always doing shifts here there and everywhere. My sister Cara wasn't far behind, she loved an early night. Weirdo.

Mum was the barrier. She would always go to sleep around midnight, one o clock, depending on what aunty or friend she was yapping to on the phone that night.

I looked at my football shaped alarm clock. Half bastardin one in the morning and I can still hear UK Gold on the telly downstairs.

Fuck it.

I crept downstairs. The telly was getting louder the closer I get.

Rising Damp. I recognised the theme tune. I eased the living room door open slowly, trying not to let the noise of it scraping the carpet wake mum. I could see the telly. Not Rising Damp, Steptoe and Son. I always mixed those theme tunes up.

Mum was sound asleep on the couch. Specks hanging off her face and snoring away.

Bless.

I closed the door back over but the carpet sounded even louder going against the grain. I decided to leave it open and snuck back upstairs.

It was now or never.

I scooped my stash from under the bed and unwrapped it.

I held the little ball of Moroccan up to the moonlight seeping through the sky light.

That excitement came back again. I was actually holding real drugs.

I sat the White on my bed next to my five fags and a lighter.

Then it hits me.

I've no fucking skins!

After all that. Fuck it, I'll just burn it and inhale the fumes straight off the rock. Remember at this point I knew ABSOLOUTELY FUCK ALL ABOUT WEED.

I cracked open the skylight as quietly as I could, had a listen at the door for waking parents or sister. The coast was clear.

I sparked up the lighter (I always had a lighter to burn newspapers out the back for shits n giggles) and burned just a little corner of my Morrocan White.

Black smoke started to pour from it . I breathed out, said a quick prayer then sucked that smoke like I was taking my last breath.

It stung. Then it stung some more. I tried to muffle my coughs by sticking my face into my Saved By The Bell bed sheets.

But I needed to come up for air so I jumped onto my feet and stuck my head out the skylight. I was spluttering and

24

spitting. It was awful. Truly fucking horrendous.

I started to panic. I needed to get that taste out of my mouth.

It was like burnt rubber.

What the fuck do people see in this drug, I thought to myself as I spat all the saliva from my mouth onto slanted roof outside the window.

I looked at the wee ball of White now lying on the carpet.

I slanted ,my eyes to further inspect it. It had gone all bubbly where I had lit it.

Surely hash doesn't bubble when it burns?

I picked it up, then broke it in half. I gave it a sniff it. That's when the penny finally dropped.

This wasn't white hash. It was broken off piece of a rubber.

Hammy had sold me a fucking eraser.

That fat wee greasy bastard.

I fell onto my bed feeling robbed and disappointed. But for some reason I couldn't stop smiling. You'd think this experience would have put me off. But if anything it had made me even more determined. I had already committed to trying cannabis, and now nothing was going to stop me.

That night I fell asleep thinking of ways I could earn more money to buy weed.

Real weed.

And how much of a cunt Hammy was.

CHAPTER TWO . COUCH SINK

I'm in second year.

First toilet cubicle material now.

I still hadn't smoked a proper joint. I wanted to, God did I want too.

But I was scared.

Not scared, cautious.

I like to think I was in control back then. I was going to choose when and where I got high. It had to be the right time. I wanted to be alone and at peace with my thoughts. I'd seen enough stoner movies now to grasp what the drug actually did. I didn't want anyone around to spoil my first high. I just wanted to lie back on a big comfy mattress, and watch unicorns and talking flowers shag each other.

But things don't always turn out as planned, especially in the weed game.

The day it first happened will be forever scribed into my brain like lovers initials on tree.

It was a Saturday in April. My birthday was the week before. I remember this because I was wearing my Adidas three stripe tracksuit my folks got me. Mum refused at first because she didn't want me to look like a Ned. She used to say.

-I know you are one, but wearing that tracksuit would just confirm it.

She really hated Neds. But she bought me it. I think she

still felt guilty as a few months before she bought me a fake Tommy Hilfiger jumper from the Barrras in Glasgow. I was so excited I just threw it on before school and didn't check it properly. Turns out it said Tommy Hil...Finger...Not Hilfiger.

I got pelters for months for that.

But she redeemed herself with the tracksuit.

I loved that tracksuit. I probably hadn't taken it off since my birthday, but I cared not a jot as I swaggered towards the Toll.

Every time I passed someone the swagger got wider to reveal as much of the tracksuit as I could. I was in a great mood. I was looking galus and I was about to go buy myself some hash with my left over birthday money. Real hash!

The Toll was a housing scheme of tall flats in Prestwick, split down the middle by the main road. One side of the road was the "good Toll" and the other was just called, "The Toll".

The "good Toll" was rough but not stabby rough. "The Toll" was rough. But most of my pals lived there so I felt safe enough, most of the time. And I must make clear that many brilliant people lived at the Toll. It was just stained by the usual bad eggs.

I was born working class but promoted to middle class when my mum and dad both got good jobs. Maybe that's why my Mum didn't want me being a Ned. She was probably scared of losing me to the past she had worked so hard to escape from. And I totally get that now I am a

27

parent.

If you didn't know anyone, then the Toll was probably the scariest place in Prestwick in the nineties. It's not as bad now. But when I was kicking around, there was always something to watch.

But if you were a known face like I say then you were relatively safe.

I once saw a junkie squat down inside a shopping trolley at The Toll, take a big steamy jobbie then rammed it into a parked car.

Didn't even wipe his arse.

But it was like telly for us. I always looked at them and promised myself I'd never do heroine. I know I'd never look back if I did. And thank fuck, it's probably the only promise I've ever kept. To myself anyway.

I marched up to the Toll and made my way through the tall brown flats. Two steps into the scheme and you were surrounded by red brick buildings. You could feel them looking down at you.

Every window a suspicious eye.

Gordo's flat was slap bang in the middle. I was hoping to fuck I could get to his door without running into Hammy. He lived two blocks away. Don't spark a lighter and you'll be fine Chris. Heed doon and keep walking.

I get to Gordo's block and press the button on the burnt service panel and push the door.

It's got a slim sheet of glass with chicken wire woven through.

Gordo's Mum answers the with a wallpaper scraper in

one hand, fag in the other. Grey dressing gown.

-Naw he's no fuckin in, but if you see him tell the wee cunt no tae come back!

-Will do. I reply to a door freshly slammed in my face.

What now? No mobiles back then. Gordo's got the hash!

Gordo was the one of the hardest guy in our year. He wasn't a close friend but he liked me because I made him laugh. He was the king of second year and I was his jester.

People left me alone because Gordo liked me.

Did I like him?

I was petrified of him. He was a bully. But on the flip side he really could be your best mate.

He was a cunt on the drink though. Guaranteed if Gordo was pished, someone was getting a hiding that night.

But he never battered me for some reason. He threatened to swing for me once or twice, but he never did. I'd just do something to make him laugh and all would be forgotten. Some may see it as weak. I saw it as being smart. I used him to my advantage. And most importantly, he could get hash.

I started walking back through the staring buildings. I Thought I'd chance my luck and see if they had gone to the Spar across the road.

We all liked to buzz deodorants sometimes through a cloth, and the Spar park was the perfect place to do it because we could hide under the slide and no one would see us

We preferred buzzing tins of lighter gas but only certain

places would sell that to us so plan B was always a duster and a can of Lynx Africa. Mum used to comment how I always used to smell nice. If only she knew. Well she will now. Sorry maw! But brace yersell hen, it gets so much worse.

I was almost at the end of the scheme when I heard a whistle. Not a wolf whistle, more of a "haw you" whistle.
-Aw fuck I bet that's Hammy. I thought with a shudder.
I kept walking.

Fuck talking to that rubber selling fat wee bastard. He'll probably try to sell me his pish and tell me it's whisky.

I hear two whistles now, overlapping and longer than the first one. I scan the windows, each one staring me out.
-Taylor! Haw!

My eyes fix on the two wobbly shapes.

It was Bongo and Danny. They were hanging out the third floor window, like droopy flags.

Bongo nearly fell out as he tried to show me his bottle of Merrydown. Danny nudged him back with a heavy elbow and a look of, calm the fuck down.

Danny shouts down.
-Where ye gawn?

The sun has started to peak around the corner of the building. I squint up.
-Fuck knows. How?

In certain parts of Scotland we ask how instead of why. Don't ask me how.
-Mon up!

Danny waves me up and pushes Bongo back into the

living room. They've both disappeared before I can even make my mind up.

Fuck it, what else was I gonna do?

Bongo and Danny were the year above me. Danny was as thick as frozen mince but a good guy. Bongo was just a ball of crazy energy .He would literally do anything if you dared him. Both of them were sound as fuck, especially Bongo. I always liked Bongo. Never a bully towards me but would always defend himself against the best of them.

Danny was half Scottish and half Iraqi. Folk used to call him Afghani Danny. He fucking hated it but we all thought it was funny as fuck.

He would go mental.

-Am no fae Afghanistan am fae Iraq ya cunts!

One time a wee wido in second year called him Afghanny Danny in the canteen. Danny snapped. Punched the wee guy on the forehead then threw him over a table. Split his head open.

Six stitches I heard.

I haven't seen a forehead punch like that before or ever since.

No service button required this time as the tenement door was held open by the wheelbase of melted red plastic Go Kart and the hood of an old Silvercross pram.

The pram was navy blue, (like my trackie) and had shiny grey mould all the way up one side, like slug trails under a green moon.

I could hear Bongo singing. His monotone echo bounced

off the concrete stairs.

Probably the Sash.

I hope to fuck he doesn't ask me to sing it. I'm still a closet Tim at this point in my life. All my mates were Rangers fans.

Especially my Toll mates.

Most of my family are blue noses apart from my Dad. He supports Ayr United, but has a soft spot for Celtic. I always pretended to like the other team, but I was a Celtic fan through and through. I was just too scared to admit it in case I was singled out. The catholic/protestant divide was still quite raw when I was growing up. A Celtic fan at my school was bad enough, but a proddy Celtic fan? Oooft.

It just wasn't worth thinking about the abuse I would have received.

So I always just said I liked Ayr United like my Dad. We would go to Ayr games together sometimes. We saw some great matches.

Ayr Vs Kilmarnock stands out. The Ayrshire Derby. We humped Killie that day and Andy Walker rubbed salt into their wounds by dinking a cheeky wee penalty over Gordon Marshall. Special memories those.

These days when people ask who my team is I always reply,

-I'm a Celtic supported and an Ayr United Fan. I've even been a guest pundit on Ayr Utd radio a few times".

So aye, I've definitely got a soft spot for my local team. But Celtic have my heart. Sorry if you're a Rangers fan reading this. I get it. I instantly dislike someone when I

hear they don't like my team... But stick with me, hopefully
I can win you all back over in the next few chapters.

Danny has the door open before I've even reached the
landing. I can see him through the bumpily glossed railing
as I get closer to the top. He's grinning more than usual.

Eyes bloodshot.

Ya

    fucking

        beauty.

He's stoned.

I skipped up the last three steps and grabbed the railing
to swing myself around towards the door.

He puts a palm out, we slap and clasp. He giggles.

-Sapnin mucka?

-Nothin much. You seen Gordo?

Danny still has a hold of my hand. He pulls on my arm
gently enough to guide me inside.

-Naw. Mon in but. Take yer shoes aff.

Fuck, I thought. I hate taking my shoes off. Always
been weird about getting my feet out, even with socks on.
I don't like them being exposed to the elements unless
they're my elements.

I'm a fruitcake that way.

-Do I have to?

-Aye, if ma maw sees marks on the carpet she'll know I had
folk over.

I look at the carpet. Pearl white and fluffy as fuck. One of
those carpets that changes shades if you stroke against the
grain.

33

The whole hallway looked pretty glam.

I kicked my shoes off at the door and followed Danny through to the living room. When he opened the door, the smell of hash smoke hit like a warm breeze.

Smokey heat waves danced in front of Bongo's face like drunk paragraphs. I was nearly stoned just from the smell. I remember thinking to myself,

 -Aye it'll be the footprints on the carpet that give the game away Danny.

Bongo is sat on the cream leather couch, cider in one hand, as he flicks through a pile of case less C.D's on the couch with the other. He greets me with that big smile of his.

 -Chrissy boy! Sapnin? He nearly drops his Cider again.

 Danny looks scunnered with him.

-Fuckin watch that cider you. If ma maw smells drink am fucked!

I tried not to roll my eyes and just answered Bongo.

 -No much mate. You seen Gordo?

-Nah mate, probably away meeting they wee dirties fae Marchburn again. Just chill wae us.

Danny slumps down with Bongo.

He sits a video case on his lap. I think it was Home Alone 2. He opens it, and there it is. A small brownish amber rock surrounded by tobacco dust and twisted up cigarette carcases.

Danny looks straight into my eyes. His peepers look like burnt out islands surrounded by seas of rusty raspberry ripple. Heavy on the ripple.

He's definitely as stoned as I want to be.

-You smoked afore?

- Only rubbers.

I said it with a grin because I knew they knew. Everybody knew by then. Hammy told every fucker.

In the English block toilets they called me "Durex" for months, because apparently I liked to "smoke rubbers".

I fucking hate Hammy.

Danny and Bongo got the giggles. But they appreciated I had addressed the elephant in the room. Not that you'd be able to spot a fucking elephant in that room with all the smoke.

Nothing else needed to be said. Danny just nodded his acceptance.

-Wee blast?

My smile meant I didn't need a nod but I gave one anyway.

I watched in awe as Danny put this joint together. I was mesmerised.

Fucking mesmirised.

Bongo fucked off to the toilet so no conversation was needed. I just watched Danny's ritual.

The building of the skins.

Licking down the seam of the fag and then gently pulling the strip of paper back to release the tobacco, like a small hairy log dropping onto the skins and crumbling slightly at the ends.

The burning of the hash.

He lit the end of the rock and a small stream of white

smoke raced from the surface and into the air. Danny sooked the stream down into his lungs. No wastage.

He used his thumb and middle finger to pinch off the hot soft hash and crumbled it into the joint.

But the master class was in the rolling for me. It's like an art, rolling. Every artist has their own technique and that goes the same for weed smokers.

Afghanny Danny gently teased it in his fingers, never taking his eyes off the prize. Then one big lick and a few twists and it was rolled.

Just like that.

I needed to learn how to do this I thought.

Bongo was raging when he came back from the bog because Danny hadn't built a five skinner.

But this was the most excited I'd ever been.

The danger of being caught.

The thought of feeling something new.

I loved every fucking second of it.

Danny ripped a piece of cardboard from his fag packet lid and rolled it up into a cylinder to make a roach. (Filter) He inserted it inside the joint with so much concentration you'd think he was defusing a bomb. I now know that this really is the key part of the build.

You fuck the roach then the whole joint is gubbed. Roll it too loose and you end up with backy and weed shrapnel flying into your mouth and sticking to your tongue like pebbledash.

Too tight and you'll end up bursting blood vessels in your eyes just trying to get a draw. It's

36

all

    in

        the

            roach.

Danny pulled the plastic flint stick from his clipper lighter and used it to poke the loose tobacco down into the joint to make it more compact.

To finish off he twisted the loose paper at the end of the joint to seal it and tapped the base three times on the back of his fag packet.

To me the twisting of the tip at the end of rolling is like a painter signing off on his work.   Some people fold their tips but in my opinion ......they're fucking lunatics.

-Windae.

Danny says as he hops up off the couch.

Bongo is already at the window, leaning out trying to catch a glimpse of scheme fanny.   His oversized blue chequered boxer shorts were sticking out from his waistband and his wee cider belly was poking out like dough trying to escape from a sealed paint tin as he leaned against the window sill.

Danny nudges him to the left a bit.

-Rollers rights.

Bongo moves to the side and gives Danny most of the window, but still keeps half an eye out for loose scheme birds.

Rollers rights by the way means whoever rolls the joints

gets to light it. That was the rule.

Danny bit off the twisted end and spat the paper out the window. He sparks up the clipper and lights the joint.

He was one of those inhalers that collects all the smoke in his cheeks first, like a hamster then sucks it all in with enough breath to revive a corpse. He took pride showing everyone he could handle big draws.

It impressed me right enough.

He took another few draws then a double reek before he passed it to Bongo.

I'm sat there just watching them.

Heart racing, gauntlet style.

The radios start to come on one at a time.

It's my turn soon. If they even give me some. I mean I don't know them *that* well. What if they're at it.

Am I being set up?

I can't tell if Danny is smiling with me or at me. But he is smiling.

Bongo rips the hole right out of it. I counted at least seven tokes, but he was still puffing away.

Danny yaps at him .

-Haw! Haw ya hoggin bastard, get that passed!

Bongo takes another two hefty draws, then holds the joint out. He eyes me up.

-Mon then. Take it.

I just stared at it.

The reality of it all turned excitement to anxiety. Dreams are great at the time but reality is a different beast altogether. But I'd come too far. It wasn't how I'd imagined it, unicorns and cartoons shagging and all that, but fuck it. It was free hash.

I tried to act cool as fuck walking to the window but probably over did it. Bongo and Danny were sharing this smile now.

Please be smiling *with* me.

Danny plucks the joint from Bongo's grasp and literally cries out like an emperor summoning his next fighters.
-Blowback!

Bongo fights a laugh and nestles his shoulders into his ears.

I fucking knew there was gonnae be a catch. My radios were right.

I knew fine well what a blowback was. We used to do them at the urinal but with fags.   The person giving a blowback would take the lit end of a cigarette and out it in their mouth, using their teeth to keep the fag secure. They then cup their mouth around it and blow the smoke out through the end of the filter. The person receiving the blow back would cup their hands around the filter of the fag and inhale all the smoke coming their way. It was like taking ten draws at once.

I had done it twice before and both times it nearly killed me.

And that was just a fag.

I'd never smoked hash but here's Danny and Bongo wanting me to take a blowback to pop ma Cheeech and Chong cherry!

My response was obvious.

-Aye nae bother.

Danny looked as surprised as I was by my outburst. But I'd committed. And a blowback is better than last draws. What harm could it do?

I didn't think.

I just leapt right in..

Danny had the joint in his mouth already. I could see by Bongo's expression he was both proud of me for going for it and surprised at Danny for letting me. He kept looking at us alternately like a stoner that's just accidentally staggered onto centre court at Wimbledon.

I cupped my hands around the filter. The sides of my palms met Danny's as he blew an almighty cloud of smoke through the channel our hands made and straight down my throat into my fresh pink lungs.

I knew it was going to hurt but I sucked that smoke like I was siphoning petrol.

My eyes started to sting. The smoke was snaking up through my knuckles and whirling around my tear ducts.

I jolted my head to the side and sprayed a cough all over Bongo. Saliva started to fall down off the insides of my cheeks and filled the canals around the sides of my tongue. The second cough was better aimed as I emptied my canals onto the carpet.

This one was black with glitter.

-That was shite, dae it again or you'll no feel the effects, Danny said as he put the joint back in his mouth.

I had no time to argue. He grabbed my wrists and pulled me towards him.

40

He blew again, and I sucked again. I inhaled slower this time, which allowed the smoke to build up in our hand caves and attack my eyes with more aggression.

I sank to my knees coughing. Danny let go of my wrists
I'm regretting everything already.

Danny and Bongo helped me up.

Their faces looked guilty.

They knew they had taken it too far for a first timer.
-Sit on the couch mate, Bongo says with concern.
- I'm all good.

They sit me on the couch.

The coughing passed after a minute or two.

We make small talk, can't remember what about, I just remember trying my hardest to look as if I was hardcore.

Then it hits me.

No build up, no easing it in….

I was fucking stoned.

Really fucking stoned.

Sounds cliché but I genuinely felt I was sinking into the couch. I got a warm tingle around my neck and face, not a huge tingle but warm enough. And as I sunk, Danny, Bongo and the window got higher.

It felt so good. I was relaxed. I was at peace. I was in my fucking element. But it was short lived. For as the higher the window got, the more the paranoia started to set in.

Are they looking down at me?

Are they laughing at me?

Do I look stoned?

I must look stoned.

When will I stop sinking?

How the fuck am I gonnae spin this to my mum? Danny shouts at me in a way that makes me feel it must be the second time he's tried to catch my attention.

-Haw! You okay mate?

I think I've had plenty time to respond but Bongo's input tells me otherwise.

-Fuck sake mate you're mongoed.

They both laugh and the sounds jolts through me like a spear through the head.

PARA FUCKIN NOIA.....

Their laughs fade out. I'm too far gone. I'm too busy trying to match my heart beat with the music blaring out Bongo's pink ghetto blaster. I say blaring but it sounded more like underwater music.

Half an hour passed as I sat full of anxiety, fear with the odd flash of delight. I was nearly enjoying it, but it was all too much too soon...with too many people around...two too many.

I needed to get out. I contemplated going back to my bush at the Oval to try and enjoy the rest of my high. But the thought of wee Sheila sniffing about my balls again set my heart racing.

Danny and Bongo were smoking a freshly rolled one at the window, which was now almost back to eye level. They didn't offer me any. They knew a casualty when they saw one.

I couldn't go back home. Mum and Dad would sniff me

42

out straight away. I'd have to go to Gran and Papa's. I could always get away with things if I stayed at theirs. I used to think it was because they were gullible and would believe anything. Now I'm older I know it was because they had both been tearaways back in the day so were just playing the game.

Good old Gran and Papa.

Fucking legends.

But more about them later.

The couch was feeling firmer so I decided to make my move. I had to think of good excuse. If I admit I was too stoned they would spread it round school and I'll never be able to get hash off anyone else. I had to come out of this with some credibility. I thought long and hard before looking at Danny with pleading eyes and saying,

- How do I make this stop?

The boys loved this. They laughed so hard I felt their voices vibrate through my chest. Bongo blows an arrow of smoke through his tight wrinkled lips and looks at me with pity. Not pity, empathy.

- You cannae make it stop mate, you just gotta let it pass.

He takes another draw and passes it to Danny before he even inhales. Danny pipes in.

-Or eat.

Bongo exhales with a nod of agreement. He sounds like he has a cold as he confirms,

- Aye, or eat. That's why you get the munchies. Body's telling the brain to get straight. More you eat, quicker you'll feel normal.

Bongo turns to Danny just in time for a blowback. It looked almost planned.

This was my chance. No offence to the lads, but I needed out, and pronto. I stood up and staggered back towards the fluffy white hall carpet. I was too anxious for goodbyes. I'll apologise on Monday.

I just fucking ran.

Right out that door, down the concrete steps, passed the shitey old slug trailed pram and Go Kart and out through the nosey red bricks onto the main road.

Two Toll's either side, I just kept running.

And running.

And running.

Every step felt like a chore.

I wanted to keep running but I was fucked. It was like jogging on pillows. My body and brain were jelly.

I had to get this feeling away.

Eat something. That's what they said.

Fucking eat something.

There was a Safeway beside the Toll on Prestwick Road.

It's an Aldi now.

I rummaged through my silky navy blue trackie bottoms.

One pound eighty.

-I can make this work I thought. My tongue channels had re-filled with saliva to the point of overflowing. An overwhelming hunger consumed me. Not like any hunger I had ever felt before.

This was the Munchies.

For anyone who has never experienced, "The Munchies", then just picture the thirst a vampire would get for blood....That's the same thirst a stoner gets for food. Especially chocolate ,cereal and maze based crisps. Especially the 10p variety. (Well fuckin 30p now!) The munchies heighten all senses when eating. It's honestly one of the best parts of being stoned.

I walked into the supermarket but now my tracksuit felt less like a superhero costume and more like an orange jumpsuit. I needed to be covert, but I was standing out. Navy blue, white stripes and raspberry ripple eyes....Heavy on the ripple. I was a walking example of a "hooligan".

Space Raider Crisps, 10p a pop. Five of them straight into the basket. One pound thirty left. Taz bar 10p? Three in the basket. One lands on its side and slips through the metal grate. Cannae be fucked bending down so I grabbed a fresh one and slung it in. Went sideways again. Fuck it, two Taz's will do. Pound ten left. I saw a Pepperami and it made me think.

It was a quid, but it was the closest to a meat diet as I could afford. Fuck it. Pepperami and I'll go back and grab another packet of Space Raiders. Job done.

What a feast I had.

I walked and ate, and I walked and I ate.

This food was more amazing than anything I'd ever tasted. Every crunch of those pickled onion Space Raiders like a gourmet meal. It was the closest I'd come to ejaculating without touching my willy.

Every taste was a new adventure.

45

It's hard to explain but the munchies are more than just being hungry. The brain comes alive to tastes and textures. And swallowing food feels like it's just meant to be. It's almost as if the Weed Gods are teaching us how we should appreciate every single bite we take.

Give a man three bongs of Mary Jane then blindfold him. Feed him a bowl of dry pasta and brown sauce and he will tell you it's the best Michelin Star meal he's ever eaten. That's the power of weed. When you're stoned, your senses aren't judgemental.

Next thing I remember I was on Midton Road. It's a long residential back road that runs parallel with Prestwick Main Street.

Gran and Papa's front door looked right onto the Main Street but I was fucked if I was chancing walking by so many people looking like this. Everyone knows everyone in the Wick.

Papa's back garden led onto a patch of land beside the local bake house, about a hundred yards from where I was. I just needed to turn right onto Kyle street and cut past the Electric Bakery without anyone seeing me and I'd be safe.

I'd just tell Gran I felt dizzy and go straight upstairs to bed. She was a hypochondriac so I knew she'd empathise.

I could see the bakery entrance in the distance. A big grey stone square building with a blue and white peeling sign reading "Murray's Electric Bakery". The entrance was draped with those vertical plastic strips that you see in serial killer movies. Once clear but now ash grey with wear

46

and tear.

I felt safe. My Old Uncle Jimmy worked nightshift in the bakery. Anytime fresh rolls came out the oven my Papa sent me down the garden to see him.

-How's Bill? Tell him we're due a dram soon.

Bill was my Papa. Jimmy was his best pal so not a real uncle. But still an Uncle to us.

He'd bag up twelve hot rolls and throw them my way.

-Grab a few cakes on your way out son.

I always did.

More than a few.

Creamier the better.

The cakes were stacked on trolley trays six feet tall. The trolleys lined both sides of the entrance. Every cake you could imagine.

Best gauntlet I ever ran.

This time the dayshift were on. Drivers were packing the van for the nightshift workers. No Jimmy in sight. Paranoia kicked in again. They know I'm stoned. I can feel it. They aren't looking at me. But I can feel it. I put my head down and went into "stealth mode.

I ran like an escaped convict with a hunch back.

I got to Papa's back gate.

The bolt's off.

Thank fuck.

I'm safe.

Just get to the house, tell Gran you're dizzy and get to that bedroom. And for fuck sake try and salvage what's left of this fucking stone.

Gran fell for it. Papa was too busy in the kitchen shouting at his lentils for not soaking quick enough.

-Ok up to bed. I'll check on you soon. Take this water.

Gran filled a wee green plastic cup with water from the tap and pushed it into my hand. Papa glanced up from his soup pot and studied my eyes.

He knew.

I knew he knew.

But just like the Janitor, Papa chose his battles with me.

And this time he was on my side.

He broke his stare from me and looked to Gran.

-He'll be fine, don't make a fuss. Go to your bed son.

I nodded into my wee plastic cup and put all my energy into remembering how to walk again.

I got clear of the kitchen and made my way up the stairs. Every step lifted some weight from my mind and the closer I got to the top the more excited I got. I was stoned...and I hadn't been caught.

Closing that bedroom door was like shutting off the real world for the first time. I remember grinning as the last bit of light was sucked into the hallway. It was pitch black. But my mind was brighter than ever before.

Getting undressed wasn't an option. I stumbled backwards, until the end of the bed swept my legs from under me.

I crashed onto that bed like a sleepy stunt man and sank into the mattress. I think I may even have gasped. If I didn't I should have...because I felt fucking amazing.

The darkness helped to block all the anxiety out. I was

48

alone with my thoughts.

My real thoughts.

Thoughts I never even knew I had.

Or wanted.

I felt a state of mental relaxation for the first time in my life.

All radios stations off bar the one, my inner monologue.

So this is what normal people think like?

All I'd known before was a racing brain and a faster heart. It was just who I was, full of beans and full of shite.

But not now.

My thoughts were finally moving at a pace I could process.

I wasn't scared anymore.

I could focus.

I could relax.

I didn't ever want this feeling to leave me.

I must have lay there for an hour, just soaking up the silence and thinking about all the ways I was going to conquer the world. I could hear Gran and Papa's tones downstairs in the kitchen. Papa had and irritable tone, Gran had an innocent one. What were they arguing about now? Me? Probably. They weren't daft. But in that moment....

.... I just didn't give a fuck.

I'd found a new me

I'd found a new state of mind.

I'd found weed.....

..... And I refused to let it go for the next twenty years.

CHAPTER THREE. ANOTHER DOG IN A BUSH.

Weed was my new thing.

I smoked as much as I could get my hands on and any time I had the chance.

I smoked at break times, lunch times, in between periods and any time Mum and Dad were out or asleep.

But the problem was, I couldn't ever fucking afford it. I was always scadging bits off my mates, who were mostly all smoking by now as well.

So I did what any respectable school kid would do. I went down to that English block and sucked as many cocks as I could to raise the money.

Kidding.

I got a job working at a fast food takeaway called The Picnic Basket.

Hash wasn't cheap. You could buy a fiver bit, that would get you three or four joints. A half dig (half quarter) would skin you about fifteen quid but it would last you a week if you were clever about it.

I could only ever afford last draws.... A quid....Well they

were Hammy's going rates anyway.

I was getting sick of smoking everyone's dregs.

I'd been sacked as a paper boy from every Newsagent in Prestwick Main Street and was black listed by the rest around town. Bear in mind the main street had five paper shops. And I got sacked from every one. Most sacked me for sleeping in and turning up late. I think the other ones sacked me purely because I was so shite at the job. I was always getting lost or damaging peoples papers. Have you ever tried ramming a soggy Sunday Herald with all the magazines inside through a letter box in the pishing rain? Oh and I nicked someone's porno mag once. I think I got sacked from somewhere for that. All five merged into one for me so I can't really remember.

I needed a job.

So I started doing the rounds, going into shops and pleading for work. I even went into an antique shop and asked if they needed any staff.

The Picnic Basket was on the Main Street about two hundred yards from the New Yorker. It sold the usual stuff, Chips and cheese, chips cheese and gravy, chips cheese and curry sauce, chips and chicken curry and the odd salad roll. It was a real lunchtime hotspot.

It was really busy when I walked in. The owner Nathan asked me what I was after.

-Any jobs?

He almost looked relieved.

-Do you know how to cut and butter rolls?

-Aye.

I didn't, but how hard could it be?

-Good, get a pinnie on and start on that pile over there.

Nathan pointed over to a big batch of rolls in the corner.

And just like that I had a job.

My main tasks were to peel and cut the veg, mop floors and sort the bins.

I actually took it quite seriously.

I loved working. I always have. I may be a stoner but I've always worked and I've always worked hard.

Was I stoned while working?

Mostly yes. But I still worked and that's what counted.

I used to work Friday's after school and all day Saturday. I'd take away about thirty five quid a week. That was enough to buy me my a half dig, fags ,skins and still have enough left over for a bottle of Buckfast and a Garlic bread with cheese from the Topkapi Kebab house across the road.

And that was my routine. School, Picnic Basket on Friday and Saturday, then on a Saturday Night , I'd go meet my pals down the beach, get wasted, , then stagger home together talking the most shite you'd ever heard in your life. And if I got lucky I'd get a wee winch. It didn't happen often but when it did I can assure you that they always just wanted to stay friends the next day.

Best days of your life.

In a nutshell that was how my stoner life progressed from second year to third year. It was bliss. I was more at peace . I functioned better in class. I really loved life. I didn't realise it until writing this but that was probably the last time I truly remember being free from any stress or negative thinking. That was when I was the real Chris.

No bitterness inside me.

No anger.

No radios.

Just Chris.

I was happy.

Then just like that, it all started to get a bit messy.

I found alcohol.

And I don't mean that in a deep sense. I mean I literally found a bottle of alcohol.

On top of my job at the Picnic Basket I ended up getting my job back at one of the Newsagent's in Prestwick run by old Jimmy Young. His shop Young's was directly across from my Gran and Papa's on the Main Street. They knew him well and got me back in. And I think he was desperate so had no choice but to agree. Good paper boys were few and far between then. I'm living proof of that.

It was an extra fifteen quid a week , bonus cash as I called it. I would fritter it away on shite. I've never been a good saver. Money burned a hole in my pocket, and still does to an extent now.

I always felt if I didn't spend it then I would lose it or have it taken off me. Even now I worry that everything I have worked for will all disappear one day, and that's the reason I never stop working if I can help it. Fuck knows where that stems from but it's just how I am.

My paper round was easy, only twenty five papers. Old Jimmy didn't trust me with a bigger run, so I guess my incompetence actually worked in my favour for once.

I was only a few houses into my route one morning, it must have been about half six because I remember it was still dark but the ora of the sun was starting to poke it's head up.

I was cycling across the grass at the Spar Park when my tyres got stuck in the mud. They slid away from me and I toppled into a bush. I used my hand to cushion my fall and as I crash landed I felt my knuckles hit something hard. I heard the dunt only a glass bottle could make.

A full glass bottle.

I knew what it was instantly. I'd seen it in all the shops, and everyone always talked about it.

And there it was in all its neon glory.

A bottle of Mad Dog.

MD 2020

Orange Jubilee flavour.

My eyes widened as the now rising sun glinted off the shoulder of the bottle. Almost as if it was winking at me.

I now had a predicament. Do I stash the bottle in my bag and risk being caught by my parents, or even worse by the people that had stashed it in the first place? Or do I do the unthinkable at six thirty in the morning on a school day and drink it there and then?

I drank it there and then.

Looking back on it even I think I'm mental. I was due at school in and it was SIX O CLOCK IN THE FUCKING MORNING.

But an urge just came over me. I hated school and just thought, ah fuck it. This'll get me through the day. I was only thirteen. Where did that come from?

Something inside me just craved the feeling of being drunk.

Something took over me that morning. And we were about to make friends for a long time to come.

It tasted like oranges at first but the aftertaste quickly kicked in. It was fucking disgusting. Like what you'd imagine licking rotten fruit off a wet rusty cake tin would taste like. But I was committed. I never even got off my bike. I just glugged a bit, then looked out for dog walkers. Then I glugged, looked.

Glugged and looked.

Glugged.

Looked....

Then it was gone.

I forced out a burp and my mouth filled with hot wine. I swallowed then boaked, then swallowed again.

I felt warm.

I threw the empty bottle back into the hedge and had another look about. I could see a woman walking her dog in the distance, coming towards me. That better no be fuckin Sheila.

It was time to go.

I felt strong, as I pushed my legs hard to get my bike through the muddy field. I was smiling. Same smile I had when I collapsed onto Gran and Papa's bed.

But bigger.

Much bigger.

I was loving life.

I felt that glow I always heard them talk about on the telly, I felt giddy, happy....I was in my element. I felt confident.

But again, it was short lived.

Next thing I remember, I'm lying in some cunts shed covered in my own puke. I'd been sleeping, but had no idea for how long or more importantly I had absolutely no fucking idea where I was.

And where the fuck were my newspapers?

I knew I'd fucked up.

My cheek was stuck to something cold and plastic. The glue was half dried sick. It was my paper bag. I'd been using it as a pillow and it was still full of papers.

-Aw naw man am fucked! I let out as I jolted upright.

I bounced up and grabbed the bag. The hut smelled of damp wood and grass cuttings. I opened the door to peak out. It was still day time but I didn't recognise the garden.

I made a run for it and bolted out of the hut and through the side gate, which was already open thank fuck.

I recognised the scheme.

It was Mossbank .

How the fuck did I get to Mossbank? My route was the opposite side of East Road about a mile away. All I could thinks was,

-I'm so fucked.

I didn't even know what time it was. I didn't have a

watch and we didn't have mobiles back then.

And bare in mind, I am still absolutely pished at this point.

I had no option but to brave it out and head home. If Mum and Dad were still in then they'd know I was drunk and I'd be fucked. If they weren't home then that meant they were at work, and if they were at work then that meant I'd missed school. Either way…. I was fucked.

I cycled home feeling "the fear" for the first time. I was in tears as I tried to cycle in a straight line. I was having a full blown meltdown.

I snuck in the back door not having a clue what my excuse would be. The house was silent apart from my heavy breathing.

They were all gone.

I looked at the old brass clock on the mantelpiece in the living room.

One thirty in the fucking afternoon!

-    Yup I'm fucked.

Radio Taylor fired all stations on at once at full volume.

My mind went like this….

-What if the school phone and report me absent?
-What if Jimmy Young sacks me because I never delivered his papers???
-Gran and Papa are gonnae be mortified!!
- What if that was one of the Sweeney's Mad Dog I

57

tanned?!?!

- What if the police find it and fingerprint the bottle??

-Gran and Papa are gonnae be mortified!!

-How am I going to explain the puke on ma jacket?

-What if a paedo saw me cycling about pished then kidnapped me and stashed away.

-Is my arse bleeding?

- Who the fuck drinks Mad Dog Orange Jubilee?

-Gran and Papa are gonnae be mortified.

Now picture all of that overlapping and playing on a constant loop. That is what happens in my brain when all of my radios come on. There isn't enough time to analyze or question any of my thoughts because none of them stay still long enough to do so. So I'll just pluck one out of the air and analyze that. That's my brain. And that's my struggle.

   I was in so much trouble and I knew it. I ran upstairs to my room, shut the door and started to roll a joint.

   May as well go out as Lion.

   I smoked it out the skylight. It was some really tasty Moroccan black. Much better than their white cousin Hammy shipped over.

   I slumped onto my new wee green and white stripped Japanese Futon. (All the rage back in the day by the way).

   I should have been uptight at that moment, but once again weed had come to my rescue. I was as calm as could be, almost accepting my fate. With weed I just didn't care as much anymore. It always took the edge

58

off......

......Always.

I drifted off .

Next thing I know my Mum's in my room.

-Dinner's ready. Not like you to sleep at this time.

I was feeling rough as fuck. I gave a covert sniff to make sure there was no smell of smoke left over in the room. I was still half pished as I tried to think of something to say.

-We had cross country. I came first.

Well if you're gonnae lie you might as well gloss it up.

She had that Mum smile that makes everything okay. Either she didn't know yet or she's doing that thing mum's do where they lull you into a false sense of security to see if you are going to admit it first. I used my tiredness to buy me more time to suss her out before responding.

-Aw well done. Do you want me to bring your plate up to you?

I was so confused. Surely she knew.

-No I'll come down.

Why the fuck did I say I'd go downstairs.

Dad and my sister Cara were getting tore into their dinner.

By the way I have another sister. Her name is Hannah. She is ten years younger than me. She is the most level headed out of the three of us. I don't mention her much in the book but I wanted to give her a wee shout out. She has been my wee rock during the toughest parts this past few years and never gave up on me. Cara has been the same. For all we argue at times but the bond the three of us have

59

couldn't be stronger.

Right soppy bit over...

Dinner that night was Dad's signature dish, corned beef and mash tatties with grated raw turnip and carrot on the side. Sounds mingin but it's the dugs baws by the way.

I was starving so got tore right in about it. Mum was chatting away but I can't really remember what she was saying. I was just waiting for someone to pull the trigger and out me. Dad knew Jimmy Young so was he in the loop? Cara was at the same school as me, did she twig that I wasn't there? If she did then sure as fuck that grassing bitch would have given the game away by now. I love my sister dearly, she has a heart of gold and is an amazing mum to her four kids. But back then I hated her. She was a bitch when it came to dobbin me in for every little thing. But she knows this is how I felt and she will probably tell you that I was a wee prick as well. And that would be fair enough. The important thing is we love each other now.

But not one of them seemed to know a thing that night. And if they did then they were hiding it well.

I relaxed enough to join in the conversation for a bit then excused myself. I needed time to assess the situation. I'd just missed a day of school and cost a guy about £40 in newspapers.

Had I actually gotten away with it?

Surely not.

When everyone had gone to bed I smoked a one skinner out the skylight then got into my pit. I tried to sleep but I just kept picturing my mum storming up the stairs and bursting into my room, leaving a maw shaped hole in my door.

-Caught ye ya lying wee jakey bastard! I gave you the chance to admit it but you didn't! Gran and Papa are gonnae be mortified!

But she never did.

And still to this day it has never been mentioned. I honestly see this as one of my finest moments where luck was concerned.

The school never reported my absence. I'm guessing it was because it was the first ever day I ever missed school since the start of first year. I was always late but never absent. They must have just trusted I was ill.

And as for Jimmy Young, only three customers complained they never got their paper that day. I just played dumb and nothing else was ever said about it. I never got sacked. He just took the value of the papers off my wages. Losing four papers was a good day for me usually.

I got sacked a week later though when I got caught stealing a pint of milk off one of the customers neighbours doorsteps.

Give Jimmy his dues though. He never grassed me to Gran and Papa.

Jimmy had an inner Jannie too.

But a small price to pay considering I'd escaped Scot free from the Mad Dog escapade.

And that was that.

I had a taste for it now.

I wanted that warm feeling back again, that glow up the spine. But this time without the puke induced coma in a stranger's shed.

Smoking hash was getting too expensive as I was down to one job now.

And that feeling I had when I was cycling away from that hedge just wouldn't go away. I knew the only reason I blacked out was because I had drank it too fast. I was going to savour it next time. Drinking was going to be my new thing.

But it wouldn't be easy. I could get hash without much hassle through my mates at the Toll. And you could easily conceal a half dig in your pocket without the polis driving by and spying it.

But getting a carry out was a much more complicated operation.

Luckily we had that local shop that sold single fags, and they also didn't mind selling the odd bottle of cider to selected and trusted under-agers.

I had a supplier, and I had a plan.

All I needed was an accomplice.

Steven Rice was his name. He lived a few doors down from me and was in the same year. He had a real distinct look about him. Long wiry mahogany hair and his eyes were so narrow you could never read him. He was painfully quiet but had a sense of menace about him.

He always had money because his mum wasn't on the scene anymore and his dad was a total push over. He gave him at least a fiver a day just to get sweets. A fuckin fiver!

For sweets!

But it wasn't his money I was after. I still had my Picnic Basket wages coming in and my single fag enterprise was booming. I was selling ten a day by now at fifty pence a pop. I didn't need money.

I needed Steven for the drink.

He was braver than me and would swagger into the shop no bother. Again, I was a shite bag and always had the fear the shop keepers would tell my parents.

We came up with a plan that on the Saturday we would tell our parents we were going swimming and that way we could use our swimming bags to hide our bottles. When we got to the pool we would hide in a changing room and tan the drink.

Fucking genius I know.

I got prepped early and told my mum I would be staying at Gran and Papa's but I had really planned to do an "all nighter" and just sleep down the beach or the Oval.

The plan worked a treat. Mum even flung me a few quid for the vending machines at the pool. Only reading this will she now realise she actually chipped in for my cargo. Cheers maw! (Social Services anyone?).

Steven marched into the shop and got us two cold bottles of Merrydown cider, gold label.

No questions asked.

We stuffed them down our rolled up towels then tucked them into our swim bags and sleeked off towards the Oval. We were trying to look covert and stay small I guess, but on reflection we probably looked like two teenagers trying to disguise the fact they were concealing alcohol.

What a rush though.

Looking back again it really was all about the build up for me and not just the end product.

I felt alive.

The fear of being caught.

The danger.

Every time a car passed I shat myself but the rush was incredible.

We got to the pool, paid our money and went into the changing rooms. The place was empty. Prestwick baths had a tiny wee changing room and it still looks as old today as it did back then. I think their lockers still take farthings. (That joke was shite but I promised I wouldnt edit the book....Aw shite that last "wouldn't" I typed should have had an apostrophy......APOSTROPHE!!!!!....Bastard.

We agreed we would stash the booze in a locker and go swim for a bit. We wanted to get the smell of chlorine on our Bermuda shorts so we had an alibi if anyone asked questions later on. We really did cover all angles looking back on it. What a team.

With our Merrydown hidden away, we headed for the pool. Laughing and joking about how pished we were going to get.

The pool only had a few people in.

An old guy doing two mile an hour laps width ways, and a dad with his wee girl.

We swaggered up to the deep end. The lifeguard looked up briefly. She looked as suicidal as they usually did in there. A quick glance at us then back down to her flip flops with a yawn.

Steven cannon balled in.

I was raging he was drawing more attention to us. He knew bombs were banned. But luckily the lifeguard was too engrossed with her feet.

I got into the water slowly.

Probably too slowly. Like Mr Bean getting off that diving board.

I dunked my head under to acclimatise, but by the time I had re-surfaced Steven was already out of the pool and halfway back to the lockers.

-That'll do! He cackles as he starts running back towards the changing room.

The lifeguards head snaps up to attention.

- Haw you, nae runnin!

Steven bounced his scratchy/screechy giggle off the old tiled walls then shouted back,

-Get tae fuck ya paedo!

All colour and life drained from my face.

The lifeguard went to blow her whistle but the cord holding it around her neck got tangled in her fingers. So she shouted instead.

-Right that's it you're barred!

I could hear Steven's cackle echo as he disappeared into the changing room. The lifeguard turned her glare to me. Before she could say a word I jumped to my defence. With a squeaky tremble in my voice I blurted out.

-I'm so sorry I didn't know he was going to say that! Please

don't bar me, ma granny comes to your aqua trim classes!
I actually said that.

I always blurt out the strangest things when I feel under pressure. Always have and I think I always will. One time a mate put me on to a dealer of his but warned me he only had one leg so not to stare etc. I turned up at the guys house and walked into his bedroom and he was lying on the bed with two legs but one of them was in a cage thing and looked beaten up to fuck with lots of bruises and stitches. Turns out he was about to get it amputated but I didn't know this.

I stared at it for a wee second and froze up...then I just blurted out.
-Alright mate! Davie telt me you only had wan leg! Much for a half ounce??

Most folk have a filter but mine gets lost amongst all my radio signals.

The lifeguard understandably didn't know how to filter my outburst so just snapped back at me.
-Well get your pal telt that I'm wanting an apology or I'll be telling your Granny about the company you keep!

I nodded with wide eyes and scrambled out of the pool like a nervous jellyfish and bolted for the changing rooms. A whistle stopped me dead in my tracks.
-Nae runnin!!!

I didn't even look up.
-Sorry!

I started speed walking like a piece of wet cardboard until I was out of sight and in the changing rooms.

66

Steven was there to greet me. Wee Satsuma pubes was standing on a wooden bench, baws oot and a bottle of Merrydown in each hand.

I was fucking raging.

-What the fuck was that all about ya clown? And get them away!

 - Ach who cares? Mon let's just get these tanned.

- I fuckin care! She said she's gonnae tell ma Granny!

Steven paused just a wee second before bursting out laughing.

After a few seconds I saw the funny side too

. I decided to let it slide. I didn't want anything killing my buzz.

-Right, but we need to be quick, she'll be in here to check that you've gone.

We picked two cubicles next to each other and locked the doors. All I can remember is feeling so scared but I knew I had to get rid of this cider one way or another.

We glugged. Then we giggled. Glugged then giggled.

Glugged.

Giggled.

Glug

Glug

Glug.

Then it was gone.

It couldn't have taken any longer than five minutes, no exaggeration. Steven was quicker by about a minute.

I got dressed as quickly as I could and wrapped the

empty bottle back in the towel and stashed it at the bottom of my bag.

Then came the glow.

I got the last of my burps out, took a deep breath and opened the cubicle door. Steven was waiting. Not smiling this time. I think he was fighting the boak but I never mentioned it.

We left the pool and headed straight to my wee bush at the Oval for a fag. The second the fresh air hit me, I felt the glow burn hotter. Like a fuse had been lit at the bottom of my spine and was sizzling up my back, then the neck before an explosion of euphoria in the brain. I could see Steven was feeling it too. We just looked at each other burst out laughing and started running full pelt towards the bushes. The faster we ran the harder we laughed.

A cocktail of adrenaline and relief.

What a rush.

We sat in the bush for about fifteen minutes, smoking fags and laughing. No idea what we were talking about I just remember feeling so happy I was even half hoping for a visit from wee Sheila!

Weed made me not care as much but alcohol made me not give a fuck.

Unfortunately after the first fifteen minutes of bush patter, I blacked out again. My next memory of that day was about four hours later.

I vaguely recall being stood outside St Nicholas Church on Prestwick Main Street having a screaming match with Steven.

A few days later at school I found out the full story.

According to Steven I started giving him shit for calling the Lifeguard a paedo and wouldn't let it drop. He said I changed from happy to angry in the flick of a switch. One minute I was laughing and joking then, click.... A psycho was born.

Apparently I stared him down for a while then just flung a punch out of nowhere. Missed his face and hit his shoulder. He said he ran off and I gave chase but ended up falling over and hit my head off a parked car's bonnet.

I can't remember it at all.

The only vague memory I have of any of that day was me crying outside the church.

I totally blanked out. From the bush to the church I remember nothing. Don't even remember going home to Gran and Papas. I was obviously so drunk I couldn't find the beach.

I woke up that Sunday morning in their spare room with not a clue to how I got there, or what state I was in when I arrived.

The fear hit me again.

The hangover/ come down fear really is the worst feeling in the world. That feeling of having absolutely no clue what happened the night before, made even worse if you have a wild imagination.

I knew I was in trouble this time. No way I'd have convinced them I was sober last night. I tried to come up with a story but it was hopeless. I had nothing.

I went downstairs. Papa's wee tray with his teapot, mug

69

and newspaper was still untouched on the living room table so I knew he was still in bed. Gran always made him up his wee tray in the morning.

I could hear the dishes clinking away in the kitchen. Gran was washing up her breakfast bowl.

-Oh there he is!

- Gran I'm so sorry about last night. I just wasn't feeling well.

Gran dried her hands on a tea towel.

-And do you feel better now?

I didn't want her to think I had a hangover, although I did, and it was a fucking killer.

-Yeah I'm fine now, must have been a bug or something.

Gran looked me up and down.

-Ok good. Now go sit down and I'll make you some breakfast. Get your strength back up.

I walked through to the living room thinking, ya beauty, she's bought it again.

Little did I know of the harsh lesson that awaited me.

With my guts churning and Gummy bears on the telly, Gran appeared twenty minutes later with a fry up on the biggest fucking plate you've ever seen.

It was overflowing with fried sliced sausage, a link, a runny fried egg, beans, two tattie scones, mushrooms and a side bowl of cornflakes filled to the brim.

Now too many of you that probably sounds like a cracking wee scran. Especially if you're blazing some weed as you read this. It's maybe even put you in the notion for one. But if you're reading this with a bastard of a hangover then I'm sure you can empathise.

She sat the plate of food down. The fry up was swimming in grease, even more so than usual. When the plate hit the table the wee bits of black frying pan dust started to jiggle on top of the wobbly egg yolks.

The mushrooms were the worst. Like sweaty limp corpses piled up in a heap. This was going to be my toughest acting role yet. To eat this plate of death and pretend I'm enjoying it. Gran sat on her wee floral yellow padded chair with bamboo frame and started knitting while staring at me like a sadistic nurse on suicide watch.
-Come on don't let it get cold. You need to build up that strength seeing as you were ill.
 That's what she said, but what she really meant was,
-You think I'm daft? I'll teach you to pish on my head and tell me it's raining. Now eat ya wee dick!

She never broke character. Not once.

But neither did I.

It was like a stand- off.

Toughest thing I've ever had to do. I can still taste the dry oily sausage as I write this. I ate every mouthful as if I was enjoying it but every single bite made a tiny piece of my soul disappear.

I managed to eat most of it but she let me off with the tomato. She knew I had learned my lesson.

My Gran was from Germany and her inner Gestapo was certainly on show that day.

What a woman.

So my second experience of alcohol was pretty much a

carbon copy of my first. I felt terrible but this time I had well and truly learned my lesson.

I had to drink slower.

Third and Fourth year of school were pretty much a waste of my time, the teachers time and the governments money. I had no interest in School at all apart from English and P.E. I just wanted to spend my time smoking and drinking with my mates and playing Tekken 2 on the Playstation.

I'd spend all my hours in class just dreaming about the antics of the weekend past and what kinda shit we could get up to the following weekend.

I'd had a few girlfriends by then and had joined a Youth Theatre with loads of beautiful girls so now I had, weed, booze AND lassies to distract me from my studies. I was still a virgin but I'd winched a few.

I had been going to a youth theatre on and off since I was nine but I always took the huff when they didn't give me a speaking role so it was always stop start.

My first ever experience of acting was when I was eight years old. I was in the chorus of the Youth Theatre's production of Bugsy Malone at the Civic Theatre in Ayr. It really was an amazing venue but the Council knocked it down a few years back. Something to do with asbestos but more likely running costs were too high. I still get a real sense of sadness when I drive past the patch of land the old girl used to sit on. If I was a millionaire I'd buy that land and re-build the Civic.

I was aching to play the part of Bugsy Malone, it was my

favourite film as a wee kid (before Home Alone came out) but I was only nine and couldn't sing so they cast a guy called Euan instead. It was the first time I ever remember feeling properly jealous of someone. Euan was a great guy and perfect for the part and we actually have remained friends since then and played in the same Sunday league football team many years later. But at that time I was bitter with envy.

   My next hope was for the role of the villain Dandy Dan. But Graham got that part. I didn't even get a role of one of the gangsters. I was gutted as I sat in the auditorium of the Civic, listening to the director call out one name after another as everyone cheered. The good roles were disappearing and my name still hadn't been called. And it never was.

-Okay see you all next week! The director shouted to the sixty odd kids in the auditorium.

   Fifty nine hyper under sixteen's ran past me to the exit in slow motion as my heart sank. Why the fuck wasn't my name called? I couldn't help myself as I ran, and I mean literally sprinted to the front of the stage and shouted up to the director,

-What about me?

-What about you?

-Do I not get a speaking part?

-Not a principle one.

-Please! I've seen the film more times than any of them. The director could see the pain in my face and softened his stance.

73

-Don't worry we still have a few speaking roles left. You can audition next week.

-Can I audition for the magician?

-Sure.

The magician was a great wee part. I knew the dialogue off by heart so I left the theatre with a bit more of a skip in my step. I knew I had to stand out, prove myself.

I went home that night and watched the scene with the magician on VHS over and over again. I was going to get that part and show them all what I can do. The dialogue went a little something like this.

"I am the great Marbini! I am the finest magician in the whole of Norfolk Nebraska and from this hat I will produce not one rabbit, not two rabbits, but three rabbits!"

I practiced it all day every day for the next week. Pulling loads of daft facial expressions and doing an American accent. I really worked hard at it. Nothing was going to stop me getting that part. I knew it wasn't a big role but all the good parts were gone and this was the one that gave me the most chance of clowning around and doing what I loved to do most. Make people laugh.

That next Sunday I sprung out of bed, got dressed and ran out the door to meet my pal Janine.

Janine lived on the main street just across from the Golf Inn pub. . In fact it was her mum that told my mum about it and that's how I ended up joining. We always got the bus together every Sunday. Unless our parents were feeling flush, then they would all chip in and send us in a

74

taxi.

Janine was the nicest girl you could meet. A tiny wee smiley bundle of joy. And boy could she perform. I was always in awe of how courageous and confident she was when performing. I remember she was always able to do any accent. Something I am terrible at, even now. Any accent I try just sounds Indian. But if you ask me to do an Indian accent I sound Welsh. But Janine could flip from Spanish to Swedish in the same breath. But most of all she was a great pal. She had lost her Dad the year before and he was her best pal. A great guy.

But despite this she was always the most positive person in the room. Everyone loved Janine.

We jumped on the bus and talked about how excited we both were to audition. For some mad reason she hadn't been given a principle role either so she was hoping to get the part of Lena Marelli, the diva that gate crashes the auditions to demand her job back.

She practiced on the bus.

-Oscar! Oscar, I'm gonna give you one more chance!

Meanwhile I'm sat beside her muttering,

-I am the great Marbini.

As the bus pulled up I could see all the other kids piling into the Civic and my heart started to race. A new anxiety I hadn't experienced but one that would never leave me when it came to auditions.

There was no messing about. As soon as we were all sat on those old red dusty chairs the director was on stage starting the auditions.

75

-Okay all girls auditioning for the role of Lena Marelli make your way to the wings!

I turned to Janine to give her my good luck face but her arse was already halfway out the door.

The houselights went down as the hopeful girls auditioned one by one. Some decent performances, but most were pish. One girl was really bad though. She was one of the seniors. Stiff as a board and basically just shouted the lines like a nineteen fifties housewife calling her kids in for dinner.

Janine outshone them all. Her accent was perfect and her comedy performance had everyone in stitches. I knew she was going to get the part.

So obviously she didn't get the part.

For some reason big Shouty McstiffFace face got the role. When the director called out her name the whole building gasped. It was a real shocker. I still don't understand why but looking back it must have been political. Her parents must have been heavy donators or something.

I watched Janine walk down the treads off the stage. I was heartbroken for her but she was as bouncy and upbeat as ever as she just shrugged an "oh well" out to the seats with a smile. I had no idea how she could remain so positive. If that were me I'd have had a face like an abused blobfish.

She didn't come and sit with me but instead sat at the front of the stalls to reflect.

That's when I knew she was disappointed.

They called name upon name for role after role. It was never ending. And sure as fuck the magician role was the last audition of the day. But I was ready.

There were about twelve of us cramped together in the wings, all going for the same part.   I scanned the line.

I fancied my chances. These were the kids that just came for the tuck shop. I had this.

I stood at the back of the line because I wanted to be the last person the director saw.

The competition was poor as they all stuttered and stammered through the dialogue. I was growing more confident with each shite audition. Then it was my turn.

I didn't even think about it. Auto pilot kicked in as I bounded on stage with a big leap and a big swish as if I was wearing a cape. I was going all out.

-      I am the great Marbini! And I am the finest magician in the whole of Norfolk Nebraska!

As soon as I delivered the opening line the director and all the senior cast erupted into fits of laughter. I hadn't expected to nail it on the first line. I was well chuffed so I started throwing even more into it.

-From this hat I will produce not one rabbit, not…

I had to stop talking as the laughter had now rippled throughout all the kids in the auditorium. I had dreamed of this kind of reaction before. But something wasn't right.

The director wasn't even looking at me, he literally had his face in his palms crying with laughter, along with sixty other kids.

I felt the blood rush to my cheeks. They weren't laughing with me, they were laughing at me.

I looked down at my flies in case my wee tadger was hanging out because it sounded like a, "his wee willy is hanging out kind of laugh". But my flies were fastened tight.

What the fuck were they laughing at? I was mortified but didn't know why.

-Did I say it wrong? I asked the director with a tremble in my voice.

There was a beat before the theatre erupted again. The director tried to hold his laughter as he waved me off the stage.

-No that was just perfect. Brilliant.

-But I've not finished.

-Honestly it was great. Have a seat.

I should have stood my ground and demanded to know what the fuck they were all laughing at but I was so embarrassed I just ran down the treads sat in my seat and used my grey duffle coat as shield to deflect my humiliation as I pulled the hood over my face.

I had never been so confused or humiliated in my life. What the fuck just happened there?

Then one of the seniors Martin poked his head through the seats and gently said,

-They are laughing because it's pronounced, Norfolk Nebraska, not NorFuck Nebraska.

I crumbled in my chair.

I'd even emphasised the fuck part.

No wonder they were laughing. But on reflection that director should never have allowed me to feel humiliated like that. I was nine years old and felt my dreams had been broken. I was shaking like a leaf with shame and for the first time, a lot of anger. Anger I had never felt before.

When all the sniggering subsided the Director stood up from his laughter squat and looked down at Janine in the stalls.

- Janine, you fancy auditioning for the magician?

I knew there and then my chance was gone.

Without a beat Janine ran up those stairs and smashed the audition out of the park. She even put on this amazing comic Russian accent. The director gave her the role on the spot.

I was devastated.

I wanted to be happy for Janine because I knew she deserved it, but I just couldn't. For me my career was over before it had even started. Even though I was only eight. Maybe I wasn't cut out to do what I'd always dreamed of doing for the past three months.

I ended up being given the role of the barber who gets shot in the first twenty seconds of the play. That was me until the end of act one where I got to be in the chorus. The scene was the audition queue in the background as the lead roles Bugsy and Blousy have their big moment in the script.

We were told we could create our own costumes at home for this as we were only background artists. (The

79

budget only ever stretched to the speaking roles at Ayr Youth Theatre).

The brief from the director was.

-Okay listen up guys and gals! If you are in the chorus for the audition scene then you need to make a costume that looks show bizzy! Dancers, ventriloquists, whatever, just tell your parents to use their imagination! Funnier the better!

And that last comment was the biggest mistake he ever made in his directorial career. You want funny mother fucker? I'll give you funny. Then we'll see who's laughing. I really did say that to myself in my head. Ones last time...I was eight.

Some say psychotic but I say "driven".

I burst through the living room door that night.

-Mum I need a costume that's going to make me stand out!

I explained the whole situation to her.

My mum knew how disappointed I was not to get the magician role the week before so she was right on board straight away. She turned off the telly with the big switch complete with blue leckie tape headband and put a fag in her mouth to think. She picks up the fire stoker.

-A Chippendale! She blurts out as she stokes the coal fire with one hand and lights her fag off the flames with the other.

-What the stripper guys?

-It'll be hilarious! I'll cut the collar and cuffs off an old school shirt, stick your boxers on, wee bowtie, sorted!

The Chippendales were a group of male strippers in the nineties. All bronze with big muscles and a chip fat glaze. All the rage for hen parties and girls nights out. Even the thought of an eight year old boy trying to impersonate them would be out of the question.

I didn't need time to think as this was the greatest idea I'd ever heard. Most boys that age would have cringed at the thought of doing something as outrageous as that, but I didn't care.

I just wanted to make some people laugh.

Mum whipped the costume up in a day because she is in short, a fucking legend.

The director didn't see me in the full get out until the dress rehearsal. The lights came up and I was stood in the background wearing only a pair of black boxers, two white cuffs cut from a shirt and a cut collar complete with black bow tie. I was built like a malnourished racing snake but I was up there striking poses like Mr Universe. I had the whole cast in stitches. Bugsy and Blousy were loving it and it was the first time the Director ever really noticed me. He was laughing just as hard as he was at my Norfuck routine.

I was back in the game. I had gone from utter despair to sheer delight in the flash of my bony body. I was buzzing

Opening night came and I was about to perform in a theatre for the first time in my life.   Needless to say I was like a puppy on crack.

I can still smell the theatre that night. The waft of the canvas sets. The hemp ropes above, the dust burning on

81

the lights.

I was in my element as I stood in the wings listening to the hustle and bustle of the audience. That's always been my favourite part of performing. Hearing the buzz and knowing your actions created it. It's not an ego thing, far from it. Just knowing you are about to make people happy is the most satisfying thing in the world.

And there I was dressed as a 1950's barber about to get killed in the first few seconds of the show and I couldn't have been happier. I may have been getting shot but I was going to make sure my death was the most memorable.

I milked my debut and death scene then ran up to my shared dressing room to get into my Chippendale gear. I was full of beans because I knew the costume was going to raise a laugh or two. But nothing could prepare me or more importantly the director for what was about to happen.

As the backdrop lifted to reveal all six of us chorus members the sound of the orchestra was replaced with the sound of gradually building laughter.

It took a second or two for the audience to notice the four foot one skinny nine year old striking muscle man poses dressed as a Chippendale, but when they did the place was in an uproar.

The laughter got louder with every pose. Mums and Grannies especially were literally snorting and slavering with laughter.

I'd never felt so tall.

The more they laughed the more I played up to them.

I didn't want the feeling to end. They were laughing because of me, not at me.

Next thing I know the stage goes to a blackout so I filtered off into thw wings with the rest of them. I remember thinking that this was the happiest moment of my life.

I see Martin in the wings.

-Directors raging at you by the way. You totally just upstaged Bugsy and Blousy.

I was clueless.

-What does upstaged mean?

-You were making the audience laugh when they were trying to say important lines. Director's gonnae kill you.

He walked off shaking his head. I think he was actually jealous I got so many laughs.

None the less I was petrified. I'd gone from euphoria to anxiety before I'd even made it back to the dressing room.

I burst into tears in the wings. Not just a wee cry but a full on sob.

A few of the seniors tried to console me before the director burst through the crowd and grabbed me by the upper arms.

-Don't listen to anyone else. I don't care that we lost a lot of the plot, that's the biggest laugh we've had in this theatre for years. Just do the same again tomorrow and the day after that. But make it bigger. Just not when Bugsy and Blousy are talking.

And then he ran back to his prompt corner, put on his head set and continued to direct the rest of the show.

I ripped the hole right out those next two shows. Blew the roof off with my skeletal muscle poses and rubber facial expressions.

I'd caught the buzz.

I was now officially a certified laugh whore.

After my stint as the Chippendale I was cast as the lead role in the following Youth Theatre show The Incredible Vanishing written by Denise Coffey (Like the drink but not spelt the same).

From what I remember the script was about this mad Queen Marsh who had three cheeky troll disciples that ran havoc throughout Victorian times. I may be off with the plot here but that's what I remember. I played the hero P.C Parker and Janine played the Queen. She was brilliant. And we were both chuffed to bits that we were cast as the two lead roles off the back of our Bugsy debuts. All unjustified resentment from my side was gone now. We made some team.

The shows went great apart from one minor blip. But it was a blip that would define my whole outlook on theatre and how it should be done for the rest of my career.

During one of the shows one of the Principal actors broke character and starting waving to his parents. He was about ten years old the same as me. But I was fucking furious that he broke the forth wall. And this was before I was taught what the fourth wall even was. It took all my energy not to walk over to him and tell him to stop. I may

84

even have let out a hiss across the stage to deter him at one point. I think I did. I definitely did.

I felt a real surge of fury run up my back, over my shoulders then into my cheeks.

When we got off stage I squared right up to him and we had it out. He couldn't understand why I was so angry. -Jesus it's just a laugh. It's my mum and dad, I'll wave if I want.

The way he laughed and walked off along with the reaction of my fellow cast members made me realise that my passion for selling the story was different from the rest.

I wasn't playing at acting anymore. I'd tasted the lead, and now I wanted to keep it. I was ten.

Performing in shows really helped me realise what I wanted to do in life. I grew more confident after my first lead role. Perhaps too confident.

I didn't get another big role for the next few years after that. In all fairness the Youth Theatre had lost funding so it was only one show a year now not three. After the Incredible Vanishing I was launched back into the bowels of the big shows with the same old seniors playing the lead roles. I spat the dummy if I didn't have a speaking role in a show so I wasn't in many over the next four years. Obviously now I realise that was not the way to behave but at the time I felt I could do better than the guys in front of me.

My sensitivity couldn't handle my passion.

By the time I got my next speaking role I was in the

senior group. They were just about to cast for "The Lion The Witch and The Wardrobe". I wasn't excited because I thought it was the most boring fucking book I'd ever pretended to read, but I knew there were some meaty parts available. And when I say meaty I mean they had lots of dialogue and stage time.

The script had at least twenty really good speaking roles and there were only twenty three of us in the senior class. I was pretty sure I'd bag a decent character to play.

By now the Youth Theatre had moved home.

The Gaiety Theatre had built a brand new studio upstairs from the main auditorium and we were the first class to ever use it. When I was growing up there were three main venues. Borderline Theatre, The Civic Theatre and The Gaiety Theatre.

I can still smell the fresh varnish on the newly laid pine floor boards as I was sat amongst the rest of the hopeful kids looking up at the director and a few select senior arse kissers by his side. He started with the usual build up.
-Now this hasn't been an easy decision for me, but the cast is as follows.

He began to read out the cast list to the room.

Principal role after principal role read out with cheers from the loving cast, but yet again not a mention of my name. It was Bugsy all over again.

After about an hour of gushing congrats every time a name was read out the director concluded.
-Congratulations everyone, now time for the hard work. See you all at rehearsals!

Then he left.

Everyone got a part bar three of us.

Me.

A girl that had just joined that day

And a boy who's name escapes me. All I can remember about him was that he didn't even know why he was there and he was wearing a vampire costume.

Rejected.

Again.

I was fourteen or fifteen by now I think.

I spent the next week or so getting wasted on weed and cider with the odd tin off gas to buzz in between.

I just couldn't work out why I was being overlooked again. I still don't fully understand it. Maybe I was too hammy, too energetic. I have a tendency to let adrenaline overcome my composure. Or it could have been a case of my inability to force myself to shine. For all the confidence I have in myself I tend to struggle in portraying it.

A few bit parts in shows weren't feeding my hunger and I was about to give it all up for drugs. I didn't need to work as hard for that kind of buzz.

But then I got the first ever role of my dreams.

Little Shop of Horrors was one of the best Youth Theatre shows any kid in the country could hope to be cast in during the nineties. I was obsessed with the film. My Papa let me watch it when I was staying it his and I was instantly hooked. The actors and characters fascinated me, especially the role of the Dentist played by Steve Martin. Steve just owns that character. I'd watch it on a loop and copy his every mannerism as best as I could.

I felt confident this time around as I had matured physically and I looked more like the Dentist than anyone else at the Youth Theatre. My main competition was a guy called Jonathan Ross. Not the talk show guy, but still a really funny guy. We called him Jono.

Jono's comedy timing was second to none. I should have been jealous of him but because he was so funny I could only respect him. He was and still is a good friend. He looked a bit like a working class Hugh Grant with the same dry humour.

We both knew we were the two leading contenders to bag the role. Jono had the better singing voice but I had the highest energy and if truth be telling, more arrogance in my performance. But we were neck and neck.

When casting day came, everyone kind of knew what the cast list would look like, apart from the role of the Dentist. It really was that close.

The Director played on the excitement and left me and Jono on edge until the last kick of the ball.

- And the role of the Dentist goes too...Chris! (By the way I know book cover says Jerry Taylor but that's my stage name...can't remember if I've covered that yet but I'm not allowed to look back on what I've written)......And I've written most of this stoned.

I was over the moon I got the part. I felt accepted. The fuse lit in my spine again, but this time the flame was friendly.

Our first performance was at The Gaiety Theatre. A place that holds a very special place in my heart. The venue was packed that night.

Four hundred and odd people.

I nailed it. I truly did. I gave it everything I had and more. What a rush. The minute that curtain came down I knew this is what I wanted to do for the rest of my life.

I was going to be an actor.

The after show party was epic for a few reasons. One of the parents decided it would be a good idea to let some of the older kids have a party at her house, and bring drink if our parents allowed it. So obviously we all lied and said that wouldn't be a problem.

I don't know if you've ever been to an after show party full of drunk emotional teenagers still high on adrenaline, but just picture the scene in the movie Gremlins when they are watching Snow White in the cinema. Times that by ten and that'll give you fair idea of the utter carnage that took place.

Needless to say we were all booted out after a couple of hours.

But some of us weren't ready for home yet, we were just getting into the swing of things so we decided to find somewhere we could finish our drinks and hopefully get a game of spin the bottle going.

Truth or dare at the least.

We snuck around the back of a big school called Queen Margaret's Academy to lay low for a bit.

Turns out we didn't need spin the bottle because one of the girls that was with us, Shelly pounced on me the minute we turned the corner. She pushed me up against the roughcast wall and started kissing me. I dropped my bottle of lemon Hooch and started to kiss back.

I'd kissed girls before but this was getting steamy. I was thinking,

-Oh here we go, this is it, this is finally it.

Shelly was a really good looking girl too. Dirty blonde wavy hair, freckly nose and big brown eyes.

After a few minutes of kissing she pulled down my pale blue baggy jeans and Bugo Hoss boxers fae the Barras and lifted up her dress to her belly button. I'd never seen a real life fanny before. I definitely stared too long. And my mouth and eyes were one hundred percent too wide.

I had no idea how to work one but by God I was gonnae try.

We fumbled around to try and guide me in but it was no use, I had no idea where my willy was meant to go. Obviously I knew the general area because of magazines and Channel Five soft porn movies, but I just couldn't get my angles right. I was scared I put it up her bum or even worse that clitoris thing I'd been hearing about!

Eventually I found where I was meant to be and slotted the wee soldier into the barracks. It didn't feel how I expected but what did I know?

I started to pump away like a wee Jack Russell . We were standing up so it was hard to keep balance at times. The Hooch wasn't helping. After a second or two I knew it just

90

didn't feel right.

Then it hit me.

I wasn't having sex ….I was shagging the gap between the top of her thighs.

But she's too polite to tell me.

First chance to lose my virginity and I've penetrated her legs.

I tried to pretend I knew it wasn't in yet and gave an awkward laugh. I positioned myself again but luckily Shelly took control of the situation, and just dropped to her knees and gave me a blowjob.

My first ever one.

Result.

It was only for a minute or so but still a blowjob I could tell my pals about.

She pulled my trousers back up then gave me a cuddle.

Sympathy probably.

Good on her though, because if someone had just pumped my thigh gap they'd be getting fuck all sympathy from me.

We joined the other guys who were now sat in the doorway of the back entrance of the Academy. Shelly sat beside me while I rolled two joints to share among the group.

And what a group it was.

I don't want to name any of them due to drugs being involved, I don't grass on pals. But trust me they were some of the finest people I ever met in my youth. We were all misfits together. Some of us don't talk anymore due to either me being a bit of a cunt or them being a bit of a cunt. I don't want to dwell on that though. No matter what we all think of each other now, we had some really special times together.

We smoked, laughed, cried and drank until five in the morning. One of the troops had their acoustic guitar so they played and sang while we all listened. I'd made a wee bonfire using two empty cans of Miller Lager. Spilt them in two and folded the two edges together to make a wee base plate. I curved it at the sides so it basically looked like a big ashtray. Then I used paper and wee twigs that were scattered around and got a tiny wee fire going. It didn't have much heat but it lit up our wee den just enough to create a cracking wee atmosphere.

Music, drink, weed and pals.

It really was a perfect night....

.....Apart from pumping Shelly's thigh gap.

We started to get tired so we started our journey home. It was a half hour walk to Ayr Town Centre. There was a taxi rank just outside the train station.

Kelly looked tired as she blew me a kiss and got into her cab. That was the last time I ever saw her. She moved away and I've never heard from her again.

I decided to walk back to Prestwick. It was freezing but I didn't care. I wanted to think about everything that had gone on the day before.

I walked with my chest puffed out and couldn't stop smiling as I thought about that show....that audience....that party...and of course....that blowjob.

I had tasted popularity and I wanted more.

School couldn't be further from my mind.

I think I've repressed most of my school days. I don't remember too much about them. The odd thing here and there but when I was in class I reckon my brain just went into hibernation mode, especially Maths. I fucking hate mathematics. It does something to me. When I knew I had maths that day I felt depressed. Sometimes anger or pure rage. I don't know why I'm like this but even now if I see a Sudoku puzzle I have a sudden urge to scream and rip it up. I'm not even exaggerating. That's pure psycho behaviour that isn't it? But that's what maths does to me.

But words? Give me words all day long.

English was my favourite subject. I craved learning new words and their meanings, and I've always been a fan of reading. Even though my spelling is utter pish.

Ever since ma old maw slung a Secret Seven book at me to shut me up, I've been hooked.

One of the best teachers I ever had was my third year English teacher Mr Rankin. Sadly he passed away a few years ago at a young age. I was devastated when I heard. He was known to be very strict but to me he was one of the biggest influences of my career. He had a brilliantly dry and witty sense of humour that I really enjoyed.

He had a tanned complexion, ear length straight jet black hair and glasses. A bit like a David Badeil now I think about

93

it.

One thing I have to tell you about Mr Rankin and I swear on my son's life this is true. He had a speech impediment and couldn't pronounce his R's. His R's came out as W's and with a name like Rankin you can see why this created many a laugh in the classroom. But he dealt with it so well, always a knowing smile any time he had to introduce himself to a new pupil. He demanded respect but he also knew that kids were always going to find that funny.

He noticed early on my passion for reading. I always had an Andy McNab S.A.S book in my bag, so he recommended I venture more into the fiction side of things from more established authors. He loaned me a copy of Bram Stokers Dracula.

If you've ever read it then you'll know the chapters are made up of letters and newspaper extracts and not always in order, so to say it was a step up in reading was an understatement. But I got tore in. It took me an hour or so to really get into it but once I did I hardly lifted my head for weeks. These days it would only take me a few days to read this particular book but I was still young and had to go back and read chapters twice to stop me getting confused.

I would wait until mum and dad were asleep, smoke a fat cone and lay on my futon reading all about Jonathan Harker and his dealings with Dracula. I was absorbed into the world. My life didn't exist when I was reading. I was addicted there and then.

So that was reading added to my , do anything but school

list, after weed, drink and girls. School was really fucking up my social plans. I hated it.

Thank fuck for Mr Rankin though.

One day in class we all had to read the play, Educating Rita. Every kid had to take turns at reading out a part of the play. It's a two hander with a male and female character.

I volunteered straight away. No one else wanted to do it but they were forced. And God were they shite. Nae commitment. I couldn't understand why at the time.

Obviously now I get we are all different but back then I just thought my class were a bunch of weirdo's. Even Mr Rankin was getting bored so for a laugh he told me to just read both parts. I grabbed the challenge with both hands.

For the role of Rita I put on a screechy scouse accent, and a Michael Caine accent for the male role. I went for it. I had the whole class in stitches, especially Mr Rankin. It was the first time we all saw him smile properly. It was nice. I thought he would stop me after a while but he didn't. He let me perform right up until the bell rang. I got through the full first act in forty five minutes.

That for me was my first ever one man show. And I loved every single second of it. Not because I was getting all the attention, but because I just loved making people laugh. To me it's one of the greatest feelings in the world. Creating an emotion in someone and making them happy. That's what it's always been about for me. A whole class room including teacher just all enjoying each other's company for forty five minutes, and all because of what I did.

It was that day I realised that maybe, just maybe I had a shot at being an actor in the future

But it wasn't just my interest in books, or letting me show off that drew respect for Mr Rankin. He actually believed in me, and in my writing. And the reason he believed in me so much all stemmed from the first imaginative essay I wrote during my third year prelim exams…. Stoned.

In third year we had to sit our mock exams, Prelims. I hated them, so naturally to help us all get through, some of me and the boys from my year would go to the English block before each exam and have a cheeky wee joint to help us get through the next few hours.

On the day of my English prelim I headed to the toilets as usual to meet Gordo and the others, but this time they were nowhere to be seen.

I could hear whispering coming from the top cubicle so I went to investigate. I was in third year now so I was allowed to venture further up the bog.

It was Danny and Bongo.
-Fuck are you two up to?

They nearly shat themselves. Danny was raging but Bongo was relieved.
-Chrissy boy fuck sake don't dae that.

I could now see Danny was trying to push the roach end of a joint into a small hole he had burnt into the side of a small empty plastic bottle with a fag. I think it used to be Red Kola, could tell by the shape. Curries…none of that

Barr's shite.

-Fuck's that?

Bongo looked excited.

-You never seen a bottle bong afore?

-Naw.

Danny had managed to put the roach end through the hole and was now holding it up for me to see.

-Just light the joint, sook the top of the bottle, pull the joint out and clear the smoke from the chamber.

Danny lit it up to demonstrate.

I kept edgy.

I'd never seen a cloud of smoke so thick as Danny blew his lungs out. He doubled over like a half shut chib coughing into the toilet bowl as he held the bong up for Bongo. A big line of saliva bungee jumped from his bottom lip a few times then snapped off and fell into the pan. He looked in pain.

But I was still game.

Bongo took a hit and then joined Danny's head at the bowl.

The two of them were coughing and slevering like rabid dugs in a gas chamber. It wasn't the best advert for their product but Gordo was a no show and he had the hash. No fucking way I was going to that exam straight.

Luckily the lads were in a generous mood and let me take a blast. I think they were buying themselves time to recover thinking about it now.

Like every other time I didn't weigh up my options, I went in full steam ahead with conviction. I sucked the neck of that bottle like I was taking my last breath. I sucked and sucked then pulled the joint out. The smoke piled straight into my lungs. I held it in as long as I could. It wasn't as harsh as I thought. Maybe I was getting better at this. I actually felt proud. Here's me holding my own while Danny and Bongo have their heeds doon the pan.

Just as I went to exhale I heard him.

-Bells rang.

It was the Jannie. I'd been holding the smoke in my lungs for about fifteen seconds already so I had no choice but to blow it straight in his direction. Danny and Bongo had already grabbed their bags by now and had made a bolt past the Jannie, but I was just stood there like a dick, the last ant left. Mouth wide open and a fucking bottle bong in my hand. I knew he was a good guy but surely even he couldn't let me off with this.

In a panic I stashed the bottle in my school bag.

-What was that?

I froze. It felt like an hour. I didn't know what to say.

Then out it came.

-It's my inhaler.

I don't know if it was the fear on my face or the daftness of my answer but he laughed.

-Beat it and don't come in here again.

I took that as a win and bolted past him with my heart racing.

-Sorry! Thanks!

I legged it to the assembly hall where the exams were being held. My sprint started to feel a bit spongy beneath my feet the closer I got. I was in a panic but still relieved the Jannie didn't stick me in.

The bottle bong was kicking in.

I entered the hall with a swagger .I always liked to make an entrance to show off to the rest of the year.....I always loved making people laugh to annoy the teachers.

As I passed some of my mates desks I pushed their exam papers onto the floor. I was a wee dick that way. One of the exam officials or whatever the fuck they were called clicked their fingers to get my attention and signalled with a downwards pointing index finger to sit on my arse. I thought it best not to draw any more attention to myself so I did as I was instructed, found my desk took a few minutes to enjoy the stone coming up.

It was a real nice mellow stone. My body felt loose but my brain was still sharp.

My favourite kind of stone.

I didn't know at the time but have now since learned that when you don't mix weed with tobacco you get a much purer stone. The chemicals they put in fags and backy bring on anxiety for me.

I don't know if it was the type of hash I'd smoked or the fact I'd used a bong, but I felt so fucking good. The perfect mind state for writing I've found over the years.

And this state was ideal for this particular exam as the topic was," imaginative writing". Right up my street!

The exam paper gave you the choice of three headings and you had to write a story based on the one of your choosing.

I don't remember the other choices but the one I went for was, "Journey through the Stars".

It's the happiest I ever remember being at school. Stoned, relaxed and knowing I had two hours to create something from my own mind with no rules or restrictions.

My pencil scribbled on that paper like the needle on Donald Trump's lie detector.

I had to sharpen it at least eight times.

I was ....IN... MY ....FUCKING.... ZONE.

I wrote a short parody about spoof Star Wars characters hitch hiking through space. I'd never even seen Star Wars but knew enough about the characters and story to make something work. If I'm being honest I have no recollection of what the story was about, I was so stoned and it was about twenty fives years ago now. I remember one character based on Chewbacca was called ChewBacky . I wrote him as a big redneck hillbilly backy chewin loudmouth. He was on a mission to find his two sisters, aunty and mum who turned out to be the same person. I'm raging that's all I remember. I'd love to be able to read it again.

I know I had great fun writing it though and something clicked in my head. It was a release, a tonic even.

When the marks came back a few months later, Mr Rankin announced everyone's grades in front of the whole class. I was dreading hearing mine. I knew Mum and Dad had high hopes for me in English but all I'd researched in my study time was different strains of weed and how not to pump a thigh gap.

I wasn't holding out much hope.

The scores were graded from one to six. One being the best mark you can get, six the worst. If I didn't get at least a three then I would have some serious explaining to do to maw.

Mr Rankin was going through the marks alphabetically. Most were getting twos and threes.

The odd four or five here and there.

He got to me.

-Taylor, one.

Did I hear that right? Did he just say, one? I saw the class all look at me.

I was just as fucking surprised as the rest of them.

Fuck knows how, but I'd passed with top marks. Mr Rankin was delighted. He kept me behind to chat to me that day.

-For all you do my head in some days Chris, you really do have a unique imagination. I loved your whole working class spin on the story.

He then went on to talk passionately about Star Wars but I stopped him.

-I've never seen Star Wars.

After saying this he was even more impressed. We sat for about half an hour talking about structure and what other writers I should research. Then he ended the conversation with…..

-Now, your story was great, but it "genuinely pained" me how bad your spelling and grammar were at times

He insisted I was to do the ground work before I focussed solely on the story telling.

Great advice still to this day, although believe it or not I still do really struggles wif spellings and grammars to this very week.

Thank God Mr Rankin teached me to spoke right since I was a wee children.

I spent the next year studying English with more gusto than ever before. It got me wound up at times but I never gave up. I loved the challenge and my thinking was if I got great marks in English then Mum would turn a blind eye to my maths results. Did I tell you I fucking hated maths?

I've had a passion for writing ever since my chat with Mr Rankin that day. And because of his encouragement I started to try harder. He gave me belief in myself and I'll never forget him for that.
God Rest His Soul.

If you're listening up there Mr R, then thank you from the bottom of my heart, for seeing through my dunce mask and taking me under your wing.

My eyes are filling up with tears writing this as I think of your family and the fact that no other kid will have the chance to be inspired by you the way I was. I wish I was good enough a writer to put into words just how grateful I am but I can't. And even if I could you'd still find the spelling mistakes.

I wanted to write LOL after that but apparently it's not good "book etiquette".

Mr R would have loved that line by the way so if you didn't laugh you're a heartless cunt.

The problem I now had was that I immediately put my new found writing skills down to the fact I was stoned. How else could I have pulled that out of the bag? I thought, it must have been the weed, it was expanding my mind... all that pish.

For the next few years to come, writing and weed would come hand in hand. If I couldn't afford weed, I wouldn't write.

.....So not much writing was done after that for a long time to come.

Drink and girls were my main focus come fourth year at school. I still liked weed but I had become fonder of the drinking scene as it made me more confident around girls.

Every Saturday night I would have the same "party routine".

By the way before I get into it, I should tell you now, a huge character in these weekly routines was the best friend I've ever had.

Mark Anderson.

Mark is my cousin. Our maws are sisters. We were born 2 months apart with me being the oldest. We've been best mates since birth, genuinely. I've argued and screamed at pretty much every person I've ever been close to. But in the thirty eight years Mark and I have been friends, we have never argued once. Not even a raised voice. We were joined at the hip as kids. We did everything together (no not that ya creeps).

We couldn't be more different on paper. I'm a loud mouthed bundle of noise and anxiety but Mark is the most chilled out, reasonable guy going. He may be the quietest man you'll meet but believe me you won't find a bigger heart.

When we got to Academy we didn't see each other as much the first two years. We met new pals and mine were more into drugs, so we remained friends but just didn't hang out as as often. That all changed in fourth year though when Mark started to get more interested in the bevy rather than the baw. Mark was an outstanding footballer. He was the captain of the Primary Seven team when he was in Primary five. I think if he was more confident he would have gone Pro. (That was his knickname-Pro).

But like most kids in Scotland, the opportunities were few but the drink was a plenty. And let's be brutally honest about it. Mark was choking for his hole anaw.

We used to stay at Gran and Papas every Saturday night. By then Papa knew I smoked and Gran has resigned herself to the fact we were coming home steaming every weekend. I think she actually quite liked the fact we used her house as a hideout. And I know old Papa was proud. So long as we didn't disrespect their house or rules, they were willing to turn a blind eye. Papa would even pour me and Mark a wee whisky now and again when Gran had gone to her bed.

We really had it good when I think about it.

Mark worked at the electric bakery bake house every

Saturday. The same bakery I walked past after my first joint with Danny and Bongo. I was still grafting away at the Picnic Basket. We would both finish at five and head straight to Gran and Papa's.

Gran would always be sat in one of her wee jogging suits, feet up on a poofy watching some shite on the telly.
-Oh there's the workers, she would say. How are my boys?

Mark would greet her with a floury hug as the white dust fell off his white overalls and I'd smother her in the smell of grease with my huggy hello.
-Oh you shtink, she's always say in her wee tartan laced German accent.

Papa was always in the kitchen .

Not just then.

Always.

The kitchen was his sanctuary in the winter, but he would move to the garden in the summer.

Dinner was always a three courser with Papa no matter what day of the week it was.

Soup

Main meal

Pudding.

Lentil soup mostly, but it was tasty so you could suffer it week in week out. Main meals always varied.

Standard Grandparent cooking.

Mince n tatties, fish n chips, haggis neeps n tatties. Anything with an "n" in the middle.

Pudding though was always by request. And every time Mark and I only every asked for one dish. Bananas

105

and custard with hundreds and thousands on top. Honest to God it was fucking glorious. I used to rattle through my first two courses just to get to it. In the winter Papa would serve the bananas and custard hot but in the winter it would be cold. Either way, it was fucking heaven. If you've got the munchies reading this right now then I IMPLORE you to get rattled in.

So that was us, full bellies and ready to rumble. Mark would have a bath and I'd use the shower upstairs. Papa put a five minute timer on the shower so we wouldn't use up all his leckie.

Talk about a pressure wank.

With our Ted Sherman shirts hanging off us and stinking of Joop aftershave we kissed Gran goodbye and made our way to meet our pals Mikey and Sean at our newly acquired drinking destination.

Buckfast Bridge.

Mikey and Sean were two boys from our year that also went to the same Primary school as Mark and I. Mikey was an athletic type. Right into his basketball. He was taller than the rest of us and had golden blond hair. He was queit but funny especially on the wine.

Sean was a diamond too. He was right into his computers but not in a geeky way. He had this great full head of glossy mahogany hair swept to one side. We used to call him ginger to wind him up but in truth it was a dark red colour I'd never seen before. He was a real warm character and was the first person to introduce me to the game "Sensible Soccer" on the P.C. Me him, Mark and Mikey used to spend hours playing that game. Sean would always win because he got to used the joystick and made us use the fuckin keyboard.

Sean if you're reading this, poor form mate, poor form.

You won't find Buckfast Bridge anywhere on a map of Prestwick, we came up with the name. I won't insult your intelligence by telling you why.

It was the perfect place for us to tan our cairy oot.

All angles were covered, literally.

The Oval was too risky by then. The Polis were always turning up and surrounding everyone. Every Saturday night we had to watch them pour our bevy out in front of us with a big cheesy grin on their coupon. I mean come on tae fuck, I know they have to do their jobs, but who in their right fucking mind smiles when alcohol is being wasted?? That's what put kids off the police when I was a younger. The pure smugness of it all. They didn't just do their jobs, they rubbed it in as they did it.

We did find a wee quiet spot for a few weeks once. It was know by everyone in Prestwick as "The Rope Swing". It was a wee secluded nature spot by a wee burn (stream). It was hidden behind a football ground called Calley Park. It's where the famous Caledonian Boys Club play. I played for them once when I was nine or ten, but I got sent off in my first game. I was playing shit. I was a goalkeeper but they had me playing left back. We got beat ten nil. Every time a goal went in I got the blame from the other boys and the manager. When the tenth goal went in I ran over to the sideline to get a drink of water. The coach walked

107

up to me and said,

-Water? You've done nothing all game and you want water?

My mini Hulk took over as those angry tears filled up in my eyes like flash floods.

I snapped and threw the water bottle at him.

-Who you talkin tae ya fat cunt? Am dain ma best!

The minute the bottle cap burst open off the bridge of his nose my rage hid behind my fear. The whole pitch froze. The referee blew his whistle but I don't think he even knew what to do.

The coach jerked the top half of his torso forward as if to lunge at me, but his peripherals spotted the witnesses and the potential ramifications so he stopped in his tracks. He knew he couldn't hit me. But I swear to fuck he was aching too. The rage poured out him faster than the water from the bottle that maimed him. I think it's the darkest colour of purple I've ever seen anyone turn. But he composed himself long enough for the referee to intervene.

The referee was and still is a legend to this day in Ayrshire....Wee Joe McGill. He was a notoriously fair referee and a well respected member of my Gran's church. He knew me so I was hoping he'd go easy on me.

-Right son, you're off!

He pulled his red card out and flashed it in my face. I should have just accepted my punishment and walked off to the dressing room, but as always I felt like playing up to the rest of the boys and shouted back at him.

-Are you fuckin kidding me man??

He flashed the red again.

-That's another. Swear again and I'll keep them coming.

I pointed at the coach.

-Blame that baldy bastard not me!

He blew his whistle and flashed the red again

The assistant coach grabbed me by the collar and guided me off the pitch.

I was so angry but also I have to admit I was kind of enjoying the drama of it all. I felt like I was in a film. I swaggered to that dressing room like Danny Dyer in...well any Danny Dyer film.

I always cry when I'm angry. My eyes fill up like those quick speed pints glasses you see at festivals. If you see my eyes fill quickly you know I'm either about to trash the room or pounce on you.

It's a bastard of an affliction though because sometimes people mistake the tears for fear and see it as a sign of weakness , and that in turn makes me even angrier. I don't bubble away like a soap star or anything like that. I just get so full of rage that tears pour from my eyes.

I never played for the club again after that.

Aye so as I was saying, me Mark Sean and Mikey used to drink at the rope swing down by the burn behind Caley Park! But word soon spread about how good a spot it was and all of a sudden everyone started going down there. Aw the neds and pricks we were trying to avoid. Including Hammy.

One Saturday we decided we had had enough of shite over crowded drinking spots, so we decided as a team to try and explore potential dens down Prestwick beach. We loaded up our swimming bags with bottles of Buckfast (My new poison) and headed for the shore, and that's when we found Buckfast bridge.

The bridge sits just off Midton Road and takes you over the railway line towards the shore.

The four of us were heading over the bridge trying to think of good spots when Mikey stopped at the top, and had a look about.

-Here look! You can see in all directions for at least two hundred yards here and there's only two ways over this bridge. If two of us keep edgy at each side of the steps then two of us can down our bottles.

Mikey was a genius.

There were houses all around the bridge but if you ducked down at the top then you were totally concealed.

We took turns as look outs, one at each side. We rotated every few glugs. The more we rotated the more we laughed.

That was the day Buckfast Bridge was christened. But it wouldn't be the most prominent "Buckfast bridge" of my life. I found another one a few years later... But we'll get to that a few more chapters down the line.

As soon as we had downed our bottles we would spark up two fags, I'd always leave Mark twos because he wasn't really a smoker so I'd get away with giving him last draws. Mark only smoked when he was drunk. Oh aye and one

more thing you should probably know about wee quiet
fourteen year old Mark....

When he was drunk, he was a fucking psychopath.

Not in an angry serial killer way, but by fuck that boy
could party. Picture Frank the Tank in the film Old School.

One time my friends Ricky and Roddy had an empty
when their mum and dad were away on holiday so they
threw the most epic party you can imagine, pure American
Frat Party film standard it was. About two hundred people
all crammed into that house that night and by fuck was it
legendary. People still talk about it to this day.

It got so out of hand that the police busted the party and
threw everyone out then started searching the place for
contraband.

Mark was wasted so we hid him in a cupboard in one of
the bedrooms then some of us hid under some beds.

The police found us all straight away and when they
opened up the cupboard where Mark was stashed he was
stood there with his top off and was holding a pair of
nunchucks in one hand (Ricky collected martial arts
weapons) and an empty bottle of Thunderbird in the
other. He could barely stand but squinted at the
policemen and slurred.

-Fuck you lookin at?

Luckily for Mark the police got a more serious call over
the radio and had to leave. They made us promise we
would put him straight to bed then left. Obviously we
continued to party, but we did put Mark to bed after
prising the nun chucks from his hand. He wouldn't part

with the Thunderbird though. He fell asleep nursing it.

The bridge became the norm for the four of us every weekend for about two months. But like with everything else, I was losing the buzz, I needed a new high. I never liked routine.

I was missing something. I loved making Mark, Sean and Mikey, but it wasn't enough. I was missing a proper audience.

The Youth Theatre was about to announce the casting for their next big show, The Crucible by Arthur Miller. It's about the trials of the Salem witches.
Real drama.

I was pretty sure after my performance as The Dentist I'd be in with a good shout of getting the role of the lead John Proctor.
But I was wrong.

Even though I'd burst the roof in Little Shop of Horrors, this was the time to bring me back down to earth. I get the reason now, but at the time I fucking hated the Director for what was about to unfold.

I didn't get the lead role, or any of the real good meaty parts I wanted. I was cast as Thomas Putnam. Compared to others I only had a few scenes. I was bitter with rage. Although now I realise it's a great role to get the teeth into but back then I was jealous of every other male actor at the youth theatre. This is the point I started to feel like they were all against me, even though that couldn't be further from the truth.

I couldn't be arsed with rehearsals half the time. I still

felt I didn't really belong.

I was either too hungover or too stoned to turn up. When it came to show time I was so unrehearsed and knew I was going to have to blag my way through.

I was awful.

Truly fucking awful.

Worst performance of my life to date.

I was unprepared, I was bitter and I played the role full of resentment.

I screamed my way through every scene. I even remember hearing one of the cast members saying off stage, "There's Chris shouting again". I hated the girl for saying that, but on reflection she was right.

When I think about how bad I was I get a beamer.

The rest of the cast were amazing though. And that made it even harder.

I didn't go to that after show party.

I went straight home, gave maw and paw the usual small talk then disappeared to my room and smoked a joint with a wee bottle bong chaser.

I turned on my T.V to drown out the silence.

Only Fools and Horses.

My worries disappeared again...Not disappeared... Hid.

I could feel the blood vessels in my eyes bulge. The weed was good...Really good.

I slouched on my pillow against my wall and tuned in to Del and Rodney's capers.

I was more stoned than I needed to be but all my

worries were gone for that moment in time.

This was the first time I used hash to blank out my feelings and I was now understanding what the phrase "medicinal" meant.

I sat every one of my Standard Grades absolutely....fucking....... wasted.

Every single one of them bar my P.E practical. Fuck running cross country stoned.

I really did love P.E. Sport was always an addiction for me too, but unfortunately I chose blunting my endorphins as opposed to using them to my advantage,

I've always been into sports, any sport. Apart from Cricket.

I was just turning sixteen and knew I could legally leave school then so I didn't give one thought to my education. I can honestly say that in the whole of fourth year I didn't study once. Not one single page. I just didn't give a fuck. I just wanted to be an actor. In my opinion actors didn't need to be able to count.

The only thing I cared about in my last year at Prestwick Academy was winning the school talent show.

It was the biggest event of the year at school. Hundreds of parents and students would fill the assembly hall to watch the show and I was determined to win it, even though the year before my performance had almost ruined all hopes that I could make it is a performer. I went into the show totally unprepared and thought I could wing it. I tried to do an "adult singing kettle show". Even to this day I've no fucking clue what I was trying. I'd somehow

114

talked Mark into being a double act with me. The basis of the act was that we were ripping off the singing kettle but there was no script. Poor Mark had to try keep up with me just making things up on the spot as I tried to do stand up comedy. I didn't prepare anything, I was just winging it, thinking I was good enough to make an act out of something that wasn't an act. It totally fell on its arse to the point that even the teachers joined in with the kids booing us off the stage. We were literally ridiculed for the whole next year. I was broken after that so Christ knows how poor Mark felt.

But I didn't let it stop me. I knew how bad the act was but I also knew I was the funniest kid in school. I had a fucking point to prove.

Christ knows how but I somehow managed to convince Mark into doing the talent show with me again the following year. I sold my idea to him that we were going to replicate the Sweet Transvestite song from the Rocky Horror Picture Show. I was going to play Dr Frankenfurter and he would play Brad.

Looking back he had some baws to stick by me and go again. Maybe he had faith in me more than I had in myself or maybe he just wanted to prove something to all the haters just like I did. Either way I'll never forget that he stuck by me that year and in total truth if it wasn't for this I probably would have given up on performing altogether and would never be writing this book.

For the three months leading up to the talent show we rehearsed at my house once a week. I'm not the best singer in the world but I knew if I sold the performance I could redeem my reputation as the performer of the school. I knew we wouldn't win. All I wanted to do was prove a point.

All my Youth Theatre pals helped me find the costumes and my Mum bought me some fish net stockings in Semi Chem. My art teacher/guidance teacher Mrs Hughes did the makeup on the night. After Mr Rankin ,Mrs Hughes was the best thing that ever happened to me at school. She understood me, she encouraged me but most of all she listened to my thoughts. She knew I was different from all the other kids. She didn't pigeon hole me but instead taught me that being different was better than following trends. I still love her to bits to this day.

I was lucky to get another shot at the talent show as the two teachers in charge, Mr West and Mr Burns (Both Science teachers) were very wary that my act would be as shite as it was the year before. And quite rightly so. So they made me audition.

I was called to the assembly hall one lunchtime to show them my act just to prove I was actually rehearsed this time and it could have gone either way.

I remember them sat watching me as I minced around the stage belting out the lyrics to Sweet Transvestite and thrusting my corset wearing torso out to the audience. Mr Burns was laughing his head off but Mr West looked more reserved.

When I finished I saw them turn to each other and start a deep discussion. I knew Mr B was onside but Mr West was a tougher nut to crack as he turned and looked up to me on the stage.

- Right well, I mean it's great and clearly well rehearsed but...Well how the hell can I justify putting a fifteen year old boy on stage wearing that without getting sacked?

I was ready for this question and had already rehearsed my response with Mark.

- But Mr West I'm not playing a fifteen year old boy! I'm a fifteen year old boy playing a famous transvestite. If I was an actor playing Hitler would you automatically think that I hate Jews?

In my head it was the perfect response but it only seemed to make him more anxious.

Mr West stood up and made for the exit.

- Sorry Chris, I just can't justify this. Maybe next year, try something different.

I was distraught but something took a hold of me. I looked at Mark who looked as gutted as me. I needed to make a stand so I jumped off the stage and grabbed Mr w=West by the arm to stop him from leaving.

- Mr West you can't do this to me. Look at how bad we were last year! I need to do this! I can't take another year of abuse. I'll get my mum to sign a letter saying she is fine with me doing this!

I went to say more but I didn't have any words. But no more words were needed. He saw the desperation on my face and turned to Mr Burns who gave him a look of "just let them do it".

-Right fine, but if anyone asks I had no clue what the act was!

He gave me a playful slap across the head and left the room.

And just like that we were in.

God fucking bless Mr Burns. And by the way I was a cheeky wee cunt in all Mr Burns's classes so the fact he took my side meant even more to me.

More on him in a wee bit.

Mark and I were chuffed to bits and started rehearsing even harder for the next few days. We were either going to redeem the whole of the previous year or fucking regret the next one.

The whole school was buzzing on the day of the show from students to teachers, especially as we had all just found out that one of the guest judges was Ally McInally the former Celtic and Bayern Munich player. One of the girls in the show had a dad that worked for the Daily Record and she convinced him to get him along. The pressure was well and truly on now....and doubled!

All of the acts had to meet four hours before the show took place in order to go over music and lighting cues with Mr Burns. I remember sitting in the hall watching all the other contestants approach Mr B at his lighting desk at the back of the hall. All of them handed him their CD's to play, but none of them discussed any lighting. I knew I had an advantage straight away. To me it wasn't just about the sound. I wanted a show.

118

I was one of the last to go over all my cues with him.

-   You better prove me right here son, I've stuck my
    neck on the line here.

I could see the genuine fear on his face.

-   Aye and I'm putting my whole head in the block Mr
    Burns, if this goes tits up for me then I'll be getting
    bog washed fae playtime tae hometime. At least you
    can hide in the staff room then handed him my CD.
    He laughed.

-   Right, cheers. Don't suppose you need any lighting>

-   Too right I do. When I enter from the winmgs keep
    the lights low but bright enough to light us both. But
    when I pull my cloak off fire them all up then just
    freestyle the rest of the song.
    Mr B's face lit up just as I wanted the stage too. This
    was what he was wanting.

-   Aw ya beauty, I can finally user these light the way
    they are meant to be used.

He was thrilled that I had a vision and that he could
show his knowledge of the lighting desk. That's when I
knew at least I had one person on my side apart from
Mark.

All that was left now was to get prepped. And by that I
mean go out the back of the Tech block and get stoned.
Mark stayed in the staff room with most of the other acts
and just shat himself for the next few hours.

I walked around the corner of the tech block to be met
by my good matesJay and Ryan Bharaj. They were
brothers and good pals of mine from the Youth Theatre.

119

They had their own band. Jay on drims and Ryan on Bass and vocals. The most sound guys you'll ever meet. They had to audition too the same day as me. They played some generic wholesome song, Beachboys I think or something like that, I can't really remember. Anyway the song they sang got them through but I was just about to learn that they had something totally different planned. Something that would sit with me for the rest of my career, and still does.

The two brothers and the rest of their band were all smoking weed and drinking Jack Daniels, and of course I got tore in with them. Ryan just kept saying, "Just watch this, it's time we fought back" or words to that effect. At the time I didn't really take on board that they were planning something big as I was that nervous about my own performance my arse was eating my Malvin Klien boxers ma maw bought fae the Barras.

I was well and truly oiled by the time I got back to Mark at the dressing room. He was pacing up and down but still well and truly up for it. Mrs Hughes turned up and helped me into my costume and did my make up. Before we knew it we could hear the crowd in the assembly hall chanting away etc. The place was buzzing.

Mr West came through just befor the show went up, congratulated everyone for getting this far and then nodded to me and Mark,

-    And good luck boys.

We were up last and had to watch all the other acts disappear from the dressing room and return to rapturous applause. A group of girls including my pal Val Wilson went on as the Jackson Five and totally smashed it. I knew they were the favourites as well as big Paul Tomkinson. Paul had one the year before and had just played Danny in the School's version of Grease. He was an amazing singer and a real good guy.

Mark and I would have been happy with third place but would also acceot just acknowledgement if anything. Whatever would take the heat off us from the year before!

The second last act was Jay and Ryan's band. We heard the crowd cheer as they came on, but all of a sudden we felt the atmosphere drop. The noise went from adulation to shock, to silence. I turned to Mark and said.
-Fuck's going on out there?

He shrugged to mirror my thoughts.

The Jackson Five came thorugh and explained that Jay and Ryan's band had gone on stage and totally changed their act. They played some heavy metal and started wrecking the set on stage whilst telling the crowd they were a bunch of cunts for following trends and not allowing people to be different. They even brought chalk and wrote things like "FUCK THE SYSTEM" all over the set and stage. They were literally man handled off the stage by Mr West and the Headteacher Mr Dunsmuir.

Fucking legends.

And they were totally justified. They were bullied all the time but as soon as they were on stage people cheered them, They didn't want false love, they wanted to make a difference and I'll never forget how powerful their

121

statement was...although now I had to follow that drama and I was the next and last act!

My nerves got worse as I knew it was down to me and Mark to lift the spirits of over three hundred people again.

But we didn't have too much time to think. We were called up straight away and before I knew it my music was playing. Mark hugged me at the side of the stage and we both just looked at each other as if to say, "it's now or never".

I half expected Mark to shite it but he burst onto that stage more confident than I was in that second. And that's when I knew we were going to smash it.

Mark set the scene with dialogue and then on I came all wrapped up in a cloak from shoulders to toes.

The audience were confused at first but as soon as the chorus hit along with Mr B's lighting and the reveal of me in a corset and fishnets...the audience were putty in our hands.

We fucking smashed it. The laughs and cheers were deafening and I never wanted it to end. I Remember looking at my best mate on that stage and sharing a smile as if we were both invincible.

When the song ended, whoever wasn't already on their feet jumped up to give a standing ovation.

I still chase that buzz to this day.

I wasn't the greatest singer but they just loved the originality and surprise factor. Talk about euphoria.

As we came off the stage Mr West winked at us both with a tongue in his cheek and said, "I told you it would work".

Waiting for the result was more nerve racking than the wait to perform. I knew we would be top three now but still knew The Jacskon Five and big Paul would be top two.

Mark and I stood at the back of the hall with our arms around each other as big Ally McInally announced the results. I didn't care about winning now. Just having Mark by my side knowing I hadn't let him down again was enough of a win for me.

That's utter bullshit by the way, I was dying to win.

Ally did a wee spiel then got into the nitty gritty. He announced third place...

-   How amazing were these girls, please give it up for third place, The Jackson Five!!!

Credit to Val and the girls, they were ecstatic to get third and bounded onto the stage to claim their trophy.

That's when Mark turned to me and said... "Holy fuck we might actually win this mate".

I didn't believe we had a chance until Mark said it, but I was still convinced Paul had it in the bag. He had sang Robbie William's "Let Me Entertain You" and had the spandex cat suit on with make up and everything.
Ally took the mic again.

-   And in second place. This boy had the make up, the costume and the confidence to pull this off...

I knew It was me now. I just waited to hear my name.

-   Paul Tomkinson!!!

I looked at Paul, he looked surprised but still humble as he ran up to claim his trophy.

For some reason I thought that meant we had come way lower in the ranks than I thought. In my head Paul was always going to be ahead of us.

Then I saw the whole hall turn to me and smile. Mark looked ecstatic but I was still in denial until...

- And the winners, and not just purely for originality but also for courage, gusto and bravery.... Chris Taylor and Mark Anderson!!!

The whole hall erupted! I fell to my knees as Mark jumped on top of me.

We had done it.

Me and my best mate after a year of abuse picked ourselves up and showed them all. And that was the day I knew that no matter how low things could get, there was always a way to get back up.

The first thing I did to celebrate was head round the back of the tech block again for a five skinner and to tan the quarter bottle of vodka I had stashed in my costume bag, still with full make up on. Mark had already left to go home and I just sat there glugging straight vodka and puffing on my joint. I was already as high as a kite through pure adrenaline but for some reason I wanted to add to the buzz with drink and drugs. Something I continued to do for the next twenty years after a show. I was never good at taking compliments after, I always liked to be alone for a while and analyse my own performance. I'm always my biggest critic even after success.

I sat for about half an hour just looking up at the

stars and getting shit faced.

One of the Jackson five, Morag was throwing an aftershow party and I didn't want to show up sober. Most of the kids there were seniors so I was nervous about attending. That and Mum had told me I wasn't allowed to stay out past midnight as I had my paper run the next day so I wanted to get as oiled up as I could in the short time I had.

I turned up at the party but felt really anxious even though everyone there couldn't have been nicer or more complimentary. I just felt like I didn't fit in. They were all the cool kids. I would rather have been sat outside somewhere with Ryan, Jay and the band smoking weed.

I stayed at the party until about half eleven then headed back home for a joint or two of soft black out my skylight then crashed onto my bed with a wee smile, just recreating that ovation in my head on a loop.

I never made my paper round that next morning and ended up getting the sack.

CHAPTER FOUR. PILLS, POLICE AND PARTIES

I turned sixteen the month before my final exam. I knew that would be my last day ever in school. Despite my mum and Dad's protests I was adamant. They knew I hated school and to be fair to them they let me follow my dream. They have always encouraged my career and never stood in my way.

Legends.

Ayr College was just about to launch an N.C course in Acting and Performance and I had an audition date set up. School couldn't be further from my mind.

I was like a prisoner counting down the days until release and rehearsing my monologue for my college audition kept me distracted from actually studying for my standard grades. I just didn't give a fuck about my exams; all I wanted to do was perform.

I didn't know about monologues so someone from the Youth Theatre suggested I use Mercutio's "Queen Mab" speech from Romeo and Juliet.

I had no clue about Shakespeare or what any of it meant but on the day of the audition I put my all into it. I had no idea what I was saying but it must have gone well as I was given an unconditional offer on the day. I was over the moon. As a fifteen year old you think you've made it when you get accepted even though it was just an N.C.

I was going to live my dream.

I was going to be a student of the arts.

The last few weeks of school dragged in, but I managed to sit every exam.

Stoned out ma tree for each one but I still sat them!

I was quite surprised with my results. Two 2s, four 3s and two 5s. In other words I'd passed English and P.E at credit level, scraped through four other subjects and failed Maths and History. Which is Ironic because I'm obsessed with history now.

I had a great history teacher. Shout out to Mr Fowler who was a great man and extremely patient with me. I still see him in the street now and again. I was a right pain in the arse in his class but he was a good sport.

One time I climbed out the class window walked around the building and came back in through the classroom door. He looked angry and barked,

-Where the hell have you been?

-What you on about? You said I could go to the toilet.

He looked confused but the whole class backed me up. Well most of them. Mr Fowler must have thought he was going mad. He just nodded with a bemused look and I went back to my seat. Ten minutes later I did it again. Snuck out the window and came back through the door. This time he saw me and jumped up from his desk.

-See you ya we fffff...

He stopped himself from swearing.

-Go sit on your arse and get that window shut!

The whole class were buckled. Well most of them.

Mr Fowler took a few seconds then even he had a wee giggle at my daft prank.

That was one of the good memories from school. I always liked Mr Fowler.

When I left school I picked up a part time job in wee call centre on Wellington Square in Ayr cold calling local people and trying to sell them gym memberships. Turned out I was really good at it and was earning about two hundred quid a week off commission alone. That was some amount for a sixteen year old stoner just fresh out of school, and this money in my pocket would prove to be a huge Factor in how the next chapter of my life was about to turn out.

I had always wanted to be independent and move into my own place from a young age. No harm to my parents, I just wanted my own gaff. Mainly so I could smoke as much weed as I wanted without worrying about being caught.

I found a bedsit in the middle of Ayr High Street that only cost fifty quid a week and with all the cash I was making at the call centre I knew I'd still have plenty cash left for partying and smoking. I didn't factor utility bills or food into my budget. I was just focussed on the life of riley.

Mum and Dad tried to talk me out of it but I was adamant. And they could see I was working hard and at this point still trusted me so they soon backed down. And that was it. Within a week of seeing the place I had moved in.

It was a total dive.

Four rooms all filled with young guys all intent on getting wasted on a nightly basis with a shared kitchen and bathroom.

One guy was a serious bong smoker, cool as fuck and really chilled. He worked at Burger King. Let's just call him Snoopy.

Snoopy always had some real cool hippy like folk in his room. They just sat all night passing around a bong Snoopy had made out of a coffee jar and a piece of white tubing from under a sink while listening to Cyprus Hill and Snoop Dog albums. I liked Snoopy and still talk to him to this day if we bump into each other in the street.

Across the landing from me was a guy called Joe. He had a job as an apprentice joiner or something like that as far as I remember. He had a girlfriend and would often bring her and some of her pretty pals up to the bedsit. They liked a good party. He was a funny guy but you wouldn't want to get on the wrong side of him.

The last room was taken up by a guy called Rob. Now before I tell you about him I need to stress that Rob was a great guy, pure heart of gold, but he was FUCKING MENTAL. Absolutely bonkers. He would have drank and smoked twenty four seven if he had the money and guaranteed if a fight was going to kick off then he would be slap bang in the middle of it. Rob scared me at first but when we got talking I realised he was just a troubled soul.

All the boys in the bedsit welcomed me and I felt at ease straight away. I became closer with Rob though.

I had started college and was loving it. I was the youngest but I felt I was one of the strongest performers there. Maybe it was ego and the fact I had just won the talent show but I truly believed it at the time. But I only lasted a few months as I was too intent on working more shifts in the call centre to make money for partying. I would sleep in for college, or not even turn up to class at all as I was too wrecked. I got worse by the week but the final nail in the coffin was when I discovered my next addiction, and one that would change my life forever.

The nightclub of choice when I was younger was a place called Xess. Everyone went there for many reasons. Firstly they hardly ever asked anyone for ID and secondly the drink was so cheap you could get smashed off yer tits for a fiver. I remember at one point they were even selling vodka and dash for thirty pence! It really was a dangerous place for a just turned seventeen year old horn monster with too much money in his pocket.

It was open Wednesday to Sundays and I would be in there every night drinking until I either pulled some random girl and took her home for a shag or until I was incapable of walking. The latter happened more than the pulling. Me and Rob would tan a few bottles of Buckfast beforehand and smoke a few joints then rock up to the club feeling like rockstars.

One night I was ordering us more drinks at the bar when Rob bounced up and asked me to sub him a fiver.

- I swear I'll pay you back when I get ma giro mate.
- What's it for? I'll buy your drinks fur ye, it's cool.

131

- It's no fur bevvie it's fur a Mitsy.
- A whit?
- -A mitsy...an Eccie!

I wasn't clued up on ecstasy by then, but Mitsy was short for Mitzsubishi, a type of ecstasy tablet that had a Mitzubishi stamp on it like the make of car.

I was always brought up to fear that type of drug but I was so drunk I was actually really curious.

-Aye alright but as long as you get me one anaw.

I handed a smiling Rob a tenner and watched him disappear into the sweaty crowd.

And just like that I had made my mind up ....I was going to try ecstasy.

Rob appeared back at the bar within a few minutes and handed me my pill.

-What does it do?

-Makes you feel like fuckin superman mate. Swear to fuck, best feeling in the world.

Who was I to argue. Just like the mad dog in the bush I didn't think. I just did it.

For the next ten minutes I remember I kept telling Rob how I wasn't feeling anything and that I think we had been bumped.

-I cannae feel anything.

-Just gie it time.

-But I cannae feel anything.

-Gie it fuckin time! He snapped at me before heading upstairs to get out of my way. Looking back I must have been killing his buzz so he left me to it.

Another five minutes passed as I danced away on the sticky dance floor underneath the cage dancers above. Yup that's right they had cage dancers.

Then all of a sudden....Wooooosh! It hit me. I was coming up and I was coming up hard. Rob was right, it was the best feeling in the world. Like the adrenaline rush I felt at the talent show times by a hundred. I'd never felt confidence like it. I danced all night and told every person I met how much I loved them, and I truly believed it. There is a reason it was called the love drug. Although looking back it was the worst mistake I could have made. But it was genuinely the greatest night of my life.

When the club turned the lights on and switched the music off I didn't want the party to end. I invited as many strangers as I could back to the bedsit, about twenty turned up and we partied the night away until about ten o clock the next morning before I crashed out onto my bed surrounded by three or four people I'd never met in my life.

I slept for about ten hours and woke up to Rob forcing a bottle of Buckfast towards me.

-Round two, time to get up.

I didn't even have time to reflect on what the fuck had just happened the night before, I just started all over again.

I tanned the Buckfast, had a quick shower and headed back to Xess with Rob for more pills. I wanted to feel that love all over again, that confidence, that buzz.

This became my new routine for the next few weeks until

133

I was kicked out of college. But I didn't care as I still had my job at the call centre part time and could now just focus on having fun. Without even thinking I'd given up my dream of being an actor all because of drugs. I was taking pills at night then smoking weed all day to help battle the intense come down.

I was living off Burger Kings and crisps and just spending any cash I had on drink and drugs.

I was seriously deteriorating physically and mentally but I was too set in my ways to even notice or care even.

I got to a point where I wasn't even showing up for work so they had no choice but to let me go. I was one of the top salesmen but what use to them was I when I wasn't even there.

That night after being sacked I decided to buy myself two pills this time and double dunt them. I'd only ever taken one per night before but this time I was on mission to block out all the negatives and get seriously fucked up.

Rob's brother Billy had turned up out the blue. He was a psycho and got kicked out the club after only five minutes. I gave him my keys and told him we would met him back at my room after. He was off his face at the time and I thought he would just go back and have a kip.

If only I knew.

When we finally left the club and turned the corner we could see glass and furniture lying on the high street pavement. It was only when I got closer that I realise the furniture was my fucking bed and chair. Billy had obviously launched them through my window in a rage.

134

Rob ran up the close and upstairs while I just stood there staring up at my broken window. Anyone else would have been shocked but I had just double dunted two pills and was feeling great. Nothing could have bothered me that night. I was kind of hoping Billy was going to throw something else.

I heard Rob screaming at his brother followed by the sound of sirens coming down the high street.

I legged it upstairs to get away from the police and help Rob hide his brother in a cupboard. I was convinced I had the situation under control. I didn't feel phased at all. I was superman times two remember.

The place was trashed.

Billy had completely wrecked my room. He had punched that many holes in the walls they didn't look like walls anymore. My telly was broken and all my things were thrown about the window.

But yet I still didn't care. I was buzzing out of my tits.

I looked out the broken window and could see two police cars below with four officers investigating the scene.

Don't ask me why but for some reason I thought it would be hilarious to pull one of the remaining shards of glass from the window pane and throw it down below at a police car. I missed and it landed right beside a policeman's foot. They all looked up and one shouted, -Right you, get down here now or we're putting the door in!

I tried to hide behind the half ripped down curtain but

135

was clearly still in view as the copper shouted again.

- You in the blue shirt, down here now! Last warning!

I should have been scared, anxious even but I think I was enjoying the drama of it all due to the pills. I thought I'd be smart and try and trick the police by changing my shirt and then just walk out the front door as if I had no clue what was going on.

I quickly grabbed another shirt from the floor and got changed then headed outside with the most innocent look I could muster while high on pills.

The plan might have worked had I not changed into another almost identical blue shirt.

The policeman grabbed me, put my arm around my back and planted me firmly face first onto the bonnet of one of the cars. One of the coppers blurted out.

-Watch he's bleeding.

I hadn't noticed but I had sliced my forearm on the window when I was taking out the shard of glass from the window. I had blood all over me.

The policeman let me go and looked really concerned.

Again I should have been worried but because of the pills I was actually loving all the attention I was getting from a crowd of pilled up night clubbers that were now surrounding us.

A female police officer came closer to inspect my arm which was now soaked in dark red blood. She winced as I held it out to reveal you could see all the tendons and bone through the gash. But I couldn't even feel it.

-   Just sit down on the curb, we need to get you an ambulance.
-   Ach I'll be fine! Mon upstairs and party!

The crowd were all laughing ....that encouraged me more. I was in my element, drama and an audience. I was back inside my own film again. What a rush.

Two officers gently but firmly sat me down on the curb.

They knew I was off ma tits and starting engaging in conversation, asking me what drugs I'd taken etc. They were really nice from what I can remember.

I explained that I had had my first double dunt and that it wasn't me who smashed the window but it was me that threw the glass. I apologised to them and pleaded that they let me go. I just wanted to keep on drinking.

Obviously they told me I was under arrest and they would be escorting the ambulance up to Ayr hospital where I would be formally charged with breach of the peace.

I vaguely remember being up at A&E and trying to chat up the Nurses who were less than impressed with the state I was in.

I had to get twelve stitches but I refused any anaesthetic as I was still scared of needles at that point. I also thought I was playing out some kind of film scene and was trying to act like the hard man.

When I was all patched up the police charged me with a breach and then drove me back home. I said I get a taxi but they didn't trust I would go home to bed. Idiots drove me straight back to the party.

When I got in all the boys and some party goers were there to greet me with cheers. I felt like a hero.

They all commented how mental I was etc then we all partied into the early hours again. It was good at the time but the next day I was about to feel anxiety and depression than never before.

What the fuck had I done. My first charge and an arm that was already looking infected. The physical and mental pain is one I'll never forget. And to top it all off I had to live with the realisation that I had now spent all my money and had nothing left for food or rent.

It was time to call Mum.

I moved back home for a few weeks but it was never the same. I still wanted to party but didn't have the money.

This is where it all goes a bit blank for me and I can't exactly remember the timeline but I found another flat on Ayr Main street owned by my sisters boyfriends Mum and Dad. I lied to them I could afford it but in truth I didn't even have a job. But I had a plan. I was going to sell pills.

I had made enough contacts in Xess and all the dealers knew me and also knew that I would talk to anyone. So they trusted me with fifty pills a week to sell. That was enough to pay for my party lifestyle again. I never intended to pay rent. I regret leading the landlords on as they were very trusting but I was selfish and only cared about my social life. A lifestyle I could not afford.

I still met up with the boys at the bedsit now and again but I tried to stay away as much as I could as I was mental around them. So I started hanging out with old school pals

138

again who were now also just finding out how good Mitzys were.

We had some parties. Every night the place would be packed after the club. Even the bouncers started joining us. The place was a cesspit of drugs and sex. You couldn't get into the toilet as someone would always be getting pumped and every room was filled with dope smokers and coke snorters.

I was always too out my face at this point to care about sex. I was into selling and taking pills.

On one fateful night I did something that I still to this day have never forgiven myself for. I was so out of my face in Xess that I offered a girl some ecstasy not realising she was my younger cousin. She refused but when she got home she told her Mum who then quite rightly so told my mum.

The next morning, with the party still in full swing my Mum turned up at the flat. I remember her face drop as she witnessed all the carnage around her. Naked bodies slumped on the floor, trays of cocaine out in full view, people smoking weed...it must have been a total nightmare for her. She lost the plot and started screaming at everyone to get out, I'd never seen her so heartbroken and even writing this now breaks my heart in turn. I can't even imagine now I am a father what was going through her mind. But at the time I was angry with HER.

I took her by the arm and led her outside.

All I can remember is she sat on the front step with me and lit a fag, her hands trembling as she fumbled with the lighter.

I tried to talk with her and reassure her everything was okay but I kept drifting in and out of consciousness as I was on about five pills that night, a good few grams of Charlie and copious amounts of weed. I think I had been awake for two or three days by this point.

-Look at you! You can't even stay awake. You're going to kill yourself!

She was beside herself yet all I could do was jump to my own defence. I'm ashamed to admit that I stood up and screamed at her to fuck off and stop interfering in my life. I'll never forget the look of pain and hurt on her face as I walked back inside and slammed the door in her face. We have spoken about this night many times since and I have apologised many times but I will never ever forgive myself for that. I'm still ashamed. She was my rock and I crushed her.

My life carried on this way for a few months as I moved from one flat to another until no one else would take me in.

The bouncers in Xess even had enough of my cavalier approach to selling in the club. I felt untouchable and wasn't even trying to hide it anymore so they threw me out and barred me. A few other pubs caught on to this and they all decided to bar me as well. I was blacklisted in Ayr.

So that was me, no home, no clubs to sell in so all dealers stopped supplying me with pills.

I moved in with a pal for a few weeks but things got so bad that we got thrown out of there as well. One night I was so out my face I even took some valium that was

140

prescribed for his dog. I ended up shaving my head with a bic razor. I was as bald as Kojak.

But I just wouldn't learn.

I had pushed all of my family away despite their many attempts to help me. I was really nasty towards a lot of them. I had lost control.

Breaking point came when I was staying with another friend Beth. She was a good pal I met on the club scene and knew I needed a roof over my head. I had no money, no job, no friends anymore. But she gave me a bed and a roof over my head at one of my darkest times and I'll never forget her for that. She liked to party too but nothing like what I was in to. So being at hers helped me settle a bit and lay off the pills to an extent.

Although one night at hers one of her pals came over and he was selling acid tabs. I had no cash but he offered me one anyway. Again I didn't question it, I just took it. And fuck me did I have a good night.

I was the only one on it, the rest were just smoking weed and having a wee drink but I was in a world of my own. A whole new universe had opened up for me and I truly believed I was in touch with a higher being. I could think like I had never thought before. Everything was bright and beautiful.

I needed to get out of Beth's flat that night. I wanted to explore.

I was walking all around Ayr taking in the sights. It's as if the whole town had regenerated into some kind of paradise. The trees were pink and purple and all the buildings were smiling and winking at me. I walked across the old brig that leads into the town centre and looked down onto the river Ayr. The lights on the bridge turned the water into a mirror and reflected the bridge below so it looked like another world down there. I was convinced that if I jumped in then I'd be transported to a better place, a place even better than Heaven. Luckily my brain kicked in enough to remind me I was on acid so I decided against it and kept walking.

I ended up down the pier on Ayr beach. Just sat there mesmerised by the lights across the sea. I was so happy.

I pulled a joint from my pocket that I had pinched from one of the drinkers at Beth's and smoked it slowly. I closed my eyes and lay back for what must have been an hour or so. But when I opened them my whole new world had disappeared.

The acid had worn off and now all I could see was the dingy old Pier and grey skies. I looked down and there was an old sliced off fish head sat right beside me. Talk about a come down.

I instantly got the fear and started to run back to Beth's, my heart racing faster with each step as I put my hood up in order not to make any eye contact with the early risers and dog walkers. Not today Sheila….Not to fucking day.

It was an awful feeling. When I got back everyone was in bed. I jumped under the old curtain I had been using as a cover the past week and crashed out. I slept for sixteen hours straight. Best sleep of my life but the worst feeling to wake up to. That was the moment it hit me. What the fuck am I doing with my life?

I was starving when I woke up but didn't have any money for food. I had no fags, no nothing. Beth was out and I had no one left to turn to. I'd burnt all my bridges. So that's when I decided I had no choice but to go on the rob.

I took a child's buggy that Beth had stored in a cupboard at hers with the intention to head to Asda and steal some food. I thought pushing a buggy would make me less suspicious.

My heart was racing as I looked about for security guards and staff. I must have walked around for half an hour before I finally worked up the courage to steal a Snickers bar and stash it in the buggy. I didn't have the guts to try and take anything bigger. I was so hungry that anything would have done at that point.

I walked out the door of the supermarket half expecting to get huckled by a staff member, but I was in the clear. I ran around the corner, sat on the curb and ate the chocolate like a man possessed. It was the first thing I had eaten in two days.

The second I swallowed the last bite I was consumed with guilt and again more fear.

And that's when I broke.

I burst out crying and couldn't stop. What the fuck had I become. Only a year ago I was in college training for my dream job and now I'm thieving from Asda using a baby's fucking buggy as a distraction.

After crying inconsolably for a while I looked up and saw a phone box. I needed help, I knew that now.

Time to phone Mum.

I tried calling her using a reverse charge but no answer. So I phoned my Mum's sister Aunt Rhona (Marks Mum) to see if she was there. Luckily Aunt Rhona accepted the charge . I just broke down and asked if my Mum was there.

She was.

Aunt Rhona passed the phone to her.

I told my Mum everything and apologised for everything I had said and done. She wanted me to come home but Dad didn't.

At the time I was angry but now I understand. He saw the hurt and pain I had caused her and he didn't want my lifestyle in his house especially because my seven year old sister Hannah lived there. I get that now.

I was broken and about to hang up when my mum passed the phone to Aunt Rhona.

-Go get your things and come to mine, you can stay here until you get yourself back up on your feet.

I was so relieved I slid down the glass of the phone box and cried like a baby.

I had been given a lifeline.

I ran back to Beth's, grabbed the little amount of items of clothing I had , packed them in a black bin liner and headed straight to My aunties house.

The whole family were there waiting. Mum, Dad, Aunt Rhona, Uncle Andy, my sisters and all my cousins. This was the first time I had to admit I had a real drug problem.

There was a lot of crying, mainly by me and we all spoke for hours. When Mum and Dad left Aunt Rhona made us all dinner, the first proper hot meal I had had in weeks, I can't remember what it was but I wolfed the lot down then had a hot bath. Lying in that tub being cuddled by the hot water with a full belly was the first time I'd felt safe in a long, time.

The next morning I got up and decided to go and see my Gran who was now in the Ayrshire Hospice as she had been diagnosed with Cancer. I had been so wrapped up in my own breakdown I didn't even realise how serious her condition was. I should have visited her weeks before but I knew I looked like shit and didn't want to worry her. That and the fact I was always too stoned. Another regret I have to this day. My Gran was one of my best friends and I know all of my cousins felt the same way about her. She truly was an incredible woman.

I was still skint so I walked from Prestwick up to the Hospice on Racecourse Road in Ayr. It's about eight miles. I started feeling weak half way there as all the drugs were still in my system and I hadn't been drinking enough water.

When I arrived Gran took one look at me, gave me a hug then poured me a glass of diluting juice from the wee jug sat on her bedside table.

- How are you?

She didn't need an answer. My eyes just welled up and she hugged me again. She squeezed me so tight and for so long that I know now she was her trying to squeeze all my broken pieces back together.

She didn't scold me or judge me. We just talked for an

145

hour about how this was my chance to get my life back together and start following my dream again. She was the best person to talk to and always knew the right thing to say. I just kept thinking about how much I'd let her down.

We hugged again before I was set to leave and then reached into her purse and handed me a fiver. I tried to refuse but you know what Grannies are like.

- Get yourself some food and some juice and start getting some meat back on your bones ok?

I nodded as I tried not to cry again.

She walked me out to reception and told the nurses in the corridor that I was the grandson that she had been talking about and how I was going to be famous one day.

The nurses could see me still fighting the tears so one of them offered to walk me to the exit.

I hugged Gran one more time and started my way down the hall. Gran called on me one last time.

- Remember, I'll always be watching you.

We shared a smile and she went back into her room. I didn't realise how significant that comment was at the time but that was the last thing she ever said to me.

A few days later Mark, Andrew and I were woken by my Uncle Andy.

- I'm afraid I've got some bad news for you boys.

I knew straight away.

-Has Gran gone?

Uncle Andy's eyes filled but he didn't blink as he didn't want to push the tears out. He was trying to be strong for us boys. He just nodded.

My whole world collapsed.

I sat up in my camp bed with Mark and Andrew either side of me in their bed. We all just cried and cried. Gran was our God. The family glue. We were broken. It was the first time we had felt true grief.

All I could think was, "I need to be with my Mum".

I'm crying writing this as the realisation hits that not only had my own Mother been dealing with the death of her Mum but she was also having to deal with all the shit I was putting her through.

I just needed to be with her and squeeze her tight just like Gran had done to me the day before.

I saw Mum later that day when all the family met up at Papa's house. I tried to squeeze her broken bits back together for half an hour. Hearing her cry broke me and I just wanted to take her pain away. I knew I had to get better to look after her.

Later that afternoon I was feeling overwhelmed by it all, and don't ask me why but I just got a sudden urge that I had to go somewhere, I needed to go to Gran's church.

I left Papa's without telling anyone and marched down the street to Prestwick North Parish church hoping that the doors would be open. My Gran sat in the same seat there every Sunday and even had her own cushion that she left on her spot. Some say for comfort but I reckon she was marking her territory.

As I approached the church I could see the main doors were closed. I was gutted, but then out of the blue and as if some sort of divine intervention the minister Arthur

Christie appeared. He only needed to look at me with an apologetic face and I broke down again.

He put his arm around me and walked me into the church and up the stairs to Gran's seat. We both sat down. I picked up her cushion and sobbed into it for a while as Arthur spoke. I could smell her.

He was amazing with me. He knew through Gran that I hadn't been living the best life recently.

We spoke for hours about his past and how he had been lead down a bad path but God saved him and how Gran had been such an inspiration to him as well. I could tell he was genuinely devastated as well.

He was brilliant with me that day.

Just before I left he told me he had something he wanted to give me and handed me a photo of the brand new giant wooden cross the church had just had installed on the back wall behind the pulpit. Gran had fought to get this cross for years but never got the chance to actually see it in all his glory so he gave the photo to me and told me to show the family.

I ended up putting the photo in her coffin when I went to see her at the funeral parlour.

I wish I could tell Arthur just how much those few hours meant to me. He truly is a great, great man and if anyone reading this knows him then please pass on my love and thank him for me one last time.

I left the Church with a determination that I was going to change my ways, get clean off the weed and pills and make something of my life. All of these people had shown faith in me and it was my time to repay them.

But I didn't.

A few days later I snuck out my aunt Rhona's and headed back to Beths to catch up with some old pals. I ended up getting smashed on pills and weed again and didn't get home until six o clock the next morning.

That was the last straw for many. After everything they had all done I threw it back in their faces.

Aunt Rhona didn't kick me out but I knew I had really let them down so I asked if I could move in with Papa instead to keep him company now that Gran was gone. The whole family agreed on the condition that I got myself clean.

Papa didn't beat around the bush setting the house rules down. My curfew was ten o clock each night and if I missed it by one minute he was going to lock me out. I wasn't allowed a key.

I totally understood why he was doing it. This was my rehab and I had to accept it. And where else did I have to go?

Papa loved to cook and I was on his four meal a day diet again so I soon started to put weight back on and was looking much healthier after a few weeks. I was still sneaking hash in and smoking in my bedroom at night but I convinced myself that was okay so long as I wasn't on ecstasy. The only thing was I didn't have money so started to rack up a bit of a tick bill. I was getting into a rut again and the depression soon hit.

Ecstasy uses up serotonin in your brain and that's the

chemical the body needs to cope with grief. Mine was all dried up with all the pills I'd swallowed over the past year so I was really struggling. I still had no job, no money and couldn't stop thinking about how I had let everyone down.

I woke up one morning and decided there and then I was going to kill myself.

I walked to Prestwick Train station with the intention of throwing myself in front of train. I didn't want to hurt anyone anymore and my depression was so bad I was convinced everyone would be happier without me in their lives.

I stood on the wee bridge at the station and waited for the next train to come.

Five or six passed through but I just didn't have the bottle to do it. I didn't think of how my family would have felt had I gone through with it, just the pain and mental trauma I would have caused the unsuspecting driver.

So instead of jumping in front of a train, I decided to board one instead.

I thought I could just run away to London or some other city and try my luck sleeping rough on the streets. That way I wouldn't cause anyone anymore emotional trauma but could still give my family the peace from me I thought they deserved.

My plan didn't really hold much water though as I had no money to travel. I made it as far as Irvine when I saw the ticket collector approaching.

150

I decided to jump off the train and just start walking as far as I could until I either collapsed or even better died from starvation.

I was walking through Irvine town centre still fighting back tears and that's when I saw it. A big sign poking out from one of the buildings that read, "Army Recruitment Office".

A light pinged in my head and my body went into auto pilot and dragged me through the doors. This is what I need, this is my escape. If I was ever going to get clean then what better way than the military. Also in the back of my mind I thought, well I'll either get clean or killed in action so it's a win win.

I just walked in and declared to the first guy in uniform I saw.

-    I want to join the army.

The soldier smiled and told me to take a seat and he would get someone to have a chat with me.

All I really remember was some guy in uniform with a white hackle in his hat telling me that the infantry would be the best place for me after I had explained my situation. He made me a cup of tea, gave me money for my train ride home and a bunch of forms to take away and fill in.

And that was that, I had made my decision.

I was running away with the army.

The train journey home was much less depressing and I was excited to go and tell my Mum all about my knew adventure. I just wanted to make her proud and give her a sense of relief that I really was going to try and turn my life around.

I raced to her house and waved the forms at her.

-I'm joining the army

She looked at me for a bit and smirked.

-Okay.

She didn't believe I would follow through with it. No wonder considering my past record. But I was determined to prove her wrong.

Over the next week or so I spent a lot of time filling out forms and having meetings at the recruitment office. One day I had to take a test to prove that I wasn't an idiot. The questions were so simple for example…. "John is taller than Bob. Who is the tallest?". I couldn't believe it was so easy but now I realise they didn't care if I was stupid, just not too stupid to be trusted with a rifle.

I passed all my tests and was soon sent off to Glencorse Barracks in Edinburgh for my 3 day selection course. The course was to see if I could handle the fitness aspect and again to make sure I wasn't a total idiot. The days were made up with learning how to make a bed and some team building exercises with a mile and a half run on the last day that had to be completed in less than eight minutes I think, maybe ten minutes I cant quite remember.

I really enjoyed the few days but was nervous about the mile and a half run. If I failed that I wouldn't be selected and I hadn't done any fitness in the past year apart from raving all night in Xess.

152

Luckily I was fitter than I thought and passed all the tests with flying colours. After the run I was totally fucked and breathing out of my arse but I'd done it.

I also met a load of really great guys and enjoyed the camaraderie. I knew now that the army life was definitely going to be for me.

I had my final interview at the end of the course with some officer who then told me I had been successful and would be now be sent to my basic training in a week. And the regiment I would be joining after training would be The Royal Highland Fusiliers.

I was delighted.

Mum and Dad were really proud of me but most of all I was proud of myself for the first time since dressing up as a Transvestite at the talent show. Not just because I had been accepted and made my family happy but also because I hadn't even thought about weed or pills since getting home from my three day selection. The thought of failing a drug test on my first week of training played a big part in my decision.

I was feeling healthier and fitter with each passing day. I even went out a few runs down the beach to try and get a head start on all the other recruits.

I received my acceptance letter with my start date a few weeks later. I was to be posted out to Glencorse Barracks in Penicuik for my twelve week basic training and then to Catterick Garrison for sixteen weeks after that for my infantry training, providing I passed out from basic training.

153

On the Saturday before leaving my sister and her man Dougie offered to take me for a drink to celebrate and say our goodbyes. Mum and Dad didn't want to come as they said they wanted to spend time with me alone in the house when I got back from the pub.

So me, Cara and Dougie headed down to the Smugglers pub on Prestwick Main Street next door to Papa's house. I was tanning pints of Stella and had a few whiskies as I knew I wasn't going to get another chance for a drink for at least another month or so.

The more I drank the more some of the old demons started to creep up on me. I tried to make excuses and leave telling them I was going to visit some pals to say good by but in truth I was going to head out and get some weed. Old habbits die hard especially when I'm on the drink. Even knowing I'd probably get drug tested in the army I still couldn't control my urges when I was drunk.

I think Cara could see through my lies so she literally begged me just to go back home to Mum and Dad's with her and her man for a quiet few drinks alone with family. After a bit back and forth I finally gave in and agreed to leave with them, much to Cara's relief. But I was planning my escape from the house the whole walk back.

As we walked through the doors of my parents house I was greeted by an almighty cheer and cries of "Congratulations!"

Mum had only gone and arranged a surprise leaving party for me. Everyone was there, and I mean everyone that was close to me. Aunties, Uncles, Cousins Papa and all of my closest friends. There must have been about sixty folk crammed into that wee living room, all letting off party poppers and blowing into those wee plastic horns that looked like lizards tongues.

I was stunned, genuinely stunned. All the people who I had pushed away and burnt bridges with do to my drink and drug issues had all turned up to show their love and support for me. I still get overcome with emotion writing about it now. I'd never felt so grateful...so loved.

And what a party it was. I was given some amazing gifts and everyone took time to sit with me and give me words of encouragement and support. It was the most emotional yet happiest night of my life to date. Even though copious amounts of alcohol were consumed, I will never forget that night for as long as I live.

And to think I was nearly a no show because I wanted to fuck off somewhere else and go smoke weed. Thank fuck for Cara and her powers of persuasion.

CHAPTER FIVE. 25132450.

I arrived at Glencorse barracks for my basic training and was put into Alamein Platoon with about twenty five other guys all hoping to pass out on the parade square after twelve weeks. Our training Corporal was a wee guy called Andy Rhodes, or Cpl Rhodes to us cadets. He was a take no shit kind of guy as you would expect and had big sticky out ears that made him look like Mr Potato head had had a lug extension. I respected him from day one but he was a total prick at times.

We were all issued our unique army number on day one, and that's what we became for the next few months. Mine was 25132450. You use that number anytime you identify yourself, and anyone that has been in the forces never forgets theirs.

-25132450 Private Taylor sir!

I must have said that at least eighty times a week for twelve weeks, possibly more.

Training was as hard as I'd expected. Some guys were a bit taken aback at the intensity and brutality of it all, but I'd watched enough Full Metal Jacket type movies to know what to expect.

We were run into the ground every day before classes then again after class. But I loved. I was away from trouble, I was getting fit and all my meals were paid for. Army scoff is shit hot so I was in my element.

The time it really sunk in that I was being trained to be a

killer came on the day we had a class on talking about bayonets.

We were all handed one of these knives that you seen Rambo cutting about with in the films as Cpl Rhodes went on to explain how everything worked.

-If you look at the serrated edge of the blade here, we call that the rib separator. And this channel near the bottom of the blade is to stop suction when you've pierced it through the enemy's chest cavity and allows you to pull it out with ease and continue to stab through as many vital organs until the fucker is dead.

I don't know if it was the wording or the fact Cpl Rhodes was saying it so nonchalantly but I will admit I was shook for a second or two. I hadn't really thought to much into the fact that one day I may have to actually take the life of another man if it came to it. That may sound daft as it's the army but I genuinely never thought that far ahead. I was just looking for somewhere to get my head sorted. Rehab if you like.

But as the weeks went on and the more we trained in combat the less I thought about it. That's what they do though. They desensitise you in a way that the thought of killing does not faze you. It's either kill or be killed. And I joined to save my own life not let some bastard take it away.

I really excelled in all the fitness aspects of training and loved all the long power walks with full gear on, or "tabs" as we would call it. Some hated going on a tab but for me I felt hard as fuck all dressed up in the gear and walking

158

through the country side sweating. It was a killer at the time but the feeling I got later that night after I'd recovered was a better buzz than any joint or pill. Okay that's an exaggeration but at least this buzz never gave me a fucking comedown.

My weakest areas were my map reading and personal admin. I could get lost in a fucking cupboard with a compass and a sat nav and my ironing and folding of clothes was horrendous. I was always failing locker inspections and due to that my whole Platoon got punished. If it wasn't for me being a funny cunt I'm sure I would have had a doing or two in those twelve weeks by my fellow recruits.

After the first six weeks of basic training we were allowed home for the weekend. I was so excited to see my family as it felt like we had been there for months. But I also had slight anxiety that I'd be tempted by my old past again if I had a drink. We weren't allowed any alcohol the first six weeks even though the NAFFI had a bar. NAFFI is short for Navy, Army, Air Force Institution.

But I was fine. I was so happy to see my family looking so proud that I never even thought about drugs, even once I'd had a few drinks with them. They all commented on how healthy I was looking and were shocked to see how much muscle I had built up. I hadn't noticed as I saw my body every day so it's always harder to see the improvement. I think I was more ripped than I should have been though because of the amount of times Cpl Rhodes made me do press ups for being a cheeky wee dick.

The weekend flew in and I was back again for the last six weeks training. A few recruits had left by now because it was too tough for them and some had been thrown as they were not up to scratch, so I felt a real sense of achievement that I had stuck it out and hadn't been chucked out.

Everything was going really well until about week eight. We had all just passed our compulsory 3 mile run that had to be finished in a certain time, so Cpl Rhodes told us we could go to the NAFFI and have a drink. But he was adamant that it was a two can rule only. Anyone caught having more than two drinks would be up in front of the company Sergeant Major.

I think you all know where this is going.

After two pints of Tennents Igot that mad dof in a bush glow and was thirsty for more.   Five more to be precise.

I was steaming.

I wasn't the only one who broke the rule but I definitely took more of a liberty than any of the others. I was cutting about all the other plaoon's rooms that night like a lunatic, waking people up, jumping on their beds, singing Caledonia and telling jokes to people that didn't want to hear them. At one point one of the English boys that was half asleep in told me to fuck off so I pushed his metal locker onto his bed. He lost the plot and chased me down the stairs. I slid at the bottom and went head first into the wall and left a dent in the plaster board. The guy in chase just stopped at the top of the stairs, laughed and said,

-Oh you're in trouble tomorrow dick head.

  The next morning we were all woken at five by Cpl Rhodes as he screamed in his gruff but squeaky Yorkshire accent.
-You bunch of fucking wankers! Get up! Fucking get up now! I said fucking get up the lot of you!
  I was still half pished as I stumbled up and stood beside my bed to attention looking like a bag of shit on a hot summers day.
-Two fucking drinks! That's what you were told. But no you cunts had to rip the arse out of it and in doing so took the piss out of me!
  Apparently some grassing bastard had told him that some of us had bent the rules.
-I want to know who it was. This is your chance to redeem yourselves and be men. If you broke the rules then have some balls and step forward immediately!
  I stepped forward.
  No other fucker did. Bunch of bastards I thought.
-    The rest of you fuck off out onto the parade square.
All the lads ran at the speed of a thousand gazelles and disappeared out to the square.
-    Taylor! What a fucking surprise you alky jock bastard!
  Wee Andy was nose to nose with me now and screaming into my face.
-    Sorry Corporal I didn't mean...
-    Did I ask you to fucking speak you little cunt? Look at the fucking state of you. You're lucky I don't take you

out there in front of the rest of them and kick seven
shades of shit out you!

I can't really remember what else he shouted all I recall
is the more he screamed and spat in my face the angrier I
got.

And then my eyes filled up again.

- Oh don't give me those fucking crocodile tears you
  little fucking girl! Look at the state of you! Do you
  think crying makes me feel sorry for you? Do you
  think crying is going to stop me from ripping off your
  empty fucking head and shitting down your neck?
  You're a fucking joke son. An absolute fucking joke
  Taylor. These were his exact words, they are
  imprinted in my brain. It's weird but even though I
  wanted to rip his face off I was also back into thinking
  I was in film mode so I was also studying him as
  character and soaking up his monologue at the same
  time. It's crazy I know but it's all connected to my
  whole ten radio thing.

I swear I was so close to swinging a punch to the
side that wee pea heed of his that day but I knew if I did
then that was it all over for me.

After about another ten minutes of shouting and spitting
his morning breath all over my lips he took me out to the
parade square to join the boys then beasted every single
one of us in the rain. We were all still in our boxer shorts
and vests.

By the way a beasting in the army doesn't mean he
shagged us. A beasting is where they make you exercise

and put you in stress positions until you're nearly sick.

I half expected to get a doing from the rest of the platoons later that night but I think they were all thankful I didn't grass in any of the other boys that had also ripped the pish out of the two can rule. And over the weeks we had all built quite a strong bond. They don't just brain wash recruits into being ruthless killers, they also teach you to have each other's back. And that morning we all had each others.

After a few days of getting constant abuse from wee Cpl Dumbo for crying, he eventually eased off me. I think it was because I never broke and just got on with my training. I think I even gained his respect after that as he turned out to be quite supportive. Even to this day I still do respect him. He is the only training staff member that's name I remember from Glencorse so I guess that speaks volumes. Not that you'd have to speak at any volume for him. With those lugs he could hear someone rustle a sweetie wrapper during an air raid.

The last few weeks went really well and I passed all the tests required, although I just scraped by my map reading. I don't know what it is with me and maps and direction but I'm useless. Still to this day if I go into a toilet at a restaurant or a bar I'll always come out and turn in the wrong direction and end up in the fucking kitchen or staff room.

On our last day of basic training we were all given a huge passing out parade where our family would come and watch us March onto the square as a Company and receive our basic training certificates. We would all line up while some high up officer would inspect us in front of the watching crowd. It was a really proud moment knowing my parents were there and how far I had come since contemplating jumping in front of all those trains.

I remember being stood to attention waiting for the Officer to get to me for my inspection when my nose started to itch. It was a really hot day and it was fucking torture. When you are on a muster parade you cannot move or it's seen as disrespectful and a lack of discipline. I just kept thinking, don't fucking move, don't blow it in the last hour. I'd never felt an itch like it. I fought the urge that hard that I nearly passed out in more ways than one. Luckily the itch finally disappeared just as the commanding officer got to me. He took a quick look at my kit to make sure all my creases were in the right place, gave a nod and moved on to the next recruit.

There were drinks and food put on for all the family after as our training corporals mingled with them. Our platoon Lieutenant whose name escapes me told my mum and dad that he thought I was and I quote, a bit of an arsehole in the first few weeks but turned out to be a fine young recruit. I wanted to tell him he was a wanker in the first few weeks and was still a wanker now, but I resisted.

I'd now passed basic training and had a week off before I was moved to Catterick Garrison for my infantry training.

That was when the real pain would begin.

Catterick Garrison was nothing like basic training. It was

164

more relaxed .For instance we could use our own duvets instead of those itchy blankets and at night we could come and go to the NAFFI as we pleased and drink as much as we wanted within reason. We were usually so knackered by the end of training each day though, so you could only manage a few pints at most before you were ready for bed. Maybe that's an example of their brain washing...two can rule...

We focussed more on battle tactics at Catterick and weapons for the last 16 weeks of training. There were more out in the field exercises where we would sleep outside in the middle of nowhere for days on end doing combat training etc. It was a tough shift and some hated it but I thrived on it. It's when I felt like I was a real soldier. Cam cream on the face, rifle in hand and covered in mud. Practicing ambushes and learning outdoor survival .THIS was what I had signed up for.

And I was really good at it as well. My map reading was still shite though.

Our training corporals were still strict but much more laid back and less aggressive and we thought we had really struck gold when we first met our Platoon Sergeant....

....Sgt Jones. (I'm not using his real name for many reasons and this will become clear why later on in the chapter.).

Sgt Jones was about six foot four and built like Sylvester Stallone in Rocky. Even his six pack had a six pack. The guy was army barmy. An absolute machine with the strongest Welsh accent you'll ever hear. He had a jaw like a cliff edge and hands like snow ploughs. Words really can't describe just how solid and scary looking this guy was. When he first walked into the room I think at least six recruits shat themselves. But it turned out despite his looks he was a really chilled out and funny guy.

From day one he told us that he would give us as much freedom as we liked so long as we worked hard in training. As you can imagine we were all delighted.

In the first week at Catterick we all had to take a test. It was about forty questions made up of all sorts of subjects like math, English and even some general knowledge. If you passed then you could carry on training normally but if you failed then you would have to take a short college course at the end of the sixteen weeks for extra studies. It's was basically a test to make sure you were smart enough to be trusted with a loaded weapon and explosives.

I passed with full marks, forty out of forty.

I was called into Sgt Jones office.

I marched up to the door and stood to attention as was expected of me.

-25132450 Fusilier Taylor. You wanted to see me Sergeant?

When you pass basic training you take on the title of the regiment you are joining so I was now a Royal Highland Fusilier. We were the British Mountain Warfare regiment at the time. One of the toughest gigs going. Always climbing mountains and being Baltic.

Sgt Jones was sat with his feet on the desk and was drinking a can of Fosters lager. He waved the back of his hand towards me and said,

-Get in and shut the door.

　I did as I was told.

-Well sit down then.

　I sat.

- 　You got top marks on your test.

- 　Yes Sergeant.

- 　Smart fucker eh?

I was nervous as I felt I had done something wrong. Maybe
he thought I was a show off. My mouth dried up as I went
to answer but he cut me off.

- 　Good you can mark the rest of these ones, I can't be
　　fucked!

And with that he slung a pile of test papers at me, stood
up, downed the rest of his can, crushed it in his hand like
it was paper and threw it in the bin.

-That's all the rest of the boys ones. Get scoring them, I'll
be back in an hour.

　And with that he just disappeared.

　I was in shock but also felt a sense of accomplishment.
I'd never felt like the teacher's pet before so I was
delighted to be asked. I felt bad failing some of the boys
that had done poorly in the test but I didn't want to help
them cheat in case I myself was being tested. Maybe they
do this with all the recruits to see who could be trusted?

　An hour passed and Sgt Jones returned, holding another
can of Fosters and this time with his top off. Looking back
it sounds mental but what did I know? I'd seen films
where the troops cut about topless at the base so I just

thought it was standard.

He looked a bit more pissed by now as he sat and stared me down.

- Did you give any of your mates extra marks?
- -No Sergeant.
- Why not? It's not like I'm ever gonna check them.

I didn't know what to reply.

-Alright you can fuck off now. Here take these.

He reached into his desk drawer and through me a carton of Lambert and Butler cigarettes. Two hundred fags altogether.

- Are you sure Sergeant?
- There not all for you. You can have two packs and sell the rest to the lads. They all like you so you're best for the job. Bring me the cash when you've got rid of them all. I've plenty more where they came from.
- But we don't get paid until next week Sergeant.
- Well give me the fucking money next week then. Now fuck off.

I was delighted as I knew we were all running low on smokes. The boys were just as happy but they also delighted in slagging me off calling me the Sergeants wee bitch now I was his new cigarette mule.

On pay day I took him the money then he slung me another two cartons .

- Take four packs for you and sell the rest.

This happened a few times and was a great little deal for me. I didn't pay for any fags for weeks. Little did I know, that even though the lads were joking... I really was now his little bitch.

That same day the boys got dressed up in our stone wash jeans and shit two tone collar and cuff shirts and headed out into Darlington for a proper night out. Our training staff warned all of us Scottish recruits that we were to try and not talk too loud because it would be a giveaway that we were squaddies and some of the local lads wouldn't be very welcoming. That's quite a common thing not being welcomed by all as some were jealous of soldiers as we always had money and were athletic looking so they felt we were there to steal their women. We usually were.

I took no notice of the warning at the time though and headed to the club as loud as ever.

We went to a place called the Plastered Parrot and had a great night. I was in my element, dancing and buying drinks for any pretty girl I met. One girl took my fancy a lot and we ended up kissing on the dance floor for the last half hour. She didn't have a boyfriend there but just as we were warned some of the locals were not happy with me. Not that I noticed though... until we got outside.

I left the club with my closest pals from training. Big Richard Hammond, or Hamster, wee Joe Tole the crazy but brilliant Aberdonian, Wee Graham and a few other lads.

As we headed for our taxi we came to an underpass when all of a sudden a guy appeared from the other side holding a bottle. He smashed it off the wall and held the bladed shard out to me. Fuck knows why he chose me. I

169

was probably being the loudest.

-Come ahead then you sweaty sock bastard! Just me and you, come on!

I looked at the boys.

- Fuck have **ah** done?

The guy kept shouting and demanding I go over and fight him. When I have a drink in me I get a false confidence and think I could burst the moon with one punch. I started walking to the underpass. Hammy tried to grab me back.

-Don't do it mate. Something's not right here.

Hamster wasn't one to back off as he was the hardest out the lot of us but he clearly sensed something I didn't. I did my usual and ignored any advice given and marched to the guy with the bottle in his hand.

As I got closer he smashed the remains of the bottle of the floor and screamed,

-Let's go boys!

Looking back now that must have been the signal but again I was oblivious.

Just as the bottle crashed, at least fifteen of his friends started piling through the underpass from the other side. We had been ambushed...us...the soldiers.

Before I could blink the bottle dropper swung a punch at me and burst my nose all over my face.

I dropped like a sack of tatties.

Lucky for me the boys didn't run away and leave me, they ran right into the chaos and a full scale riot

170

kicked off. I'm not exaggerating when I say it was total carnage. Bottles getting smashed off faces, heads being stomped on. And that was just what they were doing to me.

A lot of it is a blur but the thing I remember most vividly is turning to run away from a big gorilla of a guy but his pal was there waiting and smashed a pint glass right into the centre of my face. It wasn't really sore because I was drunk and full of adrenaline again but I remember feeling my skin open on my forehead and cheek then the hot blood run down my face.

I curled up on the floor as they all started to kick me but I wasn't scared. I was on a high. I was back in my film again.

The kicks stopped after a while. They probably thought I was dead.

The riot spilled onto the main street. I got back up, and saw the blood drip onto my shirt. It was like taking a pill. I felt alive. I ran into the crowd and started throwing punches anywhere I could find a space to swing. I connected with a few good ones but there were too many of them. We got an absolute hiding. I got picked up by two guys and got thrown headfirst onto a car windscreen. Split the top of my head right open. You can still see the scar now if I shave my head. As I slid down the bonnet I saw wee Joe with his top off. He was dripping in blood too and swinging his shirt around his head.

-Come on then fuckers! Woohoo! Fuckin come on!!
You think I'm scared of you mother fuckers??!! Who's
next?? I'll eat yeez ya cunts! I'll fuckin eat yeez!!!

Then he started throwing more punches. The lunatic
was actually enjoying it. I'm laughing now as I think
about it.

As soon as I got back to my feet I took a bottle
across the cheek. It didn't smash first time but it did
on the third attempt, right off the back of my head. It
actually hurt less the time it smashed.

I just remember thinking, "This is it, that's me deed
now!"

Then the blue flashing lights and sirens appeared.
Police cars and vans, at least ten of them all skidding
up alongside us with too many policemen and women
to count piling out and arresting the first limb they
could grab. I turned to run away but ran straight into
a bin and fell on my arse.

The next thing I know I'm handcuffed and sat in the
back of the police wagon, absolutely soaked head to
toe in blood. Mostly my blood but I'm sure a few
others as well. I could still hear the riot as I tried to
angle my body to look out a window but I couldn't see
a thing. I was still really drunk and dazed with all the
glass that was broken off my head. I heard a
policeman shout,
-This one's Scottish.

Just at that the door flew open and wee Joe was
launched into the van head first like a sack of tatties.

172

He was also handcuffed so he had to use his face as brakes.

I burst out laughing.

Joe shouted at the police as they slammed the door shut.

-Stirling bridge ya cunts!! Bannockburn!! Never forget!

He gets up and starts booting the door.

-Aye run away ya cunts! We ripped yer Wembley tae shreds! Where were you then eh? Where were you then?!!

He kicks the door a few more times then turns to me and bursts out laughing.

-Some buzz eh mate! Any fags?

I fucking love Joe.

Big Hamster, is the next one to test out his face brakes, then the rest of the boys all appeared one by one. There were six of us huckled in the back and all of us looked like something out of the last scene in Carrie. I'd never seen so much blood. But we were all alive and that was the main thing.

The police van started up and began to drive us to the police station. We all looked at each other in silence for a second as we checked out whos wounds were worse. Then almost in unison we all burst out laughing.

I don't know if it was adrenaline, or alcohol or both but we were all as high as kites. In fact I do know what it was. We had come out as a six and we fought as a six. Brothers in arms. For all the army broke us, it also brain washed us into being loyal and to fight to the death to protect those close to us. And if it wasn't for the police turning up I honestly believe we would have fought to the death that night.

Sat together in that police van covered in blood and high on alcohol and fighting juice was one of the favourite times in my life.

It was as if we had just won the hunger games.

It was the best rush I'd had since my first Mitsubishi pill.

Getting hit and feeling that blood flood down my face and body felt better than when I actually punched someone. That night set me up for every fight I've had ever since. I'm not scared of getting hit, I almost encourage it. I don't like to lose a fight, but I like to come out of one knowing I've been in one. I don't always win but if I need to I'll fight dirty and I won't stop until I'm unconscious or victorious. Well I used to be like that before my son came along.

We laughed and joked all the way to the police station. Little did we know how much trouble we were actually in.

Sorry I'll rephrase that....Little did I know how much trouble I was in.

We were put in separate cells that night but in the morning for some reason they put us all into the same cell. Maybe they needed to free up space I don't know.

Our moods had changed from the van. Safe to say we were all shitting ourselves as we spoke about the repercussions. Sgt Jones was going to kill us. What if it made the news? It was a full scale riot and we were covered in sticky dry blood. We were sure our time in the army was well and truly over. I sat in silence thinking how much I'd let everyone down again. Why didn't I just walk the other way? If it wasn't for me the boys wouldn't have had to fight to defend me. I should have listened to big Hamster.

The hours ticked by so slowly until a police officer opened the cell and called Joe out for his interview. Then one by one all the boys were taken out leaving only me alone.

Hours passed and I still hadn't been seen. What the fuck was going on? I'd seen enough T.V to know that the one they keep to the end is always the one they have most interest in. It's the one and only time I remember having fifteen radio stations play in my head.

I hadn't even thought of a joint in almost three months but now I was craving one just to control the anxiety. The blood from my cuts on my head had now formed a crust around my skull and my body was aching all over. I was finding it hard to breath. I didn't know it at the time but I had a cracked rib and a broken toe. I think I broke my toe when I ran into the bin.

The stress of doing nothing and the pain exhausted

me so I lay down and tried to sleep.

Just as I was dozing off I heard the clunk of the cell door and jolted up.

I got up to fast and hurt my ribs. I grabbed at them and winced.

The cell door opened. The turn key was a chubby wee guy with no emotion on his face. This was my fate but for him I was his routine.

-Follow me Mr Taylor.

I was taken to an interview room where a man and a woman wearing suits were sat waiting.

Proper detectives.

This was serious.

I was nervous but I gained confidence by going into film mode again. The more I write about my film mode the more I understand it. I pretend I'm in a drama to escape the fact it's real life??....Interesting....

Big moment for me that.

Glad you were here to share it troops.

Anyway I was asked questions about my part in the riot for about two hours. All I could answer was,

-I don't remember much.

Or

-    I'm not sure.

I told them I remembered how they set up an ambush but after that everything else was a blur. And then they hit me with it.

-We have some CCTV footage we want to show you.

Aw fuck.

They played the footage on a monitor for me to watch and asked me to tell them when I spot myself. I was wearing a two tone fucking shirt so I was hardly inconspicuous. We watched footage from all angles of different cameras but lucky for me I wasn't anywhere to be seen. I saw wee Joe swinging his shirt about and had to hold in my laugh. We spent another good half hour watching all the footage until I spotted myself.

-Pause it. That's me there!

I pointed to myself on the screen as I ran into the bin and fell on my arse just before I was arrested. Lucky for me that was all the camera caught of me. There was no footage of any of us throwing a punch but plenty of the Darlington boys punching the boys and stamping on them etc.

I was gutted they didn't have any footage of me getting a pint glass smashed off my face...Even in real time I thought it looked cool as fuck.

The detectives concurred that we were clearly attacked and to my absolute relief told me they wouldn't be pressing any charges. But my relief was short lived as the male detective piped up.

- All your friends have been released but I'm afraid we are going to have to keep you in over the weekend.
- What the fuck! Sorry, I mean why?
- You've got a warrant out for your arrest back at King Street station in Ayr?
- A Warrant? For what?
- Theft by housebreaking.

177

-   Fuckin housebreaking? Are you sure you've got the
    right Chris Taylor?

I was so confused. I'd never broken into a house in my
life! What did that even mean? And then it hit me.

About six months before I joined the army I was at a
party with a dodgy crowd, popping pills and acid when
some guy I'd just met called Frank said he was going to
get money for more drugs off a guy that owed him. I had
a great buzz on as the pills fought against the acid and I
needed out of the house so decided to tag along.

Unknown to me Frank was planning on battering the guy
for the money he was owed and if he didn't pay he was
going to smash his car up with a hammer.

I didn't find this out until we were on the way and Frank
pulled out the hammer to show me. Obviously I should
have done a U Turn there and then but all I had in my
head was...More drugs. And of course...I went into
Hollywood film mode.

On the way there we were passing a window and Frank
noticed some mad lava lamp inside. And because we
were both out of our tits on ecstasy we thought it looked
so beautiful. We both cupped our eyes against the
window to take a better look at it when a police car came
around the corner. It looked dodgy as fuck but I swear we
were literally just admiring the lamp.

Frank threw the hammer into the darkness as the police
approached us. They cuffed us straight away.

We tried to explain but they were having none of it,
especially when they shone a torch on the ground and

178

spotted the hammer.

We were taken to the station, questioned and then spent the night in the cells. I was still out my nut on a cocktail of ecstasy and acid, so I spent the whole night in my cell dancing about chasing cartoons up walls and having the time of my life. Every time the guard came to check on me I just kept telling him how much I loved him and how one day he will be a real policeman like the rest of them. I didn't so much say it to him, I sang it to him. I don't remember the tune. I think I made it up.

He hated me.

Me and Frank were both released that next morning and were told the investigation was ongoing.

I had forgotten all about it.

My head was full of so many drugs and so much had happened that year it just went out of my head. I was getting arrested a few times back in the day and it was always forgotten about so maybe I just repressed this charge as I thought the same would happen again?

I had to spend the weekend in Darlington police station while I waited for the police in Ayr to drive down and re arrest me. It was one of the most miserable times of my life. I wasn't allowed a change of clothes and was due at Ayr Sherriff Court on the Tuesday morning.

The drive to Ayr in the police car was miserable but the two cops escorting me at least let me smoke a fag or two on the way back up.

I was locked up in the cells in Ayr on the Monday night and was told I'd be up in court the following day. They asked if I wanted to call anyone to tell them I was here but I didn't want to call my Mum because as far as she was concerned I was still in Catterick training. This would have killed her. So I got them to call my mate Jamie and see if he could bring a change of clothes for me. I didn't want to face the judge caked in blood and looking like a serial killer.

But Jamie didn't bring the clothes. He decided to call my Mum instead and tell her where I was. I don't blame him for it though, I'd have done the same. He was just trying to look out for me. I didn't know this though until I was walked up the stairs from the court cells and into the dock and saw her sitting in the gallery. Her face dropped at the sight of me with my blood soaked shirts, black eyes and split nose. I'd broken her heart again. They weren't told what my charge was so her and my Dad's immediate thoughts were, "He's killed someone".

My Lawyer Steven Maxwell who is also a really close family friend offered to represent me and spoke to the judge on my behalf. The whole court was looking at me in disbelief as I really did look in some state.

Luckily the judge deferred the court case for three weeks in order for him to get reports on me from the army and the Procurator Fiscal.

I didn't get to see my parents after the trial as the army had sent the Military Police to come and escort me back to Catterick. I started to know the route really well! I was put in the back of an army range rover in handcuffs and driven back down south.

The Military Police didn't let me smoke any fags on the way back. Pricks.

When we got back to the base I was marched into the Sergeant Majors office where I got this biggest bollocking of my life. He basically told me that if I was eventually charged in Ayr then my career as a soldier was over and I was going to prison. But he was actually okay about the riot stuff as the detectives told him that we were the ones who were ambushed.

When I got back to my room all the lads were desperate to hear my story so we all sat with beers as I told them everything that had happened. They all stuck by me and talked me out of my depression. Once again they all had my back, not for the first or the last time.

The next four weeks dragged in as I dreaded the court case and another drive back down to Ayr but lucky for me Frank plead guilty and told the court I didn't even know about the hammer. I was let off with a fine and wasn't charged. Somehow I'd managed to keep my career. But I knew this was my last chance.

I kept my head down for the next few weeks and worked as hard as I could in training. I made a promise that I was not getting into anymore trouble ever again.

Yup....Bullshit.

CHAPTER SIX. PASSING OUT.

We were just over half way through our infantry training at Catterick and even though I had learned my lesson I was still drinking at the weekends. We just stayed away from Darlington now. One weekend we were all skint and couldn't get any alcohol so the boys convinced me to go and ask Sergeant Jones for a sub until payday. We knew he wouldn't mind me asking as he had offered cash to some of us before in the past. The boys nominated me because as they all said I was his "favourite".

  I marched up to his office and sheepishly asked if he would sub me and the boys . He just nodded and said he would give it to us later and I was to head back to his office when training was over. The boys were delighted with the news. And I won't lie, I felt chuffed even after everything that I was still the "favourite".

  We all got our shirts on ready to go to the Jesters bar in Catterick and I headed back to the office to get the cash of our Sergeant. As usual he was tanning a can of Fosters and looked pretty pissed. He was also wearing a smart shirt.

-You'll need to come to the bank with me, I don't have the money on me.

  I agreed and we walked out of camp and into Catterick. He hardly spoke a work as we stomped into town. But he passed at least two bank machines on the way. I didn't question him. After all he was still my superior and I didn't want to push my luck.

We arrived at a wee pub that I can't remember the name of.

-In here.

I was confused.

-But I need to get back to the boys, they are all waiting for me to bring back the cash.

-What so I'm good enough to take money off but not have a drink with?

Fair enough I thought. So in we went to the pub and he bought us both a pint. We chatted about training and other small talk. Then he bought another round. Then another. I was getting anxious as I didn't want to piss the boys off.

-Is there any chance I can get that cash now Sergeant? The boys are...

-Fuck the boys. We're going to a club.

I should have known something wasn't right there and then. Looking back it's obvious but I was genuinely just overwhelmed that an actual Sergeant of 12 years wanted my company on a Friday night even though I wasn't even a proper soldier yet. This was pure Choir boy meets Pope type of honour.

He kept saying how impressed everyone was with my skills and attitude. And he was married with two kids so to me there was nothing that suspicious at the time. I just thought he was a bit of a mad alky bastard. And he was my boss. And I was scared to argue. He was built like a house.

Next thing I know he has booked us a taxi and we are on our way to a night club called tall trees. It was a huge club and was all inclusive.

After getting over the guilt of leaving the boys I had a great night. Dancing with girls and drinking all the booze I could get my hands on. Sgt Jones just kept handing me vodka after vodka, whisky after whisky until I literally couldn't stand anymore.

I sat down to try and sober up when Sgt Jones dragged me up to my feet.

- Time to get you home.

We went outside and when the fresh air hit me I almost passed out. I felt sick. We got in a taxi and started making the route back. I tried to tell him that because I left camp with him I didn't have to sign out so how will I explain to the guardroom when I need to sign back in.

- You can stay at mine and I'll walk you back into camp tomorrow morning.

-Will your wife not mind?

-Nah. Now shut up and sleep.

I was too drunk to argue, I just looked out of the window trying to work out where the fuck we were.

The taxi pulled into a nice wee looking estate that the army had bought to house all the training staff. Sgt Jones paid the fair and walked me up to his door. I stumbled into the house with a little nudge from him and nearly fell over. He took me by the arm, marched me up the stairs and opened a bedroom door. It was dark but I could vaguely make out the shape of a bed. Before I had the chance to

184

walk to it, he pushed me onto it.

I was that drunk a gentle breeze would have sufficed.

-Get to sleep.

He slammed the door and disappeared.

The room was pitch black but I could feel it spinning.

I don't know how long I was sleeping for but I was awoken by something that has haunted and scarred me until this very day.

At first I thought I was dreaming. Then the realisation hit and I froze.

I had an erection

And someone was sucking my cock.

My heart raced into overdrive as I prayed that his wife had snuck into the room. But it didn't take long to realise that my worst nightmare had come true.

It was him.

I could feel the roughness of his stubble.

Then he let out a groan that played on a loop in my mind for the next three moths. It sent an icy shiver through my soul. I had never been so frightened in my life. I wanted to jump up and start screaming but knew if I did that then there was a good chance he would murder me to keep me from going to the police. I had no chance fighting him off, the man was a monster. And now I knew in more ways than one.

My instincts kicked in so I pretended to start snoring then turned onto my stomach and put my hands between my legs acting is if I was still in a deep sleep.

I could hear him breathing heavily. He slowly tried to

manoeuvre me onto my back again but I remained rigid. He tried again but I wouldn't budge and let out another fake snore or two. I don't know if he believed me or got spooked that I was awake. But he let out a little grunt, stood up and walked to the door. I managed to open an eye enough to look and see what he was doing. He opened the door and the light from the hall lit up his naked silhouette as he staggered from the bedroom and slammed the door behind him.

I was in total darkness again.

My heart was pounding faster than I ever thought possible for a human. My mind was racing. What if he comes back? Should I run? What if he kills me? Who will ever believe me?

I tried to work up the courage to get up and run but the thought of him hearing me move filled me with so much fear I felt physically sick. I lay awake face down on the bed with my hands covering my penis for the rest of the night until the sun came up.

I still sleep like that to this day whenever I have a drink. Not on purpose, it just happens now.

I must have dosed off out of exhaustion for an hour or so but was awoken by the smell of cooking and whistling downstairs.

The cunt was actually fucking whistling.

I lay there not knowing what to do. All I knew was that I needed out of that house.

I got up and started to slowly sneak down the stairs. I reached for the key in the door and started to turn it

186

slowly.

He must have heard me.

-So you're up then you lazy bastard? Get yourself into the kitchen!

I thought about running but the fear took over. I hesitated then walked into the kitchen.

-Christ you look rough. Sit down this will sort you out.

He nodded to the table and chairs in the kitchen and sat a full breakfast down in front of me. No mention of sneaking into the room and sucking my cock in my sleep, no sign of guilt at all.

Just...... here's your breakfast.

I felt sick. But I I had to pretend I didn't remember anything. If I let on that I knew how sick and twisted he was then there was still a good chance he would do anything to silence me.

-Cheers, looks lovely. Where's your wife?

-Her and the kids are at her Mum's in Wales. Come on eat up then we'll get you back to camp.

He sat at the table and started to eat. I remember the grease dripping from his egg onto his chin. I was repulsed but did everything I could to act clueless. I even said.

-That was some night, I don't even remember getting in the taxi.

He smiled at that comment. I knew why he smiled but he didn't know I knew. He seemed more relaxed and then almost hurried me to finish the food and get me out of his house.

I ate as much as I could, which wasn't much and made

187

the excuse that I was too hungover.

-Right well fuck off then.

He walked me to the door, unlocked it and pointed to the road.

-Out there, turn right and the main road is there. You'll find your way back easy enough.

-Cheers.

I couldn't get out there quick enough and he couldn't get rid of me quick enough. As soon as he closed the front door I started to sprint. I couldn't even remember the directions he gave me I just kept running as far away from that house as I could. I was lost but I didn't care I just kept running.

It took me an hour or so to find my bearings but I finally found our barracks. I ran past the guardroom and into the dorm. All the boys were still sleeping so I jumped into bed still fully clothed and put my head under the covers

Lying face down with my hands covering my penis I cried into my pillow, trying not to wake any of the boys.

Did that just happen? Why me? What he comes back for me and kills me? Why the fuck did I have an erection? Why was I so stupid not to see him for what he was?

I couldn't stop thinking about the feeling of his stubble and the sight of his silhouette as he staggered from the bedroom. I had never needed a joint more in my life.

Anything to numb the pain.

I cried myself to sleep/.

I was woken a few hours later by big Hamster and Joe as they jumped on my bed. They were just back in from a night out and were still drunk. The minute I felt them make contact with me I felt shaken and bounced up to my feet.

-Don't fuckin touch me!

They looked surprised at my reaction. Hammy shouted back.

-Who you fuckin talkin tae?

I managed to compose myself quickly enough not to arouse anymore suspicion from them as I didn't want them knowing anything.

-Sorry lads. Must have been having a bad dream.

They weren't buying it so I changed the subject.

-Where have you two been?

Joe lay down on my bed and tried to make me feel bad.

-Well since you let us down last night and didn't come back with the money we had to borrow some off one of the Fijian boys from across the hall. Me and hamster went back into Darlington and got wur hole! What the fuck happened to you last night mores to the point?

I didn't know what to say so came up with a lie that he gave me the money and I met some girl and stayed out with her all night.

Joe bought my story but big Hamster didn't look too sure but he kept quiet. If I was going to tell anyone it was going to be him. But I wasn't ready yet.

The next few weeks were torture. Having to see the Sgt every day was bad enough but now he had started to treat me like a prick in front of all the boys during training. It was probably his way of deflecting from the fact he had

189

sexually assaulted me so he wanted to show people that I wasn't an interest to him.

He would try and humiliate me at times. For example we were out on exercise in the field one day and just for amusement he told me to pick up one of the ammo boxes and hop around the camp shouting "I'm the camp bitch" over and over again. It was humiliating watching everyone laugh at me but I'm sure if they had known what he had done to me they wouldn't have. Well I hope not. It was the worst few weeks of my life. I couldn't sleep at nights fearing that he would try and sneak into my bed. That's when the night terrors started. Even when I did fall asleep I would dream of his face popping up in all different places or have nightmares that he was raping and killing me.

I started distancing myself from everyone and instead of going to the NAFFI with my friends at night I would go into town, buy a bottle of vodka and go drink at a wee concealed wooded place behind the big Tesco in Catterick. It was the perfect place as it had a river you could sit buy and no one would see you. The boys had named that Buckfast bridge too.

I was drinking there every night just to numb the pain and get the thoughts of him touching me out of my head. I thought about killing myself every night but I couldn't do that to my family. Not after all the faith and love they showed me the days before I left for the army. I just wanted the pain to stop.

I wanted drugs. Any drugs.

Everyone always asks me why I didn't just tell someone

190

but it's not that simple. He was a respected army veteran of twelve years and I was just a spotty faced eighteen year old recruit. But most of all I was scared if I told someone then he would kill me.

One weekend I decided to go home and see my parents instead of spending it with my pals. I was going to tell them everything. I knew they would believe me. But when I got home and saw how proud they were of how I'd stuck it out I just couldn't. I couldn't bear to see the look on my Mum's face when she found out that her wee boy had been molested by a man that was meant to be protecting me. So I kept my mouth shut.

I was meant to return back to the barracks for training on Monday morning but I couldn't face it. So I went AWOL. I booked into a Bed and Breakfast in Ayr and just drank for two days straight. I thought about getting weed but only had enough money left for drink so it was one or the other. I chose drink.

I knew I had to return eventually so I arrived back on the Wednesday with full intentions of spilling the whole story. But I lost my nerve again.

I was given another bollocking from the Sergeant Major and given one more last chance. I was half hoping he would kick me out but he didn't. I'd gone from loving being a soldier to resenting the mere sight of a uniform.

And then everything changed the following weekend when I took a bottle of vodka down to my safe spot by the river.

As I approached the water I could hear someone crying. I

was going to turn around and leave as I wanted to be alone but something made me keep walking. It was one of my pals from my platoon, wee Graham. Graham was a great guy, quiet but brand new. He was swigging from a bottle of Buckfast. He tried to compose himself when he saw me.

I spoke first.

-Alright mate, fancy meeting you here. You alright?

-Aye fine mate.

Don't ask me how, but I just knew. He looked into my eyes as well and then he knew. Both our eyes filled up with tears. I sat down beside him and said,

-Has he done it to you too?

Graham could hardly talk, the tears were choking him. I just hugged him and we both cried for a moment or two.

Nothing else was said for a while. We both drank and drank and then started to tell each other our stories.

Sgt Jones had snuck into his room at night when everyone was sleeping and done the exact same thing to him just a few days before.

We cried together, got angry together and even spoke about ways that we could even murder him. For all I was devastated for him and this may sound selfish, but knowing I wasn't the only one helped. I didn't feel as alone now.

I shared my vodka with him and we talked for hours. Then without warning , big Hamster and Joe and some of the other boys turned up with a carry out. I'm a big believer in fate and those boys were meant to turn up when they did.

They knew something was wrong straight away so we didn't try hiding it anymore. We told them everything. Turns out some of the other boys had heard some things from some of the other recruits so it wasn't just me and Graham.

Big Hamster was furious, he started smashing bottles off the rocks in a rage.

-Am gonnae fuckin kill that cunt!

The lads were amazing, as always. We sat all night drinking and hatching a plan as to how we were going to get our revenge. We agreed the best thing to do was to get all the victims together and wait until the last day of training and then go to the Sergeant Major and tell him everything. We only had a few weeks left to go now. I went to bed calm for the first night in a while knowing that the boys once again had my back. We all slept wit an eye open after that day.

One of my biggest regrets is that we didn't out Sgt Jones sooner. If we had then we could have saved someone else.

It was the last night before passing out of Infantry training and the staff had organised a big piss up at the NAFFI for us all. I didn't go because I knew the Sergeant was going to be there but the rest of them did. I got pished in my room and got an early night.

When we got up the next morning ready for the big parade there was lots of chat that the Sergeant had been really drunk and acting strange at the NAFFI. We all had that sinking gut feeling. We knew something had happened but not sure to who. Then I looked across the room and saw a guy called Symonds or Simmo as we called him sat at the end of his bed with his head in his hands. He looked distraught. I was about to go and talk to him when a big dopey bastard from the platoon called Broony approached him.

-What's up wae your face Simmo?

Simmo didn't respond but Broony kept at him.

-Aw you hung over son? Suck it up and stop being a big poof!

Simmo exploded.

He jumped up and grabbed Broony by the throat and screamed in his face.

-What the fuck did you call me!? Don't ever say that to me again or I'll rip your fucking face off.

He pushed Broony away and then turned and kicked a hole into one of the big wooden boxes we used to transport all our kit.

I knew there and then that he was the latest victim.

The room stood in silence as Simmo burst out crying and ran out the door. Broony piped up.

-Fucks wrong wae that psycho.

I snapped back at him.

-Fuck up you ya big fucking lanky prick! You know nothing!

Me and some of the boys ran after Simmo but he was nowhere to be seen.

An hour before parade it all kicked off.

The training staff all came into the building looking flustered and started to ask us all if we knew anything

194

about what happened last night. Me and Graham raised our hands.

-Sergeant Major wants to see you now then, go!

We both ran to the Sergeant Majors office.

When we walked in his face was like ash. We sat and talked with him and it turned out Simmo had told him that he had been molested by Sergeant Jones and we confirmed the same had happened to us and a few others.

The Sergeant Major listened to our accounts and his eyes filled with tears.

-Is that why you went Awol Taylor?

-Yes sir.

-I'm so sorry this happened. I've failed you all.

We assured him it wasn't his fault and we all had a bit of a cry then we were told to go back to our room and wait to hear from him.

After about half an hour we found out that the Military Police were called in and when they approached Sgt Jones with the allegations he kicked off and smashed up the Sgt Majors office and had him by the throat saying things like, "How dare you accuse me of this" etc. Rumour has it the MP's were even too frightened to approach him. He was suspended and told to pack his things and go back to his regiment.

We all made it to the parade to get our certificates and pass out as fully qualified soldiers but I couldn't be happy. It should have been the proudest day of my life but it was soured knowing that if I had come forward earlier then Simmo or Graham wouldn't have had to have suffered.

And that still haunts me to this day.

I'm so sorry boys.

I went home with mixed feelings. Happy he had finally been caught but sad that so many of us had to suffer. In the end about eight guys came forward with allegations against him.   It wasn't just the nights in question that hurt. That bastard had ruined our lives for a long long time to com

CHAPTER SEVEN. ALCATRAZ

I didn't want to be a soldier anymore.

But I wasn't allowed to leave on grounds of sexual abuse until he was found guilty at a Court Marshall. It took a year and a half before the trial took place so I had no choice but to stick it out and join my new regiment The Royal Highland Fusiliers at Fort George. And I hated every fucking minute of it.

There were some great guys in the regiment and I did make a few pals but I was bullied from day one and even the thought of writing about it sends chills down my spine.

I tried to put a brave face on and look happy but to be honest I just didn't fit in from day one.

On my first night I went out for a drink and when I came back my whole locker had been trashed and my stuff was thrown all around my room. There was a note left that read, "You're not welcome here ya fuckin poofy cunt, watch your back".

Or something along those lines.

This had nothing to do with what happened in training as that wasn't common knowledge yet. Turns out one or two of them thought the clothes I wore were too posh and gay looking so automatically I was a gay in their eyes. And that was on day one.

I had bad skin due to stress so I was constantly being called spotty, or rasheed. The funniest one which I thought was quite clever was, "you've got a face like a pregnant gremlin".

I dreaded waking up every morning and tried to keep myself to myself. But like I say there were a few good guys that would back me up. But the majority just couldn't take to me. I guess I can come across quite camp compared to the wee neds and hard men of the world but that was no excuse to treat me the way some of them did.

Eventually my humour won a lot of them over and they started being nicer to me and I acted like I was their pal too, but deep down I fucking hated them.

One guy in particular was a total cunt to me, to the point I felt suicidal. And he was a corporal. His name was...let's say...Cuntface for the purpose of the book

CuntFace was a big mouth and took pleasure in belittling people in public especially me. I was meant to be fighting with these guys if it was ever war time but they I wouldn't have taken a bullet for them the way I would have for the boys in training. That was real camaraderie...not this.

It was the longest year and a half of my life.

I did two six week tours of Northern Ireland and on the second tour is when it all came out in the papers what had happened to me. It really didn't help my cause. Some started calling me a liar. Most were on my side but there were some who used it as an excuse to bully me more. I still hate them all to this day. I was thinking the chapter about the RHF would be long but I really can't think of any times when I was truly happy there. It was like a prison filled with people who just didn't take to me.

I don't want to say that everyone there was bad because

198

they weren't. I just didn't belong. Maybe it was because of what happened to me made me resent anyone in uniform. Who knows.

After a year and a half the Court Marshall date for Sgt Jones's trial was finally decided and I was called up to give my witness statement in court along with the rest of the boys. We were all put up in a hotel in Richmond and it was so good to see them all again. I felt happy for the first time in so long. These were the boys that had my back not the ones at my regiment.

We all partied the night before the trial. I knew that he was going to get found guilty because of all the witnesses and I knew that as soon as he was in jail that I could leave the army. So that night I bought some ecstasy and got totally off my face. I had a great night. Although we trashed the hotel and got our balls booted by the army I was at the point that I just didn't care anymore.

The next morning we were all about to head to court when we got a call. Sgt Jones had plead guilty an hour before the trial was to start.

I was fucking furious. He made us wait a full year and a half then admitted his guilt an hour before the trial. I could have been out eighteen months ago!

Eighteen fucking months ago!!!

I was fighting between emotions of anger and relief for the next few weeks. I was glad we didn't have to stand in court and relive everything in front of strangers with him staring us down but I was filled with rage that this piece of shit had dragged it out for so long when we all could have

199

had closure much earlier. I say closure but there never really is any, not mentally anyway.

When I returned back to Fort George I had to attend lots of meetings over the next few weeks with Commanding Officers at all levels, most of whom were very sympathetic. I was annoyed it took for him to plead guilty to encourage them to finally talk to me about it but at least now people believed me. They tried to convince me to stay but my mind was made up eighteen months ago. I wanted to be home with my family and friends.

I had to see Psychiatric nurse at the base in order for her to sign me off. I can't remember her name but she was amazing with me. She listened and understood. I would sit and cry for hours as I spilled all my feeling out to her. I couldn't or even wouldn't do that with my Mum as I wanted her to think I was coping. I couldn't bear seeing her hurt anymore. So the Nurse was my shoulder to cry on through it all.

After a few sessions with her she recommended that the army release me from my contract on compassionate grounds.

I was out a few weeks later with full pension. I don't know if that was there way of saying sorry or to try and stop me suing them but I did appreciate it. I have thought of suing them especially when I found out that someone had complained about Sgt Jones months before we arrived at Catterick but he wasn't believed and it was all brushed under the carpet. Had they acted now then the rest of us would never had to have suffered the way we did and who, knows, maybe I'd still be in the army.

For all that happened I'll always look back at my time in the forces with pride. Most of my memories are very dark but there were some good times amongst all the fear and hurt. It got me on the straight and narrow to an extent and I hadn't smoked a joint in nearly two years.

I'd gone in as a seventeen year old boy and was leaving as a man. I learned a lot in my time there.

Apart from fucking map reading.

CHAPTER EIGHT. DIVING INTO DARKNESS

During my last few months in the army I had managed to get myself a mortgage and had bought myself a wee flat in Ayr. I was letting my sister Cara and her man Dougie live there with their two kids Robbie and Eva as they were having house trouble. I was never really home so it made sense at the time. I was doted on my niece and nephew so having them all around really helped the first few weeks of being home.

I have loads of nieces and nephews now and I love them dearly. I'd die for any one of them.

When Cara and Dougie were at mine I slept on the couch as it was only two bedrooms. I didn't have the heart to ask them to leave.

I managed to find a job in a nightclub to tide me over financially. I was a PR worker, handing out fliers to encourage people into the club from ten at night until one in the morning and then I would go into the club and drink myself stupid until closing time. This was my routine every Wednesday to Sunday. I was drinking a lot now just to help me sleep and numb the pain. I was struggling with night terrors and didn't ever have a proper nights sleep. I'd wake up in a cold sweat and start drinking again just to doze back off. I wasn't even using mixers, just straight vodka or whisky straight from the bottle.

I'd also met a girl just before I left fort George called Soozy so I was staying at hers a few nights a week.

Soozy was the first woman I had been with since that night at Sgt Jones's house. It took me months to feel any kind of sexual attraction for anyone. She was ten years older than me but she made me feel safe. I fell for her quite quickly but she was not as into me as I was with her. She always made it clear that we were not an official item. I pretended I was ok with that but deep down I wanted to be her boyfriend and it killed me the thought of her dating other guys. But she was upfront and honest about the situation so I can't ever blame her for what happened next.

I was out working at the club one night and I met Soozy who was having a night out with her pals. I had been drinking a lot and hadn't slept in a few days so I wasn't in a good way. I kept asking if I could go home with her that night but she refused. We got into a big argument and I smashed a glass off the bar and stormed out the club, with a little bit of gentle help from the bouncers.

As I left the club and turned the corner I passed a group of guys that were a few years above me in school. One of them pointed at me and shouted at the top of his voice.
-Look there's that poof that got raped in the army!
I don't know what stopped me from turning around and punching his face in but I just kept walking. I felt humiliated. I started to run, just like the way I had when I left Sgt Jone's house that morning. I ran and cried and ran and cried. I felt broken.

My anxiety was at peak levels and when I get to that point no one can calm me down. I get sweaty palms and my heart beats like a piston and pumps the blood to my brain quicker than my mind can deal with. And that's the night I decided the only way I could calm down and block it all out was to buy weed.

I headed in a rage straight to an old dealer I knew and knocked on his door. Unlucky for me he was in and didn't mind me visiting so late. He only had a wee bit of solid hash left so I handed him the cash and headed back to the flat where my sister and the kids were fast asleep.

I remember standing in the kitchen trembling with an anger I hadn't felt before mixed with excitement that I was going to get stoned again.

I rolled three big fat joints one after the other and smoked only taking a breath when my mouth was filled with smoke.

After the first joint I felt it hit me so hard but I just continued to smoke and smoke and at the same time glug from a bottle of Jack Daniels.

If you haven't smoked weed before then you should know that it's never really a good idea to mix it with drink. I became even more anxious but now I was in a darker place. I wasn't in control anymore. I made the decision that I just had to end it all there and then.

My sister had a wee basket above the fridge that she kept all her pills in. Paracetamol, Iron tablets, birth control pills, you name it.

I took them all and swigged them down with the rest of

the Jack Daniels. I just didn't want to feel pain anymore.

I started to cry like a baby. This woke my sister and Dougie who rushed through to the kitchen to find me surrounded my empty packets of pills. Poor Cara was beside herself.

They phoned me an ambulance as I started to feel myself get sleepy. I don't really remember anything after that but Cara told me that when the ambulance arrived I didn't want to be saved and threatened to batter the paramedics if they touched me so they had to call the police who then hand cuffed me and forced me into the ambulance. Cara had also called Soozy who rushed to my flat just in time to see me being driven off. She was furious and quite rightly so. She thought it was because of our argument but it wasn't. I just couldn't handle life anymore.

I had my stomach pumped and spent a day or so in hospital. Cara moved the family out as she couldn't have kids living in a house where someone was so mentally unstable. I couldn't really argue with that.

When I got home to the flat after hospital, I wasn't feeling any better. If anything I felt worse. Not only did I still have my demons to deal with I had also caused more pain for my family. My mum was distraught. The guilt I felt was overwhelming.

I was so lonely the first night home, the flat felt empty without Cara and her family. So I weed out and bought more weed and drink with the only money I had left. I had been sacked from the night club because of my actions a few nights before so now I had no income.

I locked myself in my flat for three days. I had no gas or electricity so couldn't watch T.V. I just lay on the couch wrapped in a blanket drinking straight vodka and smoking weed until I was unconscious. I didn't think it was possible for a human to cry so much but I didn't stop for three whole days. I got so bad that I couldn't handle it anymore and again made the decision I was going to kill myself.

I didn't have any pills this time and there were no fixtures in the flat that I could hang myself. So I got a knife from the kitchen and tried to build up the courage to slit my wrists. The problem was I have always had a phobia of touching or seeing veins and even though I was at my lowest I couldn't bring myself to cut there. Every time I put the knife near my wrists my body hunched up and I started gagging. So I started to stab myself in the stomach instead. I could bleed out that way instead.

To build up the courage to do it I let out a huge scream and just started stabbing and slashing at my belly. Blood started to pour from me. It was so bad I got scared. Maybe I didn't want to die. What the fuck was I doing? I staggered out of my front door and hobbled around the corner onto the main road. I was so drunk and was now losing blood. I felt faint and fell onto the pavement clutching my stomach in agony. Lucky for me some passers by found me (poor bastards) and called an ambulance. I passed out and woke up in hospital as several doctors cut my clothes off and started patching stitching me up. I kept drifting out of consciousness but I remember them trying to keep me awake.

206

I woke up the next day with my mum sat by my bed. She didn't look angry or hurt or disappointed. She just looked into my eyes and said.

-We need to fix you son.

I came off the drink for a while after that night but kept smoking weed as that was the only thing that helped stop the night terrors. Keeping off alcohol helped to ease the depression and I could see things more clearly.

Soozy had every right to distance herself totally from me after what I'd done but she didn't. She really stepped up and offered to help me through it all by letting me stay with her for a few nights a week. She would cook me proper meals and was a good shoulder to cry on. Things were good when I was with her but the nights I was alone in my flat were tough. I hated being by myself.

A few weeks passed and in that time I managed to get a job working at the bar in the Durward hotel on Prestwick Road. I had some money coming in and being around people all day was helping. Although on the downside the temptation to drink grew stronger, as I watched friends and customers get drunk every weekend. I told everyone I was off it, but in truth I was downing a few pints after every shift, just enough to get a wee buzz.

One Friday Soozy me and her two kids went a trip up to the Blair Drummond Safari park in Stirling for a day out. The sun was shining and we had a great time seeing all the animals and having a picnic. This was the life I wanted. I wanted us to be a family. When the kids were off playing at the park I told Soozy that I wanted us to be a real

207

couple, no more "just seeing each other". I told her I was in Love with her. Unfortunately she wasn't in that place yet and let me down gently. She said she wasn't ready for a relationship and told me I still had to get my life together before she would even consider it. She was right to say this but I was devastated. I tried not to show it but I was quiet most of the journey home from Stirling.

She dropped me off at my flat that night and I felt more alone than ever. It didn't help that when I opened the door I was greeted by a letter from the bank telling me that my flat was due to get repossessed. I hadn't been paying my mortgage since leaving the army and just thought if I ignored the letters then it would just go away. In a week from that day I was to become homeless....again. She would never want to be with me now I've lost the flat. What a loser.

As usual I went straight to my old coping mechanism and headed straight to the off license. I only had about twenty three quid so I bought two of the biggest bottles of cheap white cider I could find and that left me enough for ten fags and a fiver bit of hash.

That night I smoked and rolled and smoked and rolled until I was unconscious.

I was embarrassed telling my parents about losing the flat and even thought they were disappointed I think they both knew it was coming. Soozy was furious as I'd lied to her about making payments and told me she didn't want to see me again until I'd sorted myself out. That should have been the kick up the arse I needed but as always I

208

drank myself through it all. I borrowed money off my mum and spent the last week in the flat drinking and smoking weed. The only thing I ate was forty pence packets of Supermarket brand noodles in order to keep as much of the cash for drink and drugs.

On my eviction day I was woken up by a chap at the door. Two men in suits and a policeman were waiting for me at the other side. I had been drinking so hard I'd lost a few days and had no idea this was the day I was to leave. Luckily they gave me two hours to pack my stuff up and leave. The place was a shit hole with empty bottles lying everywhere and ashtrays filled to the brim. I was so hungover I didn't even care about taking any furniture. I just threw all my clothes and some photos into two black bin liners and left.

I had no money in my pocket and no place to go. I sat on the kerb outside the flat and just stared into space for an hour or so. How many times did I have to hit rock bottom before I learned?

I walked about aimlessly most of the day trying to think of a plan to get my life back together. I had been sacked from the Hotel for not showing up that week and didn't have a bed to sleep in.

That night I slept on a bench down Ayr beach that had a shelter above it. I just lay there crying. I wasn't feeling sorry for myself, I was angry. And then I prayed for the first time in years. I come from a big Christian family but had lost my faith a while back. I prayed to my Gran to help me through everything and make me strong enough to tackle my demons.

I eventually fell asleep listening to the crashing waves and dreamt that she came to me. It wasn't one of those pure angelic dreams where she appeared to me with a white gown and a halo to tell me everything was going to be ok. She was furious with me in the dream and called me a stupid wee arsehole and if I was to fix this I was to go see my Papa.

I woke up about six in the morning shivering and hungry. I was nervous to see my Papa as I felt I had let him down just as much as everyone else but I knew he would set me on the straight and narrow.

I walked to his house in Prestwick and when he opened the door I burst into tears again and begged him to let me stay until I got my life together.

He wasn't known for being overly affectionate; he just looked me up and down and opened the door wider to invite me in.

- Put your clothes in the kitchen and go run yourself a bath.

And that was that. I was back living with him but under his strict rules. I wasn't allowed out past nine, no friends were allowed over and if he even thought I was on drugs I'd be out on my ear again. He even used to rip up all my roll up doubts from the ashtray to inspect whether or not there was any weed in them. Most addicts went to rehab, but I went to Papa's. The Betty Ford Clinic could learn a thing or two from old Papa Bill.

As the weeks passed I got stronger mentally and

physically. I would help him in the garden and would run errands for him then at night we would sit up smoking fags and chatting about his days growing up and he would tell me stories about Gran. It really was a great time but I started to need my space after a while and not being able to see friends started to get to me. I needed to find a job so I could afford my own place. I was so grateful for him getting me clean but I still needed to think of my future.

After a bit of soul searching I realised I was always at my happiest when I was performing so I worked up the guts to apply for the H.N.C in Performing arts at Ayr College. I wasn't sure whether I'd be welcome back after walking out half way through my N.C a few years back but luckily they were very understanding and gave me another chance. This was a lifeline for me.

I hadn't performed in a few years so I was really nervous and didn't even know if I still had what it took to be an actor, but I did know that at least it was something to focus on and I was getting some money now from student loan.

After the first day back I felt a lot more assured about my decision. I was back amongst my own kind of people. I felt I could be myself and not have to try too hard to fit in anymore.

We played some improve games and I really enjoyed being able to let go. I left class that day feeling happy again.

I was seeing Soozy again by now. I think she liked the fact I had screwed the nut a bit and wasn't acting as needy around her. Things were good.

The course lasted a year and in that time I performed in two shows. The first was an Italian play called six characters in search of an author. I played the role of "The Son", who was a ghost with a troubled soul. The play wasn't really my cup of tea but I loved being able to get lost in a character again and I could certainly relate to him. The second play was called "The Cosmonaught's Last Message To The Woman He Once Loved In The Former Soviet Union". Just rolls off the tongue eh? I played the part of Oleg, a Russian astronaught who is lost in space and delivers all his dialogue to the camera on the shuttle that is then put on a live feed to the audience. He slowly loses the plot scene by scene and I loved it. I didn't play it for laughs but the manner I portrayed his break down had the audience in stitches every night. Much to the anger of my director.

-Stop playing it for laughs, this is a serious play.

-I'm not playing it for laughs.

-Yes you are. If the audience laugh again tonight then I swear to God I'm gonna launch a fucking hammer at you mid show. Try me!

So that night I did play it for laughs. And by fuck did I have the audience in the palm of my hand. The director backed off after that. What I did was really unprofessional but I didn't appreciate him threatening me. I'd had enough of that in the army.

I passed the course with top marks and now had the choice to stay another year and complete my H.N.D. But I

212

turned them down for two reasons. Firstly I was sick of being skint and living off a student loan and second, things with me and Soozy were getting a bit more serious now. I had moved out of the Papa Rehab Centre and was now with her and I wanted to work to help support her and the two kids. I wanted to feel like a proper family, like the way I felt that day at the Safari Park

It was a tough decision as I loved performing but I also knew how difficult breaking into the industry would be and to be honest I didn't think I could handle the rejection. I still wasn't fully confident in myself yet.

Over the next few years I was in and out of different jobs. I always had work but would never last long in a job as I hated people telling me what to do. Again my army days are probably responsible for that. Here is a list of jobs I remember doing over the first five years of being with Soozy.

1. A production line in a factory making chip and pin machines.
2. A call centre selling phone contracts for Talk Talk.
3. A Barman at the Burns Tavern.
4. A call centre selling Scottish Power.
5. A door to door salesman selling Scottish Power.
6. A restoration company cleaning off fire damaged house goods.
7. Dominos delivery driver (Lasted two shifts).

These are the ones I remember but I'm sure there were more. I did stick to one job for a good chunk of my time with Soozy and that was working as a support worker for adults with profound learning disabilities and autism. I loved the job. I learned so much and it was really rewarding. That was the most settled period in my life to date the three and a half years I had that job. I was making good money and was going holidays abroad with my new family. I felt normal. I hadn't had a meltdown in a few years but was still smoking weed every day. My excuse was that it helped me sleep. It started as a few joints before bed but like any addiction my usage got more frequent throughout the day until I got to the point I'd even roll a joint before bed so I had one to wake up to in the morning.

I couldn't function without a smoke. The thought of being sober and alone with my thoughts was just never an option for me. I had a great job, I was happy with Soozy and the kids but the fear of letting those thoughts of dread back into my head were just too much too handle. I had convinced myself that I was functioning fine but in reality I was out of touch with any reality. I was stoned twenty four hours a day.

This soon led to problems in the relationship. If I couldn't get hash or weed then my moods would be terrible and if I couldn't get stoned then I would turn to drink instead. Not just one or two cans, I had to drink to get so drunk that I'd pass out.

Our relationship was on off because of this and I think we split up more times than Oasis. But Soozy still stuck by me as she knew I had a problem but also knew deep down I wasn't doing it for any other reason than to block out what

214

happened to me. She even stood by me when I was sacked from my support workers job. Again this was down to drink. I got so pished at the annual Summer ball the company was holding and decided to tell my bosses what I really thought of them. I felt over worked and under paid but instead of having a meeting about it I took it upon myself to have a drunken rant at them and basically called them all a bunch of pricks etc. I made a real scene and even threatened to throw one of them through a window. I was escorted out of the place by a few fellow support workers and asked never to return again. They did ask me back a week later but I was too embarrassed so being the fanny I am, I decided to go un employed.

It was a dream job for me and one that I was really good at, but I'd fucked that as well now.

After a few nights of begging for Soozy's forgiveness she eventually took me back and we decided that if I was to be happy then I had to follow my dream and get back to acting. Money would be tight but we both agreed that I should go back to college and complete my H.N.D.

The college were happy to take me back and within a few weeks I was in class again. The first show we were doing was the Queen Musical "We Will Rock You" and I was cast as Pop the old hippy. I was really happy to be rehearsing again and started to get the buzz for it all again. The show never happened as the director soon realised that a lot of the cast couldn't sing and it just wasn't working. So instead we replaced the musical with Liz Lochhead's "Dracula" and I was cast as the maniac Renfield. Still to this day the best

215

role I've ever played. I shaved my head down to the wood for it to look even creepier and used a high pitched old English accent. I'd never been more into a role in my life.

Unfortunately I started to enjoy my time away from Soozy too much and we began to drift apart. It was selfish on my part. I was caught up in all the camaraderie with my fellow students I forgot who it was that helped me get back into it all in the first place.

I would start going out with class mates after rehearsals and come home late. After a few months we separated again and I was sleeping on the couch at hers or dossing at friends houses.

One night about a week before the premier of Dracula I was drinking with some friends when one of them asked if I wanted to buy some valium. I'd never tried them but they told me if you mixed them with drink you would get a great buzz off them. And they were right. I ended up buying about thirty of these pills and went on a three day bender without sleep. I can't remember most of it but I was off my face. Going by what pals told me I was thrown out of most of the pubs on Prestwick Main Street and told not to come back. On the third day of the session I was so out of it I couldn't get in anywhere so bought a litre of vodka and headed to my Papa's for a drink. Next thing I know I've woken up in hospital.

After a few drinks in my Papa's I had went to stand up but my legs had finally given up due to all the valium and I fell face first through his glass coffee table and ripped my face to pieces. I had six stitched on my nose, eight on the top of my head and four on my chin. Poor Papa tried to get me in a taxi and when the driver refused to take me I started kicking his wing mirror off so he got out and battered me. I was mortified and as expected my family were furious with me. I'd come so far over the years and after a few nights of madness and weakness I'd thrown it all away again.

The college had an emergency meeting after seeing my face and had to decide whether to kick me out or not. My face was a state and Dracula was due to go up in just a few days. I begged them to let me stay. I promised I would screw the nut and put everything I had into the show and the last few months of college. Luckily the character Renfield could justify having scars on his face due to being in an asylum and being a self harmer so they agreed to let me stay on, but only on the condition that I stopped drinking.

I had clear the air talks with Soozy and begged for her forgiveness too. She had to think long and hard but eventually said.
-Last chance. You can't keep doing this to yourself. And you need to come off the weed.
-I promise, I swear.

I moved back in and didn't smoke or drink and focussed on the last few days of rehearsing for the show.

The rest of the cast were all a bit reserved with me on my return as I'd missed a few rehearsals due to stint in hospital but we all remained professional and after a few days all was forgiven.

I ended up giving the performance of my life on that
stage and got rave reviews. I was so convincing in the role
that it took my mum about half an hour to even realise it
was me. Apparently she turned to my dad during one of
my scenes and said,
-When's Chris coming on?
   He pointed to the wee maniac twitching in his padded
cell and replied,
-That's him there.
   Probably the biggest compliment an actor can be paid is
that his own mother didn't even recognise him.
   Over the next few months I just focussed on my H.N.D
and kept clean off the weed with the odd blip here and
there. If Soozy was out I would sneak a joint here and
there but nothing too bad. If I could have I'd have smoked
it every night but I knew how much I had to lose.
   The last show we performed at the College was
"Bedroom Farce" by Alan Ayckbourn. I was cast as an old
guy called Ernest. It was good fun to play something silly
off the back of Dracula and it reminded me just how much
I loved being in a comedy role. My wife was played by my
friend Siobhan who later went on to marry my cousin and
best pal Mark.
   We had a great time working together and this show built
a friendship and business relationship that would last for
years to come.
   When college ended I passed with an A and it was time to
go out into the big bad world as an out of work actor.
   I sent my C.V to every agent in Scotland and wrote to

every T.V station trying to get auditions but nothing ever came of it. After a few months of getting nowhere I had to take on my job back at the call centre and that's when I started to sink back into a deep depression.

I convinced Soozy that I needed to get back on the weed to help me through it. I used every excuse in the book and she eventually relented as long as I promised to not let it take a hold of my life again.

I was missing acting so much and my job at the centre was making me miserable. I wasn't cut out for cold calling and every time someone answered the phone and told me to fuck off I would take it personally. The night terrors were back even though I was stoned again and I could feel the demons coming back.

I agreed to seek help and went to the doctor who put me on anti depressants and sent me to see a CPN.

The pills worked to an extent but it was my first meeting with the Psychiatric nurse that changed everything for me.

She wondered if my anger and depression came from what happened in the army and advised me to write a letter to Sgt Jones. I wasn't to send the letter to him she just thought it may be therapeutic to get all my feelings and anger towards him down on paper. At first I wasn't keen on the idea but one night after a few whiskies I decided to sit at the computer and start the letter.

I was really drunk when I started writing it but was almost comatose by the time I had finished it. All I remember was crying a lot and having to stop to compose myself a lot. The anger came firing out through my fingers as I bashed

219

away at the keyboard.

I was too hung over the next day to read it back and was nervous to read what I had written. I had blanked out due to all the whisky so really didn't remember what I had said in the letter. But I finally worked up the courage to read it again a few days later. I couldn't believe what I had written. I wasn't reading it as a letter from me, I was reading it as a monologue from a play. That's when I realised I actually had a good way with words. Good old Mr Rankin was right. That night I decided to use the monologue and turn it into a full scene. A week later I had written my first ever play without even thinking about it. I titled it "Statistics".

What had started as a real life letter had become a script based on my life and struggles when coming out of the army. It was so powerful but with a lot of black humour throughout.

I took the play in to a lecturer at the college to have a read and to give me some feedback. They read it within a few hours and then contacted me straight away.
-It's fucking brilliant, I want to produce it.

And that was that. Within a few months I had the show cast with me playing the lead and we were in rehearsals. The script went down really well with the cast on the first read through so I knew I was onto something good. No one was paid as I didn't have a budget and we used as much of the college's sets as we could. It was all thrown together on a purse string but I felt the script was strong enough to get by.

We played the show for two nights to two full houses mainly made up of friends and family and it went down a storm. It was an emotional few nights for everyone due to the context and background of the script but the feedback was amazing. I was a writer now.

Reliving it all helped but also made the night terrors more frequent so my weed smoking was getting worse. Morning joints were back and I was again stoned for most of the day.

Soozy and I were falling out a lot and my new "writing career" was taking all my focus. I was on the computer every night writing new plays. It was my new release. I wasn't drinking as much anymore but I was smoking joint after joint as I felt my creative side really heightened when I was stoned. This has been a habit throughout my writing career ever since. This book is the first thing I have ever written without being stoned.

One morning we both woke up in bed and just looked at each other. We were both thinking the same thing.
-This isn't working anymore is it?

She shook her head.

I left that morning and went to stay at B&B that my friend's Eileen and Jackson owned. I met them through the college. Eileen was at my college and Jackson came in to take photos for the shows. They were brilliant with me and almost like a second mum and dad. They understood I had problems and were always there to help out when they could.

I spent a few days at theirs looking for a place to stay. I

couldn't write, I was missing Soozy too much. I thought I wanted away from the relationship but I couldn't stop thinking about her. What was I doing? I'd let my career blind me and after all she had been there for me throughout all the darker times.

One day I was missing her so much I ran out the B&B and headed to Ayr bus station. I wasn't going to ask her to get back with me. I just needed to see her. I don't know why but something in my head just made me want to speak to her.

I was stood at the station waiting on the bus when my mobile phone rang. It was Soozy.

-Hey, that's weird I was just about to come and see you.

-Where are you?

-The bus station.

-Wait there, I'm coming to get you.

-Everything alright?

-Yeah, no. I don't know, I'll be there in ten minutes.

She hung up before I could say goodbye. What the fuck was going on? I paced up and down the bus station for about twenty minutes and smoked two fags before she arrived. I jumped into the car and she drove off.

-I was genuinely just coming to see you. I've missed you.

She didn't reply, she just kept driving. I could see her eyes filling up with tears.

-What's wrong?

She took a breath and turned to me.

-Do you think we can make this work? I can't argue like this all the time. I know we have both been in the wrong at

222

times but we can't do this anymore.

-I know. I'm sorry I've not been myself, I've been too caught up in everything. I do love you.

-I love you too, but do you really think this can work.

-I do yeah. Well I know I want it too.

A tear broke from her eye and rolled down her cheek and I wiped it off. She stopped the car and turned off the engine then took my hand and looked into my eyes.

-Good, because I think I'm pregnant.

After many tears and promises to work hard at the relationship we drove to ASDA to get a pregnancy test. Soozy went into the toilets to take it while I paced up and down the fruit and veg aisle like a man possessed. It was the longest five minutes of my life. I was nervously playing about with some Satsuma's when I felt a tap on my shoulder.

Soozy smiled and nodded her head. No words just a smile and a nod. I was going to be a dad.

CHAPTER NINE. DECLAN

I was the happiest man on the planet for the next few months. I'd always wanted to be a father so the career took a back seat now and I just worked as hard as I could in the call centre to keep the money coming in. I missed acting but knew I had to do the right thing for my new baby.

I cut right down on the weed but I was an addict by now so was still relying on it at night time to "help me sleep".

My family were over the moon with the news and even they could see a real change in my personality. I wasn't drinking now, I was just spending all my time working and trying to be there for Soozy. Until one night I went and fucked up yet again.

About six months into the pregnancy I agreed to play a small part in play called "Perfect Days" by Liz LochHead that my friend Eileen was producing at the ex serviceman's club in Ayr. The role was easy to learn and wasn't huge so I decided to do it. Rehearsals were only once a week for a few months so I could juggle them with my work life and still have enough time for Soozy and the kids.

The first two shows went really well but on the last night I decided that instead of my character drinking prop whisky on stage I would replace it for real whisky. Don't ask me why. I guess I just thought I'd earned it after all the hard work over the last wee while. Any excuse will do for someone with a drinking problem.

I think I tanned about half a bottle of straight Malt whisky during the show and then the rest of the bottle at the aftershow party.

I turned up at the house pished and Soozy lost the plot. I could hardly walk. She had a go at me and I'm embarrassed to say I started to scream and shout at her. Things got really nasty and I smashed a bottle of beer on the back step. The poor kids must have been terrified. It's not easy writing this as I still hate myself for doing it and wouldn't blame the kids if they hate me too.

Soozy called the police so I ran off and went to stay with a mate.

Word started to spread that the police were looking for me that night and were going to charge me with a breach of the peace. She told the police she didn't want me charged and regretted calling them but when they saw she was heavily pregnant and the glass on the floor they decided to charge me themselves.

The next morning I went to my Mum and Dad's house and the convinced me to hand myself in. Mum took me to the police station in King Street and they arrested me in front of her. She still says to this day that watching me being handcuffed and taken to the cells was the hardest thing she has ever had to witness. I've put that woman and my dad through some amount of pain and yet they have still stuck by me and supported me throughout it all.

I spent the weekend in the cells and was due in court on the Monday morning. The police down in the cells were brand new with me as they could see I was really sorry and

225

remorseful. I was crying most of the weekend at the thought of what I was putting my pregnant girlfriend through. One officer opened the cell at one point to talk with me. He even offered me some books to read. This really helped break up the time and I ended up reading two full books. One was about the Ipswich strangler that murdered five prostitutes and the other one was an auto biography but for the life of me I can't remember whose.

I was taken to the cells at Ayr Sherriff court and had to share with a guy that was rattling off heroin withdrawal. The cells in the court are like the ones you see in films. Steel bars and you can see everyone in all the other cells. It was like a fucking nightmare listening to them all shouting and sharing stories about what they had done. They were giving the guards all sorts of abuse. I just sat with my head down praying to be called up to the court.

It was hours before they called my case. I was led up the stairs and into the courtroom. I could see my dad and my friend Craig (He had become a good mate over the years). But no sign of my mum. She would never miss a court case like this.My heart sank. Had she finally had enough?

My uncle Steven was representing me again and told the judge that I had made a mistake due to drink and recommended I go into rehab etc. The judge wasn't convinced due to my past record and only agreed to release me on bail until he could get more background reports.

I was released that day but part of the bail condition was that I couldn't go near Soozy or even her street. I was devastated.

When I got outside my mum was there waiting. She was in good spirits and happy I hadn't been given the jail. Turns out she was there in the court all along but just before I was brought up her phone rang and the judge through her out of the courtroom! Best of it all, it was Soozy calling her to ask what the judge had said!

She didn't want me to be away from the house but due to bail conditions I had to go and stay with Craig for six weeks. I wasn't even allowed to phone Soozy so we had to communicate through my Mum. Poor woman heavily pregnant and I can't even be there for her due to my own stupid actions.

Soozy now had six weeks to decide whether she wanted me back or not. It was by far the longest and toughest six weeks of my life.

After my trial I was found guilty of a breach of the peace and fined £500. Luckily Soozy wrote a letter to the judge stating she was willing to take me back and because she was pregnant with my child he was lenient but told me if I was ever to appear in court again I would be given a custodial sentence.

I never drank again throughout the rest of the pregnancy but that night I returned home to Soozy and the kids I smoked the fattest joint known to mankind out the back door. Everything was my fault but my nerves were shot. I was doubting whether I could ever be normal and my ability to be a good father.

I needed a focus other than work to get me off the drink

227

and weed. Having a baby on the should have been enough but I was hooked and needed a distraction. So I decided to start my own theatre company.

I wanted my kid to be proud of his dad. I didn't want to be working in a call centre all of my life. I wanted to write and perform. For him.

I had a great script and I knew it could sell out again. All I needed was a venue. Most of the play was set in a pub so I thought what better place to perform it. The Gaiety Theatre had just closed and the Civic was no longer open so I thought fuck it, if we can't get people into theatres then I'm gonna take the theatre to them!

I walked into the Market Inn pub near Ayr train station.
-Hello are you Billy Thomson the landlord?
-Aye son, how can I help?
-Look I've got no money to hire your function suite upstairs but I think it would be brilliant to put my play on in there. I can't pay you for the rehearsal time or performance dates but if you open the bar I promise you'll make some money at the interval.

Billy looked at me for a second then smiled. I think he liked my audacity mixed with false confidence.
-Aye why not young man. Come on through and we can look at the diary.

And so my relationship with the Market Inn and Billy was born. I would go on to produce and perform ten more shows sell out shows in that magnificent place. And that was the day my new theatre company Hipshot Theatre arrived!

228

I named the company Hipshot because my scripts always shoot from the hip. Just when you expect it to go somewhere it punches you out of nowhere.

I threw a cast together of pals and offered a profit share. Statistics sold out for five nights and again went down a storm. I paid all the actors £50 each and made about £350 myself after paying for all the props and marketing etc.

Soozy watched the show when she was nine months pregnant and was a great support throughout. She could see how it distracted me from drinking and knew I was much happier doing what I loved.

I was now a theatre producer, director and writer on top of being a performer. Obviously I was still very raw and had a lot to learn but I was proud. I had done all this with no budget and no experience whilst still keeping a full time job in a call centre. I knew that this is what I wanted to do for the rest of my life...Minus the call centre.

On the first of Dec 2009 after the first Hipshot show, Soozy was due to go into hospital and be induced as she was now nine days over her due date. Poor woman was at her wits end. My eyes were just opening when she cried out.

-Oh fuck! My waters have broken!

I leapt out of bed in a panic even though we had planned for this day for nine months. My brain was all over the place.

I looked at the bed sheet and there didn't seem to be much water there, just a tiny bit but what did I know. If she said her waters had broken then her waters had

229

broken.

We drove to Crosshouse hospital and were put into our own room. The contractions were still far apart but she was in real discomfort.

I leant in to put my arm around her and felt this sudden flow of hot water spilling all over my hand....Now her waters had broken.

Poor Soozy was in labour for ten long hours before the doctor came in with the epidural. She was in so much pain and I felt helpless. Just as the doctor went to inject the epidural Soozy had a contraction which made her back arch and the doctor ended up putting the needle in too deep. For anyone who doesn't know this is really dangerous as being too close to the spine can cause long term health problems and sometime paralysis.

Soozy had lost all feeling and found it hard to push the baby out. Just as the head was peeoping out the midwife looked at me with a worried look on her face and shouted at me.

-Quick push that alarm for me!

I looked at the green alarm button on the wall and quickly pressed it! Nothing happened so the midwife screamed at me,

-Push it!

I screamed back in a panic as I repeatedly pressed the button.

-    I am fucking pushing it!!

The midwife realised her mistake.

-    I mean pull it, quickly pull it!

I pulled on it and an alarm started to sound.

Within seconds the room was filled with doctors and nurses all pushing past me to get to Soozy. The baby's shoulders had gone a funny angle and he was suffocating. I didn't know this at the time so I was terrified.

A doctor pushed down so hard on Soozy's pelvis she let out a blood curdling scream. I watched as they pulled my lifeless baby from her womb and rush it over to the table to resuscitate him. I just kept out my own scream of despair and slid down the wall onto the floor. There was so much commotion. I was literally screaming as I cried. Please save my baby! Please!

I prayed as hard as I could still screaming for the doctors to help. It felt like a lifetime. Then all of a sudden I heard the baby cry. I jumped up and moved to the table. The midwife wrapped him up and turned to hand him to me with an exhausted smile.

-It's okay daddy, we've got baby, you go see mum.

I looked over at Soozy and she was nearly unconscious. I ran over and hugged her.

-Are you okay?

-I'm fine, I'm just tired.

She was drifting in and out of consciousness. The midwife interrupted.

-Daddy, mum's a bit too tired to hold him, sit down and you can give your wee boy a cuddle.

-Boy? You hear that Soozy, he's a boy.

I couldn't stop the tears from pouring down my face as I sat and held my little boy for the first time. I thought I'd

231

lost him but now he was in my arms and staring up at me.
Soozy was in a bad way but still managed a smile. I looked
at her and said,

-He looks like a Declan.

-Declan it is then.

  We had decided before hand that it would either be
Ben or Declan so it wasn't just a random name I'd come
up with.

  And just like that my life had changed forever. He was
my priority now. Not the drink, or the weed or my career.
This little miracle in my arms was going to be the best
thing that ever happened to me. And I was right.

  Since the day he was born the night terrors faded and
my drinking problem disappeared. One or two blips along
the way but nothing major.

  He is too important to me.

  I now had something to live for other than my own
selfishness.

CHAPTER TEN. SPARKED BACK INTO LIFE.

I love being a father. The love I feel for my blue eyed blonde haired boy Declan will never be rivaled. Having him in my life has changed me for the better. The anger I had for the army subsided. The night terrors were gone and all that remained was a fire in my heart for my boy.

Unfortunately the love we both had for Declan did not help mine and Soozy's relationship. We tried hard for a year to make things work but deep down I think we just both knew we weren't right for each other. We never argued in front of him, we always agreed her own kids had been through enough of that in the past. I wanted a career in the theatre and she had our own business. I can't even remember how we split up or what was said, we just agreed to end it and that was that.

I moved into a place in Troon and we never got back together. I'm lucky that I can say that she has never tried to use Declan as a weapon and even though we have had our ups and downs she is an incredible mother to our child.

Unfortunately the birth of the wee man didn't stop me from smoking weed although I was still only smoking at night now ,and I would never be stoned if he was staying with me. That's a lie I would smoke out the back when he was asleep. I was at the point of addiction now. I wasn't smoking to block anything out, I was smoking because I was hooked. Some people say it's not addictive or as harmful as other drugs but I can put that to bed right now and say that's all bullshit.

Over the next few years I worked hard at turning Hipshot into a proper theatre company. I wrote and produced two new plays, Cell a Secret and the Labour of Change at the Market Inn and both sold out and again to great reviews. Only thing was the Market Inn Only held forty people a show so making money was difficult. I needed a proper theatre.

I was now working in a coffee shop called Su Casa in Ayr to help me get by. I loved it as I met loads of great characters I could write about but I still wasn't happy. I wanted to be a professional performer and writer but no one in Glasgow would take my shows. Every agent in Scotland was still ignoring my emails and it all started to get to me again. I felt I really had what it took to make it in the industry. I just needed someone to take a punt on me.

Then along came Vince Hope.

Vince had been hired to become the new director of the Gaiety Theatre which was now set to re-open after being moth balled for three years. Vince had heard about my work at the Market Inn and arranged a meeting for me to chat about taking one of my shows to the theatre.

After meeting with him he revealed that he wanted me to produce "The Labour of Change" in the studio theatre when the place was back up and running. I was hoping to use the main auditorium but it was a start. I was finally going to produce and direct my work in a proper theatre and hopefully make a decent amount of money.

The opening was still a few months away and they were planning on doing a big pantomime first before any other shows could get in. So I had plenty time to prepare.

The Panto posters starting appearing all around town and there was a real buzz around Ayrshire about it. I remember looking at the poster for "Cinderella" and thinking, I'm going to be in one of those pantomimes one day.

Little did I know that that day would come much sooner than I thought.

My phone rang and it was a lady that was working for the Gaiety in the fundraising department. She was calling to tell me that they were still to cast the role of Dandini in the panto and that I had an audition if I could get to Dumfries on the Saturday.

I couldn't believe my luck but in the back of my head I didn't believe I had any chance of getting the part. I hummed and hawed for a few days and almost didn't go, but when I woke up on the Saturday I felt a sudden burst of confidence and thought, fuck it, what do I have to lose.

The auditions were being held at the DG1 leisure centre and I was so nervous my stomach was hurting. I was given a piece of script and told I'd have to sing a song, so I decided to go with the Dentist song from Little Shop of Horrors. I knew I could blag my way through that one.

I was taken into a room where the producers Mike and Karen Courtney were sitting and started reading in for

Dandini and then for the role of Muddles the comic. The producers had two pantomimes to cast so they wanted me to read for two. I really wanted the Gaiety panto so I put more effort into the Dandini audition. The song went pretty well but they did comment on how comedy was clearly stronger than my singing, but I "could hold a tune".

Just as I was about to leave the director Mike said,

-Actually, do you mind reading in for one of the ugly sisters as well?

He then handed me a piece of script with Ugly Sister dialogue on it.

-Sure, how do you want it played, camp or effeminate?

-Neither, bloke in a dress.

I nodded my head and then burst into character. I pulled the ugliest face I could muster and spoke in a gruff voice. I threw my all into it but didn't think much of my chances. The uglies were a huge role and I didn't believe I had enough experience to play one of them in such a huge pantomime.

When I finished reading the Director thanked me and said they would be in touch. I was happy with how it all went but not really hopeful. I was just proud of myself that I had the courage to go and at least try out. My first professional audition was done and dusted and I felt it was an achievement to celebrate. Big mistake.

Unfortunately on the night out celebrating I met an old work colleague who I had sacked from one of my plays the year before and we got into an argument. Nasty words were exchanged and I ended up punching him in the face.

Long story short, he called the police and I was arrested for assault and ended up in the cells yet again. Even after all my promises to myself I let my anger get the better of me and fucked up yet again.

I was released the next morning with a charge and had to appear in court a few weeks later.

I'd fucked it all. Everything was starting to fall in place for me with the theatre company and I'd let my temper get the better of me because I was drunk. I was hoping the judge would go easy on me but the words "custodial sentence" kept playing in my mind.

A few days later I was called by the Producer of the pantomime and offered the role of one of the ugly sisters at the Gaiety panto. It should have been the happiest moment of my career but all I could think of was the court case and the high probability of going to jail. The local paper ran a feature to announce I was cast in the role. My friends and family were delighted and there was some real hype about a local lad playing such a great part in the re-opening of the theatre. I felt sick to my stomach when I should have been celebrating.

I tried to put it all to the back of my mind and get on with things but the guy I had punched ended up calling round the newspapers to tell them all about my charge so a journalist from the Sun appeared at my door for a statement. He said they were going to run a story with the headline, "Ugly Truth about Ugly Sister". My whole world was collapsing around me. I didn't care as much about losing my career as I did about getting put in prison and being away from Declan. The story was due out in the papers on the Sunday so I phoned my panto producers and the bosses at the Gaiety and told them everything. They listened to everything I had to say and said they would get back to me after they held an emergency meeting to decide whether or not I was to be sacked. Emergency meetings seem to be a theme for me when I fuck up.

I didn't hold out much hope of them keeping me on as they would hardly want a criminal starring in a family pantomime.

But by the grace of God they all decided to keep me on. I don't know why, maybe because they could hear in my voice how sorry I was, or maybe it was because they heard it from me first and not the papers. Either way they showed faith in me and I'll never forget them for that.

The story ran on the Sunday and my social media exploded. But every comment was positive and hundreds of people came online to show their support. I was dreading that day but ended up feeling so overwhelmed by everyone's kind words. This gave me the final kick up the arse I needed to get a grip of my temper. All I needed to do now was pray the judge took pity on me and not throw me in prison.

Luckily the charges of Assault to injure were dropped and I was only charged with assault. I was given another £500 fine and was told to behave. My uncle Steven was representing me again, and whatever he said to the judge saved my bacon that day, and my career.

Panto rehearsals started in November and I loved every

second of it. The cast was great. It had Gary Lamont and, Leah McCrae from River City and the guy playing the other ugly sister was Fraser Boyle, who I would go on to have an amazing relationship on and off the stage. We tore it up that season and had the audience in stitches with our antics. We received top class reviews from the national papers and ended up being asked back the following year to play Abanazer and Widow Twanky in Aladdin. That was the start of our double act and Fraser and I went on to write and produce our own variety shows "The Taylor and Boyle Show". We couldn't be more different as personalities but we work so well together. I feel safer on stage with Fraser than anyone else and we just have the best fun working together. He's genuinely the funniest guy I know and an amazing human being too.

   The whole panto experience was so much fun. The theatre was packed every night for forty odd shows and I didn't want it to end. Declan would come back stage and to see his wee eyes light up when he met all the cast was the icing on the cake for me. He has spent most of his life backstage with me since that day.

   During the run of Cinderella I was seeing a girl who ended up cheating on me so I went a wee bit off the rails again. I was going out drinking after every show and then would go in to the theatre the next day rough as fuck and probably still stoned from the night before. It all started catching up on me as some days we would be doing three shows a day. My mood changed and I fell out with a few of the cast members and dancers towards the end of the run.

I let it all get to my head and burning the candle at both ends was a recipe for disaster. One night all the cast met for drinks then some of us went to a party the band were having at their digs. I upset a few people for being so drunk and for smoking weed the night before a show. I got into an argument with one of the dancers and pretty much told her to keep her nose out my fucking business. The next day she put a complaint in about me and I was pulled in by the director and told to buck up my ideas or I'd be sacked. She told him about the weed and the drinking and I didn't deny it. I felt awful about it all but also was relieved I was off the hook again. I didn't drink for the rest of the run, but I was still getting stoned every night. Not having a hangover every day helped me soak up the last few shows and I really enjoyed myself. I was gutted when panto finished. Talk about the after show blues.

But I had my first show at the Gaiety "The Labour of change" to look forward to. I started rehearsing almost immediately and now had some money from my panto wages to put into the set and props. The play sold out and went down really well with the audience. I had finally produced my own work in a proper theatre albeit the studio, but like I said...It was a start.

As the next few years went buy I was in two more Gaiety pantomimes, Aladdin and then Beauty and the Beast where I played the Gaston character, but I was called Jean Claude Van Dumb. I'd also still been producing my plays at the Market In and Gaiety Studio. The money was decent but it wasn't coming in frequently enough so I decided to use my talents to teach the younger generation and open up my own Youth Theatre.

Hipshot Youth Theatre took off almost immediately. It was handy using my name off the back of doing the local pantomimes so on the first night I had forty kids enrol and I have never really looked back from there.

I now have eighty kids registered for the Youth Theatre and we run classes every Tuesday Wednesday Thursday and Saturday.

I would be happy with my life if it was just shows at the Market, the Youth theatre and the odd panto now and again. And that's how it was for a few years.

Until the day I met Des.

CHAPTER ELEVEN. MEETING DES.

Even though the youth theatre was doing well and I was producing the odd small scale show here and there I still wasn't bringing in enough money to pay rent and bills. I was crap with money and had a lot of debt racked up from a few failed shows. And I was spending most of my cash on weed. I always made sure I had money to feed Declan but any cash spare would go on drink and hash. I got myself into such a rut that I had to move in with my Aunt Rhona and Uncle Andy again. They offered me the spare room for a few months to help build money back up and find my feet again. They were great and never asked for much rent, Thirty quid a week but in truth I think I only paid them a few times the whole year I ended up staying there.

I didn't want to stink their room out with weed so I tried to come off it and replaced it with a herbal high called Bombay Blue. There was a wee shop in Ayr that sold all these "legal high" things and promoted them as weed substitutes. Bombay Blue was much cheaper and it gave you a good dunt so it seemed like the perfect substitute. I'd only have to smoke one or two joints of it and it would knock me out. And it didn't really smell so I didn't have to worry about stinking out Aunt Rhona's house.

During my time staying with my Aunt and Uncle I produced and directed Romeo and Juliet at the Ayr Gaiety in the main auditorium. I set it in the modern day using gang culture and sectarianism as inspiration. There was a

242

cast of about forty. Most volunteers but some professional. I offered a wage to some and others were promised a cut of any profit made. The thing is though I hadn't done the math right and had really bit off more than I could chew. The show went down a storm and I was proud of it but it made a big loss and I was left without any cash to pay most of the cast. Quite rightly so this annoyed a lot of people and I was outed on social media by one of the cast members. It was a horrible time and I still feel bad about it to this day. My mistake was making promises and not budgeting properly. I went into a deep depression for a month or so after that and didn't know how I was going to recover.

Then one night when I had stopped feeling sorry for myself I decided instead of sitting about waiting for things to happen, I was going to take my career into my own hands. I needed a script that was well known so I could get it into theatres across Scotland. I was sick of being known for my work in Ayr alone.

Singin Im no a Billy He's a Tim is one of the most successful touring shows in Scotland and one I'd always fancied directing. It had a great pull so I thought, fuck it, I'll contact the writer and see if I can get the rights.

I put a post on Facebook asking if anyone had a contact detail for the writer Des Dillon and luckily another well known Scottish writer Wilma Stark got in touch with me a few minutes later. Wilma is a good pal now and without her reaching out to put me and Des in touch I don't know if I'd even have a career now. She knew Des well and

243

predicted that we would hit it off so she contacted him and he gave her permission to give me his email address. And then I wrote the most important email of my career to date. I mailed asking if I could have the rights to the show but Des replied saying that he was touring the show himself and was about to take the show to the Pavilion in Glasgow for four sell out shows. But instead of stopping the convo there I asked Des if he had any other scripts that I could take out instead. After some back and forth he sent me his play "CUNT". Yes that's really the title. I read the script in just over an hour. It was brilliant. Hilarious, dark and powerful. I told him I would love to produce it and we agreed to meet at a chippy in Girvan to discuss it.

Now bear in mind I was skint and had no idea how I was going to produce this show but something inside me told me I had to try.

I didn't have train fare to get to Girvan so I sold my telly at cash converters in order to hire a car from Arnold Clark for the day and still have enough left to buy Des his food and drink. I didn't want him knowing I was poor.

I read up on Des's career and started to get nervous. This guy had written award winning books and plays. Six Black Candles a book and a play about six sisters practicing witchcraft had just won an award in Russia. I started feeling I was in over my head but I had committed and I just had to meet him.

I sat in the wee chippie waiting for him to arrive. I had smoked a wee one skinner of Bombay Blue to settle the nerves but if anything it made my anxiety worse. The

244

nerves passed the minute he sat down and started talking. Des is working class like me and he was friendly and honest from the get go. I instantly liked him. He spoke with such passion and intelligence I was genuinely inspired by him.

We both ordered a chicken supper and a couple of bottles of red cola and started talking about his play CUNT. I was honest and told him I still had to raise the money but I would do everything I could to get the show out on a tour. We laughed and talked for a few hours and then he started to tell me all about the Billy n Tim show and how popular it was. He looked me up and down and said,

-Actually you'd make a good Tim. I need an understudy for the shows at the Pavilion. Fancy it?

And that was that. No audition or read through. I was now officially the understudy for Tim in one of the biggest shows in Scottish theatre. He let me know that he was doing an understudy rehearsal the following fortnight and told me to learn the dialogue.

-You'll no get on stage but it'll be a good experience and it's paid.

I went home feeling absolutely delighted. I didn't even care I didn't have T.V to get home to. The day was totally worth it.

I spent the next two weeks lying on my bed in Aunt Rhona's spare room smoking Bombay Blue and learning lines. The rehearsals were being held in a studio at The Scottish Youth Theatre building in Merchant City in Glasgow. I woke up that morning feeling so anxious. I

245

didn't know Glasgow well so I set off early for the train to allow more time to find the place. I couldn't afford to print the script off so I took my laptop and intended to read it from the screen.

The whole train journey I just didn't feel right. I looked pale and I couldn't get my brain to settle. My head was fuzzy, my palms were sweaty and my heart was racing.

I got off at Glasgow central and started looking for the venue. But I got lost and ended up being twenty minutes late for my first rehearsal. Des and the team didn't look impressed and my cause wasn't helped by the fact I hadn't brought a printed script. I learned a few months later from Des that he was going to sack me that day as he was so annoyed by my unprofessionalism.

-What changed your mind?

-When you started reading in for the part you won me back over.

That day in rehearsal was the first time Des saw me perform, so thank fuck I was good or I would have been out on my arse.

We spent the next four days blocking and learning the show with the other understudies and all round it was a great few days. But I just couldn't shake my anxiety. I put it down to nerves and being in such a professional environment. I knew I had impressed Des and the crew during this time as he was laughing a lot and would always take me for a coffee at breaks.

It was weird rehearsing something that I knew I wouldn't have the chance to perform in but I knew it was a step in the right direction. I just had to be patient and pray that my time would come one day.

The following week myself and the other understudies had to sit in the Pavilion and watch the four shows. That was a hard one. Watching the guy playing Tim when I was desperate to be up there and then seeing the reaction of the audience at the final bow was tough. I was chomping at the bit to play in such a huge venue like that.

And that chance came a lot sooner than a thought. The following week Des offered me the role of Tim full time and told me I'd be performing in the sequel the following Month.

This is the happiest I ever remember feeling in my career. Not only was I going to play the iconic role of Tim but at the Glasgow Pavilion. It honestly was a dream come true.

We were pretty much straight into a three week rehearsal. The script is hilarious and Des is a brilliant director so it was the most fun I had had in years. The only thing was, I was feeling really weak and to be honest looking like death.

I tried eating healthy and wasn't even smoking weed, I was on that herbal high tobacco, Bombay Blue. I'd even cut out the beer to an extent. I was determined not to blow this chance with Des. But I just couldn't shake the feeling.

I went to the doctor and my symtoms were basically pointing to the fact I was a heroine addict. I told him about the Herbal High and he said that it's a good chance it's synthetic morphine.

I was a junkie and didn't know it.

I had to go cold turkey during the rehearsals of the biggest show of my life. It was the toughest thing I've ever had to do. The sweats were insane. I had no apetite hence I was always weak in rehearsals....But I fucking did it and not one person knew about it. Come show time I was good to go again.

I remember stepping onto that stage at the Pavilion for the dress rehearsal and looking out to the fourteen hundred odd empty red seats. I felt a bolt of electricity tingle dowN my back and I smiled.
-Here we fucking go!

The show went down a storm each night and I savoured every moment. I was getting a laugh nearly every line, such is the genius of Des's writing. This not only opened up my career for the Billy and Tim shows but also for many Pavilion shows to come. The boss of the place Iain Gordon seemed to like my performance so cast me in a few of his own productions. I was Cammy the Jannie in Glesga Dance Mums. Alex in The Summer of 69. Father Boyle in Des Dillon's "Six Black Candles", (Twice). And Dandini in his pantomime Cinderella.

It was a great experience that's for sure working on that stage with so many talented performers and yes, too fucking right I'm going to name drop some. I'd gone from putting on shows to forty people in the Market to playing to thousands at the Pavilion with performers like, Dean Park, Joyce Falconer, Grado, Stephen Purdon, Holly Jack, Keith Warrick, Alyson Orr, Carole Anders, Scott Fletcher, and Julie Duncan to name a few.

I know some folk will read that and cringe that I name dropped but I worked my arse off to work with these people and to top it all off I did it all stoned oot ma tits so....allow me this one.

Here I actually got angry a wee bit there, and for comments that haven't even been written by people I don't even care about. That's a thing I do. Need to work on that.

After the last Billy n Tim 2 show at the Pavilion I felt ecstatic. Peter Mullen (Name drop), was at the show and invited us for a drink at the pub across the road. I sat drinking with him for hours. What a man.

I remember sitting just soaking it all up. Here I am sat with Peter Mullen drinking and laughing after a sell out Saturday night show at the Pavilion that I was one of the stars in. That was the very second I thought, you know what, whatever happens after this is a bonus.

I went home that night, cracked open a bottle of whisky and drank the lot as I scrolled through all the reviews and social media comments about the show. Sat on the couch, whisky in one hand, phone in the other. I fell asleep with a smile on my face.

The next day I woke up feeling so good that I thought I'd reward myself with a joint. So I went to my dealer and got a score bag. And that was me back on it for the next five years.

Over that next five years I fell out with Des then made back up again. I promised to follow through with his play Cunt but got side tracked with Billy n Tim stuff so he thought I was fucking him about. Maybe I was sun consciously because I was so nervous about touring a big show with no experience or money.

I remember the day we fell out. We were arguing over Facebook messenger and Des just wrote...
....Race you to the delete button.

Then he blocked me. I'm laughing as I type this now but at the time I was devastated. He will hate me for saying this but I see him as a father figure in my career and he is by far my favourite writer on the planet. And I genuinely don't just say that because he is my pal. If you ever meet him he just inspires you. And he is the funniest cunt you'll meet. Most people fear him because of his intelligence.

Anyway we made up about a year later when Iain Gordon cast me in one of Des's plays. I contacted Des to let him know and see his thoughts on it and he replied,
-I know, it was me that recommended you for the part.
And that was it, we were pals again and have been ever since.

I owe so much of my career to Des. Without him I

wouldn't have Billy and Tim and I wouldn't have had all those shows at the Pavilion. So aye, cheers ya dick x

In 2019 I decided it was time to take the plunge and start taking shows out across the country. I was making a name for myself in Ayrshire but I wanted to branch out. I wanted a national tour.

I was engaged at this point to a lovely girl called Laura. She was 12 years younger than me and was a dancer. We got on great but on reflection probably just good friends. Anyway I wanted to make enough money to make sure I could provide for her and Declan.

I called Des and asked him if I could have the rights to to the Billy and Timm sequel. I said I had the money in place but I didn't. But I knew if I had the rights then I would find the money.

Des agreed so the next day I printed out a contract and drove four hours for him to sign it and talk about how I saw the show. When it was it the Pavilion it was all played for laughs but Des and I agreed there was so much more emotion to be gotten from the script. We had some coffee and chatted for a while. I felt even more inspired when I left.

That night I phoned around some business men I knew from town and secured a six grand loan providing I paid twelve back. This six grand would only pay cast wages at most for a national tour, but it was better than nothing so I accepted. All I needed now was a set and I was pretty much good to go. I could blag the rest of the cash flow as I went. I had faith this show would sell out, and if it did, it would change my career for the better.

Luckily I was asked to write a pantomime for the Bathgate Regal theatre so the money from that paid to get the set built for the tour. All I needed now were theatres to book the show.

With some help from my good friend Alyson Orr (Great performer) we managed to book the play into twelve different theatres all throughout Scotland.

Shit was getting real.

The closer things got the more I was smoking.

Joint after joint in front of the laptop as I organised everything from tour transport to risk assessments to the marketing side of things. I was on social media five hours a night alone. Just drinking and smoking and trying to think of creative ways to plug the show.

I still didn't know if it was going to sell. I was already fourteen grand in the hole and bleeding cash and rehearsals hadn't even started yet.

But then Motherwell Theatre put their tickets on sale and it sold out within two days and they ended up booking another date. All the other venues started to follow suit. I'd done it. It wasn't going to make a loss. But at least everyone else will get paid. Money for me wasn't a priority. I just wanted to prove to people that I could produce and direct a national tour.

The stress of losing cash was gone and something inside me came alive. I was full of adrenaline for months. I

252

couldn't sleep so I would drink and smoke more and more.

The hangovers were always there so my moods were really bad especially at home. Poor Laura had to deal with me being moody a lot. I can see why she eventually walked, but I'll get to that in a bit.

But I was so focused on getting the job done I didn't even realise how much I was drinking. Some nights I'd easily tan three bottles of wine and ten joints. Most nights actually. Maybe I was drinking because I know it makes me more confident. Perhaps masking some self doubt, who knows? I do drink when I'm down but I also get a craving for a drink when I feel excited. You know, like to toast my excitement and all that.

I managed to get a great cast for the show. Neil Bratchpiece, Gary Morrison and Zofia Sokolowitz.

Rehearsals ran smoothly and everyone was getting paid on time but I knew that I only had a weeks worth of wages left before the cash ran out. I was relying on the theatres to pay quickly after each show so there was a genuine stress building up. I was having sleepless nights. Dreaming about the show going wrong and then waking up and having a joint at 4am to try and calm down. This happened pretty much every night the full three weeks leading up to the first show of the tour at the Gaiety Theatre.

This was a huge night for me being able to launch the tour from my local theatre, a place that I hold so dear in my heart. It was another one of those special nights. I'd directed a Des Dillon script at my local theatre and it was about to take it on a national tour. Life couldn't get any better.

The tour was a rip roaring success with standing ovations every single night. It was emotional for so many reasons. The friendships I made with the cast, the fact it was my first tour and knowing how far I'd come since stealing that Snickers bar from Asda.

Sixteen performances, twelve different venues.

I'd done it

And I was proud of myself for the first time in years.

But the more excited I got. The more the drink and weed flowed.

And now I had a wee bit of spending money from the tour. I went a bit out of control.

Laura and I took the wee man to Disneyworld after the show and got ready for Christmas coming. We had a great through weeks to celebrate the success but I was taking it too far and drinking every night. And it only got worse when I got the call from one of the biggest theatres in the country, the SEC Armadillo . It holds three thousand people. I didn't even realised I had emailed them so I must have done it when I was on my third bottle of wine.

I had sent them a message saying how successful the tour was and sent them a load of reviews from Facebook.

They were delighted to meet up and book us in. A few days later the contract was signed and Billy and Tim were about to perform at the SEC Armadillo a few months later. I couldn't believe it. Everyone wants to perform in that venue, but to produce and direct a show for it as well? I won't lie when I said I had a tear in my eye.....and then a massive five skinner.

About a month later the new cast were all in place, the big show at the Armadillo was about to happen, my wedding to Laura was only a few months away. Life was better than ever and I had even calmed down on my smoking and stopped drinking for good. No night terrors, no anxiety, no anger. It's probably the most at peace with life I've ever been. We had moved out our wee flat into a lovely house (rented) and Declan was happy and both our careers were flourishing. Life was good.

Then Covid 19 hit.

CHAPTER TWELVE- THE ARMA FUCKIN DILLO

I decided to use the lockdown to my advantage, and like a lot of writers I know, wrote absolutely fuck all the full eighteen months. I had no motivation at all. A lot of people were churning out all sorts of Covid sketches and scripts, pure inspired by the pandemic so they were. And there's me sat on my arse eating crisps, drinking beer, smoking weed and playing Fortnite on the Xbox. I got quite good at it by the end. Fortnite kept me sane the first three months.

 I was going nuts being locked up inside. Laura had a separate living room to me so we spent a lot of time apart in the house during it. We didn't really argue but looking back we didn't really interact. Not in a nasty way, just a natural, went and did our own thing way to cope. She still had all her zoom dance classes all week to focus on. I could have finished this book as I was half way through but I had no creative juice at all. I think my coping mode was to drink and smoke my way through it and black it out. And if I'm being really honest I don't remember too much about lockdown. It's as if my brain went into hibernation mode and I was just on auto pilot the whole time.

 The only time I got creative was when I decided to write and film a monologue about murdering my mother. I only used a phone to film it in my office and used a lamp for lighting. The whole piece is about eight minutes long. The Gaiety Theatre paid me and used it on their online programme that month and the video got more hits than all the Gaiety videos on You Tube combined. I was really happy with how it was received. I was inspired to do more....But I just played more Fortnite and smoked more weed instead.

I would sleep until about two in the afternoon each day and go to bed about five in the morning. Me and Laura never went to bed at the same time during lockdown. Maybe once or twice but I can't remember.

The restrictions were easing slightly and all the new phases were being announced by Nicola Sturgeon. I kept in close touch with the great people at the Armadillo and I think we rescheduled the show about three times. We had sold almost two thousand tickets and I was so stressed they would just eventually pull the plug and I would lose all that money. For the first time I was in profit months before a show was even on and it was all now hanging in the balance.

Just like everyone else I was missing the real world. And I was starting to realise deep down, that I had a serious drinking problem. This hit home when I went to put empty bottles in the bin and it was already full of glass. Laura hadn't had a drink that month. It was all mine.

Just as things started to lift restrictions wise me and Laura had to move house as our landlord sadly passed away.

We moved to a fancy big house in Alloway (Home of Rabbie Burns). It was more than we could really afford but

257

we were desperate. The house was stunning but from the minute we moved in there, things just started to nose dive for me and Laura, but I didn't even see it coming.

 The first morning we woke up in the house I could smell raw shit. It was honkin. The toilet down stairs had somehow exploded in the middle of the night and there was pish and shit all over the hallway. Laura had to leave and I cleaned it all up.

 We eventually got settled and it was six weeks before Christmas. I remember this because we put the tree up early. The three of us decorated the tree and I was messing about with Declan having a laugh and putting decorations up badly on purpose etc. But Laura seemed a bit off and was joining in. I felt like I was irritating her. When I look back the signs were there but I just didn't pick up on them.

  About a week later Laura suggested we get a rescue dog for Declan's Christmas. And that was when Buddy was brought into the family. He is a Carpathian Shepherd rescued from Romania and we just fell in love with him. We didn't realise he would be so big and I literally nearly shat myself when he came bounding out that pen. The woman said he doesn't like men so best stand off a bit. But Buddy came bounding up to me, had a sniff and then started licking my hands. As soon as it happened I thought of something Des once said to me. You don't pick a rescue dog, they pick you. And at that moment I completely understood.

 Buddy was living with us within a week. I was in love. He

was my new best pal. We went everywhere together. Three walks a day, the middle one always being five miles or more. Buddy loves his walks but fuck me if he saw a squirrel you were fucked. Dislocated my shoulder once. True story.

But it wasn't all plain sailing as anyone with a rescue dog will testify to.

Buddy had bad separation anxiety when I left. He would rip down the curtains and try and chew the front door off. We were skint at the time as we hadn't been able to work so all the DIY was killing us. We tried to buy one of those wire cages but the big bastard chewed his way through it!

We had literally just both started back at work and for two hours each day he would have to be alone. That whole two hours I was a nervous wreck. Laura and I both cried at times, it was really tough. But we loved that dog more than anything and never gave up. But it did cause tension in the house. But we never aimed the frustration at the dog. He was our good boy.

It was a few days before Christmas and we were both asleep in bed when Laura's phone rang. I knew by her tone that something serious had happened. It was her cousin Sarah on the phone. Lisa's voice changed as she asked,
-Tom who?
There was a slight pause and then she just broke down. I knew there and then that her little cousin Tom had passed away. He was only eighteen. One of the nicest most beautiful souls I've ever met. Taken far too soon. Laura was inconsolable.

I held her in my arms for about an hour as she sobbed her heart out. I didn't know what to say. So I just held her.

I'd never felt sadness like this for another family before. These were good, God loving people and their whole worlds had been torn apart. It was awful.

I tried to be as supportive as I could and run Laura a bath for getting back from work that night. I wasn't good with words in these situations so I used actions in the best way I could at the time. She lay there for a couple of hours and I heard her cry at one point. I was broken for her.

A day or so past and it was the day before Tom's funeral. Laura and I were driving to work and Declan was with us as he was coming to Youth Theatre with me. Long story short, I needed the car after I dropped Laura off but she wanted to keep it as she finished work early. She wanted me and Declan to walk from her work but the wee man didn't have a jacket. Anyway it got into a heated argument, I swore and said, "Don't fucking dare expect my son to walk in the rain without a jacket". She got out and slammed the car door and I drove off to work. Both of us with steam coming out of our ears.

That night at home we never spoke a word. She stayed upstairs and I slept on the couch. The next morning I got up to get ready for the funeral. The plan was to drop Declan off in Ayr then head to the funeral together. When I got out the shower Laura was gone.

It was a mis communication, she thought I wasn't going to go, and I thought she left on purpose to make me look bad when I was a no show. But at the time we were angrier than ever before. This was pure rage from both sides. And it was the day before Christmas Eve. I didn't fight it too much as I knew she was hurting and had a funeral to attend. I was seething so I smoked as many joints as I could and got hammered on Bells whisky out the backdoor in front of my fire pit.

I was wrapping all the wee man's presents when Laura got home. She just went straight up the stairs. I was drunk so didn't want to go bother her. That's a lie I didn't want her to see how pissed I was. I finished wrapping the presents, rolled a joint and sat out the back at my fire pit and smoked and drank into the early hours. I love a natural fire more than anything. It's when I'm most at peace. I sat for hours just thinking how unhappy I was. How unhappy we both were. I knew the drinking wasn't helping though. So I vowed that night that I was going to stop drinking and smoking. I had an urge to stop and that didn't come around often.

I fell asleep on the couch that night stinking of whisky and fire smoke.

We didn't speak the whole of Christmas Eve. We didn't even see each other. To kill my hangover I spent most of the day back at the fire pit with some beers and a few bongs packed full to the brim.

I was woken up on Christmas morning when Declan phoned to tell me that he had opened all his presents at his mum's house. Which translated meant,

- Haw Da come pick me up so I can open all your presents now. No matter what was going on in my life I was smiling

261

away listening to his excited wee voice. That boy just fills my heart with pride and joy.

I sprung up off the couch and jumped into a shower to wash away the smell of weed and wood smoke.

Laura was still in bed so I poked my head through and said,

-Look no matter what we are going through just now we need to put it aside for the wee man coming over.

Maybe I should have started with Merry Christmas but in my head I didn't think she would want to hear that from me. I was scared she would say, "Don't fucking Merry Christmas me".

I wasn't even at the bottom of the street when I received a voice note from Laura basically telling me I was a disgrace for not saying Merry Christmas and she had had enough of me. And then she said the words...

-It's over.

My initial reaction was, good I'm glad but don't you fucking dare leave us on Christmas fucking day. At least put on a show for a day and then leave on boxing day. I was furious and I will hold my hands up and admit that the voice note I sent her back was absolutely venomous. I didn't hold back. It was along the lines of, "Don't you fucking dare leave me and my boy on Christmas fucking day you horrible arsehole blah blah blah. I'm not proud of it but I was so angry. I just snapped. Having to move house again in such a short space of time, The Buddy stuff, lockdown....I just broke.

Luckily Laura did the right thing and waited for Declan to

262

get back to open his presents and she put on an act along with me. The wee man stayed for a few hours and then went back to his mums. I dropped him off and by the time I got home, Laura was gone.

I didn't even try to contact her, we were both just so sick of each other by now. And that night I outdid myself and drank and smoked more than I ever had before. It's a miracle I didn't die if I'm being fair. This is what I drank and I swear on the soul of my children that this is in no way exaggerated. Over the course of Christmas day I sat alone and drank, two bottles of Buckfast, three bottles of Prosseco and eight cans of Tennents Lager . Not a word of a lie. I drank myself into a coma and don't remember much of the day apart from dressing in a Santa suit and listening to Christmas music.

Laura didn't come home that night. She wouldn't tell me where she was staying.

When I saw all the empties in the kitchen the next day even I was shocked at how much I'd drank. I'd also gone through a quarter of weed. And that was when the penny dropped. It was boxing day and I was stood alone in the hall of that big new house looking around and soaking up every bit of silence, with the worst hangover I'd ever had. I saw a family walk past the window all wrapped up with hats and scarves. The mum and dad were laughing at the wee boy trying to ride his new scooter. They looked so happy.

I fell to my knees and sobbed for at least half an hour. That was it. I was done with it all.

I stood up, almost ran through to the kitchen and through all my weed into the bin and poured a jug of water over it all, then through the bag in the wheelie bin. Then I poured what was left of the Christmas alcohol stash, although I had tanned most of it.

Something came over me and I just wanted to get clean.

I took Buddy out for a good five miler along the beach and back. I was sad Laura still wasn't home but I was determined to show her I can get fit and healthy again. I knew it was a part of the problem. We had both stopped trying with each other over the last year or so.

She text while I was out a walk saying she didn't want to talk and that it was definitely over. I was broken.

But something happened that day. Usually in times of despair I'd turn straight to the bottle or the smoke. But I sucked it up and kept my promise to myself. It was the hardest thing I've ever done. But I did it.

Laura moved into a flat in Irvine and I moved in with Mum and Dad for a few weeks before moving into my own poky wee flat in Prestwick.

After the break up I still helped Laura move house twice (The one in Irvine didn't work out) and we tried to make it work but after four months of seeing each other a few days and nights a week it just fizzled out, for her more than me I have to admit, or so I thought at the time. I think the damage was already done and although Laura tried to get those feelings back and she just couldn't. And no harm to her. You can't feel what you don't feel. It was only eight weeks away from the wedding but Laura cancelled it all.

I've never been so broken.

But on reflection and I truly mean this, it was a great four maybe five years but it was never going to work. I'm a rugged, rough swearing nut job and she's a healthy living clean cut girl. Like I say at the time it hurt but she did us both a favour. I wish her and her family nothing but happiness, because we all did enjoy some great times together.

It didn't take long before I met someone else, Karen. Karen is a great person and we had a brilliant summer together. We made some great memories but that didn't work out either unfortunately. She thought I smoked too much weed and that it affected my moods. She didn't know I was drinking so much.

I was back on the smoke by now. I lasted four months off it but in all honesty, I was missing it. It makes me feel chilled at night when I unwind. I don't drink with it much anymore and I feel so much better for it.

So Karen and I parted ways. A couple of months back in Nov 2021.

Oh I should probably mention now that she is pregnant and I'm the father. We are not together anymore but I will not love that baby any less. It was a shock to the system to say the least but I think it's finally sunk in. You couldnae write it eh!

Sorry I got ahead of myself there.

About three month after Laura and I split, it was time for the big show at the Armadillo. At last all restrictions were lifted and we could finally have audiences through the door again! I was buzzing off ma now not so wee titties due to the lockdown diet. I put two fucking stone on by the way.

Rehearsals were a whirl wind. I had two new cast members, John Love, now playing Billy and Natalie McConnon as the Nurse. Both good friends and fantastic performers. I now had a new studio in town so we rehearsed there and had a great time. The Gaiety were kind enough to let us tech in their venue the night before the Armadillo show. Absolute legends by the way. No other theatre offers the work and support to Freelancers like they do.

Tech and dress went as well as hoped. I helped strip down the set and load the van up ready for the morning.

I went back to my flat that night with my buddy Keith Stallard who was staying with me as he had travelled from Skegness just to be my stage manager. He is a gem of a guy, a big Brummmie and the best in the business at what he does. His lighting is spectacular and with such mental show like Singin Im no a Billy he's a Tim, his input was gold.

We sat up chatting for a bit and shared a pizza then Keith went to bed. I did my usual and sat up drinking and making cuts and changes to the script. I read it every night after every rehearsal just in case I'd missed something. I do it with every show I direct. My cast hate me as I'm always sending re-writes and cuts for shows at three in the morning. But I can't help obsessing over a project as soon as I get the green light right up until that final bow.

I finished my prep for the big day and sat out the back
with a big joint. I packed it so full because I wanted my
brain to settle and actually soak up what I was just about
to do in Glasgow the following night.

I was about half way down the joint before I started to
sink onto the back step a little. I looked up to the sky and
the stars were like white paint splatter on a shiny black
canvass. It was beautiful. I smiled and took a big long draw
on the doobie. I sucked the cloud in slowly and held it in
for about thirty seconds just looking at the stars.

I let the smoke out and couldn't stop smiling. I felt my
Gran by my side. I just knew she was there.

I tried to fight the tears as I didn't want to celebrate
victory too early. I didn't want to jinx the show. But I knew
we had it in the bag. The crew were great, the cast were
top class and I knew the show inside out. I had never been
more confident in my life. And that's when the tears
started to flow.

After all these years of hurt and pain and hard work, I was
finally going to do it. I was taking a show to the Arma
fuckin Dillo.

I had a wee greet to myself, pure pat on the back stuff,
finished the joint and went up to bed. I had the best sleep
I'd had in months and woke up with firework up ma jacksy.

It was an early start and a long day but I was ready for it
all. I'd sold over two thousand tickets and most of these
people hadn't been out in eighteen months. I knew we
had to put on a show. And what a show we gave them.

The nerves I felt standing in those wigs before the curtain

went up were more itense than I'd ever felt before.

-What if people have forgot to laugh?

-What if I forget my lines?

-What if an audience member coughs and everyone runs like fuck?

-What if one of the cast forgets what they're doing?

-I should have read this script twice a night!

-I wonder if there's anyone famous out there.

-If I fuck this my Gran and Papa are gonnae be mortified, even though they're both deed (Aye Papa died a few year back....God Bless ye Bill!).

So aye every radio station was on full blast in my head. But just as always, as soon as the wee guy popped his head through to give us clearance, every station turned off apart from the one I needed.

I could hear the buzz from the audience. I hadn't heard that beautiful noise in over two years. All nerves disappeared and little eight year old Chris the Chippendale from Bugsy Malone appeared. In spirit anyway.

I was suddenly that little excited kid again with no worries in the world and all I wanted to do was go out there and make those people laugh so hard that some of them oish themselves. Because they fucking deserved it....we all deserved it.

We absolutely smashed it from the opening scene. The cast were hilarious. We got four laughs a page this time. People were choking for a good time and my team truly delivered. I was so proud of every one of them from the

268

cast to the stage hands.

And the emotional punch at the end that I'd discussed with Des all those years ago hit harder than ever before. One minute they were all laughing and the next we had grown men sobbing into their football jerseys. We nailed it.

When we came out for the final bow that was the first time I broke character and looked out into the audience. It looks huge out there from the stage. Two thousand odd people standing to applaud. I thought I would cry but I didn't. I felt euphoric.

I looked out to all those people and my mind quickly glimpsed back to the first ever show I did at the market inn. With no money and no idea what I was doing.

Ten years on and I'm stood on the stage at the SEC Armadillo getting a standing ovation from two thousand people.

It's a moment I'll never forget.

And I truly mean it when I say, if this was the ceiling of where I can go as producer, then I'll still die a happy man.

But I couldn't have done it without all the family and friends who have helped me financially and often emotionally throughout the years. I love you and you all know who you are….

….Not you Hammy,, you can still get tae fuck.

THE END OF THE BEGINNING.

Aye, so that's my story in a sixty nine thousand word nutshell.

I have another few hundred maybe a thousand stories I could have used in this book, all drink and drug related and some much darker than what you've read but like I said at the start I didn't want to drag anyone else into this book and get them into trouble. But more importantly, I don't want to incriminate myself.

I was always scared to end this book while I was still addicted to weed. I wanted it to be a big happy ending with me being totally clean.

Unfortunately that's not the case.

I still smoke at night when I'm watching a film and before bed or when I'm in the company of fellow weed smokers. But I'm in control and my work is never affected. I never smoke during the day or when I'm driving.

I started writing this book to see if I could spark a repressed memory and discover the reason to why I have smoked weed almost every day for the past twenty years. But with each chapter I wrote it became clearer that weed hasn't really been the problem.

Alcohol has.

I can't blame what happened in the army, or anything in my childhood. Just look at the mad dog in the bush I drank as a kid, the weed I chose to smoke when still at school.

The ecstasy, the magic mushrooms, the cocaine, the crack, the poppers, the acid, the DMT, the valium, the codeine…..I did it all because I wanted too. Pure curiosity mixed with stupidity. I can't blame anyone or anything for my addictions. I did it all for the thrill, the rush…………The chance to not be me for just a little while.

I don't do any other drug now apart from weed and as I write this last chapter I have now been six days sober from alcohol. The longest I've lasted in twenty years.

Two decades I've been blaming weed and trying to stop smoking, but the whole time the root of all my troubles has been staring me in the face.

I have been as honest as I can in this book so believe me when I say I have tears dripping onto my keyboard as I say this for the first time in my life….But I'm happy I am typing it….

I'm Chris, and I'm an alcoholic.

Ooooh…plot twist.

Trust me, even I didn't see that one coming until a few weeks ago.

I'm only six days in and I can't and won't promise I won't drink again, for all I know I might even have a wee whisky to celebrate finishing the book. Maybe I won't. But what I do know is that I'm sick of the hangovers. I'm sick of the depression. I'm sick of the control it had over me. And I'm going to do everything in my power to get dry. Not just for my family and the people close to me.

  But for me.

  Maybe the weed will be out of my life one day, but for now it's my reward each night for tackling the world, with all ten radio stations blaring.

  When I smoke I don't end up in a jail cell, I don't want to fight anyone, I don't cut myself, I don't fall face first through grandparents glass tables, I don't hurt people and most of all I produce my best work because I don't have hangovers.

  If anything weed makes me want to avoid all of these things more than when I am sober. And if it wasn't for weed, I'd never have written this book.

  Weed has helped me through some of the toughest times in my life. It numbs the pain. Chasing it with drink is what sent me down a bad path. The hangover mixed with a stone over is never a good mix. That's when I was grumpy and quite cold with people.

Who knows how long I'll smoke it, but for now I'm content. I have acting and writing gigs booked in for most of the year. I've got a home Declan and I are settled in and I'm happy to say I've met someone really special. We were friends to begin with but it's recently sparked into something a bit more serious.

  She is a smoker too. I told her all my flaws from day one and that's helped. I can be myself around her and she helps turn down the volume on my stations. She is as mental as me.

We just work.

It's early days but all the right signs are there. You never know what will happen in life, it could all end in tears but right now I'm happier than I've ever been before. She is the one who inspired me to get off the drink and finish this book but she doesn't even know it. So no matter what happens I'll always be grateful she came into my life.

Maybe we will encourage each other to quit smoking or maybe, just maybe... We will smoke together forever.

Whatever the outcome......

....I'm just looking forward to the adventure.

END.

ABOUT THE WRITER

.....I've just fucking told you.

OTHER WRITING CREDITS

T.V

*Only An Excuse (BBC Scotland). 2018/2020

Stage Plays

*Statistics

*The Labour of Change

*Cell a Secret

*Hogmanay Hiest

*The Walking Neds

*Britain forgot Talent

*The Fakest Showman

*Aladdin (Panto Bathgate Regal).

Comedy Shows

*The Taylor and Boyle Show (Co-Writer)

*Taylor and Boyle Tickle your Fancy (Co- Writer).

Adult Pantomimes

*TinderElla

*Booty and the Beast

*Aladdin and his Tragic Tramp

*Jakey and the Beanstalk (And his Maw's Enchanted Bean)

275

Printed in Great Britain
by Amazon

83454592R00160